HENRY SHARP, JR.

Emory University

ELEMENTS OF
PLANE
TRIGONOMETRY

Englewood Cliffs, N. J.

PRENTICE-HALL, INC.

LIBRARY OF CONGRESS
CATALOG CARD NUMBER: 58–10075

First printing.........April, 1958
Second printing.......June, 1959

PRINTED IN THE UNITED STATES OF AMERICA
26909

PREFACE

The purpose of this textbook is to present trigonometry in the language and spirit of modern mathematics. The vocabulary of elementary mathematical analysis is used exclusively throughout.

The over-all plan of the book is simple. The first eight chapters emphasize *the theory of the trigonometric functions;* the final three chapters emphasize *applications of trigonometry.* Logarithms and related topics are discussed in appendices, which may be tapped or not depending upon individual requirements. Coordinate methods are used wherever possible, particularly in formal proofs. Nearly all conventional topics are discussed, but the arrangement and approach are intended to focus attention on *periodicity* and *graphs* rather than on the traditional *right triangle.*

There are many problems which stress the importance of trigonometry in various fields of science and engineering. The final section in each of Chapters 1, 4, 7, and 10 is devoted to a *Special Topic,* which is related to the material in the chapter but is not essential to the continuity of presentation. These topics have been chosen to demonstrate applications of trigonometry to physical problems both ancient and modern.

The author gratefully acknowledges his indebtedness to teachers, colleagues, and friends who have influenced the preparation of this textbook. In addition, a special word of thanks is due both Dr. A. A.

Bennett for his many constructive criticisms of the original manuscript, and to the Prentice-Hall organization for their courteous and efficient attention in the production of this book.

H. S., Jr.

CONTENTS

vii

ELEMENTS OF
PLANE TRIGONOMETRY

1

INTRODUCTION

The word "trigonometry" is a combination of two Greek words that, taken together, mean "triangle measurement." In this sense, the study of trigonometry has an unbroken history reaching from its source in ancient Greece to the present day. But the name of our subject, although historically appropriate, is deceptive, for triangle measurement is not the only important application of trigonometry in the modern world. It is our purpose in this introduction to sketch the origin of trigonometry and to indicate its uses, both ancient and modern.

1. EARLY HISTORY

In its earliest stages trigonometry was closely related to geometry. In fact, it seems to have originated more than 2,000 years ago in Egypt and Greece with the application of geometric principles to problems arising in land surveys and astronomy. The individuals associated with its foundation as a systematic study are Hipparchus (Greek, second century B.C.) and Ptolemy (Greek, residing in Alexandria, c. A.D. 150). Isolated instances of the use of trigonometric ideas appear much earlier. The Egyptians, for example, had made use of certain trigonometric rules in re-establishing along the Nile River the boundary markers and lines usually destroyed by annual floods.

1

Hipparchus is generally credited with developing this and many other examples into a coherent theory by which more difficult problems could be solved. Most persons unacquainted with classical Greek history are amazed to learn how far advanced scientific knowledge was in that age. To illustrate, by the time of Hipparchus the Greeks had already discovered that the earth is spherical, and by geometry and trigonometry they had estimated its diameter and that of the moon with surprising accuracy. These discoveries were afterward forgotten or overlooked for more than a thousand years, and they were not popularly revived until the time of Columbus.

Ptolemy, who is famous primarily as an astronomer, refined the theory inherited from Hipparchus. After Ptolemy there were few important additions to trigonometry until about the seventeenth century. Since that time, new mathematical ideas have exerted an entirely different and nongeometrical influence on the subject.

2. PERIODIC EVENTS

The physical world is dominated by periodic events: the alternations of day and night, the phases of the moon, the appearance of certain comets, the flow and ebb of the tides, and, on a smaller scale, the swinging of a pendulum, the operation of the pistons in an internal combustion engine, the rotation of the wheels in a watch movement — these are all examples of events that occur periodically (or very nearly so). One of the basic purposes of mathematics is to furnish a symbolic language through which events in the physical world may be concisely and elegantly described. It is natural, then, to look for a mathematical scheme by which periodic motions can be represented. The algebraic ideas with which we may already be familiar are not well suited to the description of periodic motions. On the other hand, it will become apparent as the subject is developed that trigonometric expressions are particularly well adapted to this purpose.

3. GENERAL COMMENTS

Trigonometry encompasses in a single theory two widely different kinds of application. The methods of trigonometry can be used on the one hand to study the numerical relationships between the sides and angles of triangles, and on the other hand to analyze problems relating to periodic events. Questions of the former type arise, for example, in surveying, astronomy, navigation, and mechanics; questions of the latter type occur in the study of electrical phenomena, the theory of vibrations, and in many other branches of modern science and engineering.

4. SPECIAL TOPIC: THE SIZE OF THE EARTH

For almost a thousand years after the time of Alexander the Great, the city of Alexandria, founded by him near one mouth of the Nile River, was unparalleled as a center of learning. About 300 B.C. a university was established there and a great library built, into which poured many of the writings and observations of the ancient world. During their lifetimes, Archimedes, Euclid, Ptolemy, and probably Hipparchus were associated with the university, along with many other lesser known scholars. One of these was Eratosthenes (Greek, 275–194 B.C.), who for a long period was university librarian at Alexandria.

Long before the time of Eratosthenes, convincing arguments had been given that the earth is spherical. Two of these were: (1) the shadow of the earth cast on the moon during an eclipse always appears circular, and (2) a relatively small change in position north or south on the earth's surface produces an appreciable change in the height of certain stars above the horizon. Belief that the earth is a sphere led Eratosthenes to search for a method of finding its size.

Eratosthenes discovered in his library records that there was a most unusual phenomenon associated with a deep well near Syene, an Egyptian city that he believed to be about 500 miles due south of Alexandria. (He used, of course, a different measure of distance.) At noon on only one day of the year, the sun could be observed to shine straight down the well, producing a reflection on the water. He reasoned that when this occurred the sun, the well, and the earth's center lay on the same straight line. He was able to determine that, at the same time as the sun reflected in the well, a vertical column in Alexandria cast a shadow indicating that the sun was 7°12′ south of zenith. By assuming that Alexandria and Syene lie along the same meridian and that the sun's rays are parallel, he could then determine the earth's circumference (Fig. 1.1).

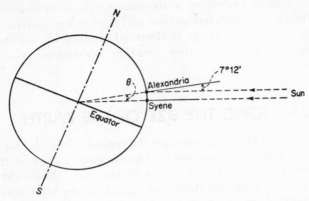

Fig. 1.1

Knowing that the angle at the earth's center is 7°12′ and that this angle subtends an arc of length 500 miles, he reasoned that the entire circumference C must be given by the equation

$$\frac{C}{500} = \frac{360°}{7.2°} \quad \text{or} \quad C = (500)(50) = 25,000 \text{ miles}.$$

────────────| **Suggested Exercises** |────────────

1. The city of Rhodes is about 400 miles directly north of Alexandria. A bright star, *Canopus*, is barely visible above the horizon at Rhodes, whereas at Alexandria its highest point is about 5°30′ above the horizon. Draw a sketch of this situation and estimate the circumference of the earth. (This method was used over a century later by Posidonius, another Alexandrian scholar.)

2. Hipparchus calculated that the distance from the surface of the earth to the moon is about $33\frac{1}{2}$ earth diameters. Using this information, with Eratosthenes' value for the size of the earth, estimate the diameter of the moon if it is observed near zenith to intercept an arc of $\frac{1}{2}°$.

3. How do modern values compare with those found here for earth diameter, moon diameter, and distance from earth to moon?

4. Assuming the earth to be 93,000,000 miles from the sun, what is approximately the diameter of the sun if it is observed to subtend an angle of $\frac{1}{2}°$?

2

FUNDAMENTAL CONCEPTS

In this chapter we discuss several concepts essential to an understanding of modern mathematics. The vocabulary introduced in this chapter will be used extensively in the pages ahead.

1. SETS

In the study of mathematics it is frequently convenient and indeed necessary to refer specifically to a whole collection of distinct objects. The objects in the collection are characterized by sharing in common a particular property that distinguishes each from objects not in the collection. *A collection that is to be considered as a whole is called a* **set,** *and the objects in the collection are called* **elements** *of the set. Each element is said to* **belong to** *the set, and the set is said to* **contain** *each element.*

We shall postulate the existence of one *set containing no element at all, which for this reason is called the* **null** *set or the* **void** *set.* In certain more advanced mathematical topics this set behaves very much like the zero in our ordinary system of numbers.

EXAMPLE 1. The positive integers less than 100 comprise a set. The elements of this set could be written out explicitly without too much labor, but mathematicians prefer to denote this set by the symbol $\{1, 2, \cdots, 99\}$. It is evident that this set contains exactly 99 elements.

EXAMPLE 2. We may also think of all positive integers as comprising a set. In this case, of course, it is impossible to list all the elements explicitly, and the usual symbol is $\{1, 2, \cdots\}$.

When a particular set is to be mentioned several times in the course of a discussion, it is desirable to assign some symbol as an abbreviation for the set. Capital letters are frequently used as such abbreviations. Let M and N be two sets. We say that M and N are **equal** $(M = N)$ *if each element of M is also an element of N and, furthermore, if each element of N is also an element of M.* In other words, M and N are equal if they contain precisely the same elements.

There is an essential difference between the sets in Examples 1 and 2 that we may indicate in the following intuitive way. Suppose it were possible to line up, either physically or by imagination, all the elements of a given set. If we then start counting these elements, one of two possibilities may occur. A definite number is reached beyond which no more are needed because each element has already been counted; or no such number is reached because there are always elements of the set that have not been previously counted. In the former case the set is called **finite,** in the latter case the set is called **infinite.**

——————————| **Problem Set 2.1** |——————————————

1. How else can you describe the set of all states larger than Texas?

2. How else can you describe the set of all planets closer to the sun than is the earth?

3. Is the set $\{1, 2, 3\}$ equal to the set $\{2, 1, 3\}$?

4. List all different three-digit numbers formed from the digits 1, 2, and 3,
  (a) allowing repetitions (for example, 111 or 122),
  (b) not allowing repetitions.

5. Specify the elements belonging to the set of all fractions a/b for which a can be any of the numbers 1, 3, or 5, while b can be either 2 or 4.

6. Give an intuitive argument for the fact that the set of fractions $\{\frac{1}{1}, \frac{1}{2}, \frac{1}{3}, \cdots\}$ is infinite.

REMARK 1. Finite and infinite sets may be defined in the following way.

*If the elements of a set A are related to the elements of a set B in such a way that to each element of A there corresponds one and only one element of B, and if each element in B is related to one and only one element of A, then A and B are said to be in a **one-to-one correspondence.***

Let A be a set. If C is a non-void *subset* of A (that is, each element of C is also an element of A), let B be the set consisting of those elements of A that are not in C. *If for some such C there exists a one-to-one correspondence between A and B, then A is called* **infinite**; *otherwise A is called* **finite**.

REMARK 2. Let A be the set of all positive integers, let C be the set of all odd positive integers, and let B be the set of all even positive integers. We establish a correspondence between A and B as follows: to each element of A corresponds its double. Thus 1 is related to 2, 2 to 4, 3 to 6, and so on. This correspondence is one-to-one, and C is non-void, hence the set of all positive integers is infinite.

7. Show by writing out all possible correspondences that the set $\{1, 2, 3\}$ is finite.

8. Prove that the set given in Problem 6 is infinite.

9. Show geometrically that the set of all points on a line is infinite.

2. REAL NUMBER SYSTEM

We shall designate the set consisting of <u>zero</u> *and the* <u>positive</u> *integers as the set of* **natural numbers,** *to be denoted by* N. *Thus* $N = \{0, 1, 2, 3, \cdots\}$. When the operations of subtraction and division are applied to the elements in N it appears immediately that this set must be extended in order to make these operations meaningful for all numbers. For example, $5 - 7$ is not a natural number, and $\frac{1}{2}$ is not a natural number. To overcome this difficulty, we extend the set N by defining first the set of whole numbers and next the set of rational numbers.

The set consisting of zero and the positive and negative integers is called the set of **whole numbers,** *to be denoted by* W.

Any number that can be represented in the form a/b, where a and b are elements of W and $b \neq 0$, is called a **rational number.** A rational number of the form $a/1$ may be considered identical to the whole number a. Thus, in a sense, the rational numbers include the whole numbers. With the rational numbers we have arrived at a set so large that the operations of addition, subtraction, multiplication, and division (with one exception) are all possible within the set. These four are called the **elementary rational operations** of arithmetic. It is easy to show that division by zero leads to contradiction, therefore we exclude $a/0$ as a number.

In addition to the operations already considered, another of fundamental importance is the extraction of roots in general and of square roots in particular. Although the set of rational numbers is quite large, even so simple a number as $\sqrt{2}$ is not rational. Any rational number can be written either as a terminating or as a repeating decimal; furthermore any such decimal represents a rational number. From this it follows that the decimal expansion of $\sqrt{2}$ is neither terminating nor repeating. *A number having a decimal expansion that is neither terminating nor repeating is called an* **irrational number.**[1] Now we again extend our concept of number, this time by defining a *set called the* **real numbers** *which includes all rational and irrational numbers.* This new set, denoted by R, consists of rational numbers and numbers like $\sqrt{2}$, $-\sqrt{3}$, $\sqrt{7}$, $1 + \sqrt{2}$, etc. Although $\sqrt{2}$ has been used to introduce the idea of irrational number, we should not assume that all irrational numbers must be expressed as radicals. In fact, one of the most frequently used of irrational numbers is not of this kind: the number π.

One of the most important properties of the set of real numbers appears in the following discussion. Suppose we draw a horizontal line in the plane and on it mark a point called the origin (or the zero point). To the right of zero we mark an arbitrary unit interval. We assume that the distance from the origin to any point on the line, right or left, can be measured in terms of this given unit interval.

Corresponding to any positive real number x we assign that point on the line which lies x units to the right of the origin. Corresponding to any negative real number x we assign that point on the line which lies $-x$ units to the left of the origin. Thus to any point whatever on the line there corresponds exactly one real number, and every real number has its uniquely corresponding position on the line. Speaking informally, we may say that the set of points corresponding to real numbers "fills up" the line.

--------| **Problem Set 2.2** |--------

1. Give five examples of
   (a) an even natural number,
   (b) an odd whole number that is not a natural number,

---

[1]There exist numbers which are not rational but which at the same time have no decimal expansion (for example, the number i, where $i^2 = -1$). Such numbers are neither rational nor irrational. These numbers are discussed in Chapter 11.

(c) a rational number that cannot be expressed as a whole number,

(d) an irrational number.

2. List the elements in each of the following sets:

(a) the natural numbers less than 7,

(b) the positive natural numbers less than 8,

(c) the non-negative whole numbers not greater than 6,

(d) the natural numbers not greater than 7.

REMARK 1. *Suppose a, b, and c represent real numbers and $a < b$. The statement that c is* **between** *a and b means that $a < c < b$.*

3. How many elements are there in the set of natural numbers

(a) less than or equal to 13?

(b) less than 31?

(c) between 13 and 31?

4. How can the answer to Problem 3(c) be obtained very simply from the answers to 3(a) and 3(b)?

5. If a and b are natural numbers and if $a < b$, state a general rule for finding how many natural numbers there are between a and b.

6. Using the rule of Problem 5, how many natural numbers are there

(a) between 100 and 1,000?

(b) between 117 and 7,801?

REMARK 2. The terminating or repeating decimal expansion of a fraction can be found by performing the indicated division. For example:

$$18/13 = 1.384615384615 \cdots \text{(period is 6)}$$
$$68/165 = 0.4121212 \cdots \quad \text{(period is 2)}$$
$$4/5 = 0.8 \quad \text{(terminating)}$$

REMARK 3. Given a repeating decimal expansion; for example $0.135135 \cdots$. To find a fraction having this expansion, proceed in the following way.

Put $\qquad\qquad a = 0.135135 \cdots$.

Since the period is 3, multiply both sides by 1,000. Then

$$1,000 \cdot a = 135.135135 \cdots.$$

Subtracting, we have

$$999 \cdot a = 135,$$
$$a = \tfrac{5}{37}.$$

7. Find the decimal expansion, and period if possible, of each of the following.

(a) $\tfrac{11}{6}$; (b) $\tfrac{12}{5}$; (c) $\tfrac{1}{11}$; (d) $\tfrac{9}{11}$.

8. Find a fraction representing the repeating decimal:

(a) $0.713713 \cdots$,

(b) $0.2373737 \cdots$,

(c) $3.1818 \cdots$.

3. RELATION AND FUNCTION

Let A be an arbitrary set and suppose there is given, in some way or other, a law which for each element of A designates at least one element of a set B. We shall assume that B contains only elements that are thus designated. In effect, *the law sets up a* **correspondence** *between the elements of A and those of B. Such a correspondence between the elements of two sets is called a* **relation**. *Set A is called the* **domain**, *set B the* **range**, *of the relation. If for each element of A the law of correspondence designates one and only one element of B, then the relation is called a* **function**. Thus a function is a special case of a relation: every function is a relation, but not every relation is a function.

EXAMPLE 1. A professor whose memory for names and faces is not always reliable avoids difficulty by assigning seats in his classroom and by making a seating chart showing the names of his class members in the proper arrangement. Suppose we denote the set of chairs in his classroom by A and the set of students (in this particular class) by B. For simplicity we will assume that there are just as many students as chairs. The professor's seating chart establishes a correspondence between the elements of A and the elements of B in such a way that for each chair in the classroom there is exactly one student. Thus the seating chart is a relation between sets A and B. In particular, this relation is also a function, for there is only one student in B for each element of A.

When we wish to designate some (perfectly arbitrary) element of a set, we use a symbol called a **variable**. A variable is usually denoted by x, y, z, θ, or some other convenient letter. *A symbol, frequently x or θ, used to denote some element of the domain of a relation is called the* **independent variable** *of the relation.* Now, if the relation is actually a function (that is, for each element of A there is just one corresponding element of B), it is customary to denote the law of correspondence by a symbol such as f, g, or other. Denoting an element of A by x and of B by y, we may express the correspondence between sets A and B by the statement $y = f(x)$, which is to be interpreted as meaning: y is that element of B which corresponds to the element x under the law of correspondence f. *The symbol y is called the* **dependent variable** *of the function.* This name is used because the particular element of B designated by f usually *depends upon* the element chosen from the domain. *Any number in the range (B) of the function is called a* ***functional value.***

In our work in trigonometry, as in most elementary mathematics, we are concerned with functions having both sets, domain and range, consisting of real numbers.

A number can belong to the domain of a relation only if there is a corresponding number in the range of the relation. Thus if a relation is described by a certain mathematical expression it is quite possible that there may be some real numbers automatically excluded from the domain. For example, in a function defined by the equation $y = 1/[x(x - 2)]$ the numbers $x = 0$ and $x = 2$ cannot belong to the domain, since either of these numbers leads to a zero in the denominator; and in a relation defined by the equation $y^2 = x$ negative values of x must be excluded if we limit the range to real numbers. To help emphasize this fact, we make the following definition. *In a given mathematical expression, any number for which that expression is undefined as a real number is called* ***inadmissible;*** *all other numbers are called* ***admissible.*** Unless stated specifically otherwise, we assume that the domain of any relation mentioned consists of all admissible values.

Although a function is expressed frequently by $f(x)$, or by $y = f(x)$, it is not at all necessary that a particular function be given by a single elementary expression. All that is necessary is that we be given some kind of law which will assign a value to the dependent variable for each element of the domain.

EXAMPLE 2. $y = \begin{cases} x \text{ for } x \geqq 0, \\ -x \text{ for } x < 0. \end{cases}$ (domain is all real numbers)

The range is $y \geqq 0$. This function occurs very frequently in mathematics and is called the **absolute value** of x. It is denoted by the symbol $|x|$. The graph of $y = |x|$ (the technique of graph construction is described in the next section) is shown in Fig. 2.1.

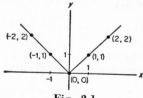

Fig. 2.1

EXAMPLE 3. Let z be a variable on the set of even whole numbers. That is, z is a variable which has the set $\{\pm 2n\}$ as its domain.[2] We define a function as follows:

$$y = \begin{cases} z - 1 \text{ for } z - 1 \leqq x < z, \\ z \quad \text{ for } z \leqq x < z + 1. \end{cases}$$

To construct the graph we assign a few typical values to z.

When $z = \quad 0, y = \begin{cases} -1 \text{ for } -1 \leqq x < 0, \\ \quad 0 \text{ for } \quad 0 \leqq x < 1; \end{cases}$

$z = \quad 2, y = \begin{cases} \quad 1 \text{ for } 1 \leqq x < 2, \\ \quad 2 \text{ for } 2 \leqq x < 3; \end{cases}$

$z = -2, y = \begin{cases} -3 \text{ for } -3 \leqq x < -2, \\ -2 \text{ for } -2 \leqq x < -1; \end{cases}$

and so on for all positive and negative even whole numbers. Below is the graph of this function, which might be called, somewhat picturesquely, a "stairstep" function.

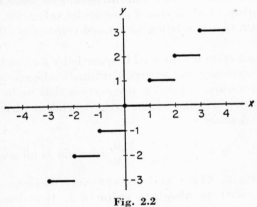

Fig. 2.2

| Problem Set 2.3 |

1. Following are a few examples of relations. Which of the relations is also a function?

  (a) To each state corresponds its U. S. Senators.

  (b) To each state corresponds its capital city.

[2] Here, and in all similar expressions in the following, we assume that n represents a variable on the set of natural numbers.

(c) To each natural number corresponds the number of times the digit 1 occurs.

(d) To each book corresponds the author (or authors).

(e) To each word in this textbook corresponds the number of its letters.

2. Describe the domain and the range for each of relations (a), (b), and (c) given in Problem 1.

3. In each part of Problem 1, state the correspondences for any three distinct elements in the domain.

4. On the real number axis plot all whole numbers w satisfying the condition:

(a) w between -6 and 6,

(b) $-3 \leq w \leq 3$,

(c) $|w| < 3$,

(d) $|w| \leq 0$.

5. On the real number axis designate the following intervals by a heavy line (notice that each of the paired expressions denotes the same interval):

(a) $\begin{cases} -1 \leq x \leq 1, \\ |x| \leq 1; \end{cases}$ (b) $\begin{cases} 1 < x < 3, \\ |x - 2| < 1; \end{cases}$ (c) $\begin{cases} -5 \leq x \leq -1, \\ |x + 3| \leq 2. \end{cases}$

6. How else can the following intervals be denoted?

(a) $-1 < x < 1$, (b) $|x + 1| < 2$.

(c) $|x - 2| \leq 1$, (d) $-4 < x < 2$.

7. Suppose the domain of each of the following functions is $|x| \leq 3$. Find the range, if

(a) $f(x) = x - 1$,

(b) $f(x) = |x|$,

(c) $f(x) = 2x + 1$,

(d) $f(x) = \begin{cases} 1 \text{ for } x > 0, \\ x \text{ for } x \leq 0. \end{cases}$

8. What is the range of each of the functions in Problem 7 if the domain is

(a) all positive numbers,

(b) all negative numbers?

9. What are the inadmissible values of x in the expression $1/g(x)$ when

(a) $g(x) = x^2 - 1$,

(b) $g(x) = 3x^2 - 4x + 1$,

(c) $g(x) = x^2 + 1$,

(d) $g(x) = x^3 + (\pi - \sqrt{2})x^2 - \sqrt{2}\pi x$?

4. RECTANGULAR CO-ORDINATE SYSTEM

Let two lines perpendicular to one another be drawn in the plane, one being horizontal the other vertical. The point of intersection is called the origin of co-ordinates (*the zero point on each line*), *and the lines themselves are called the* **co-ordinates axes.** On each axis we mark a point at unit distance from the origin and, as stated in the remarks on real numbers, this establishes for each line a correspondence between the real numbers and the points on that line. From the origin, points on the horizontal axis to the right and on the vertical axis upward correspond to the positive numbers, and oppositely to the negative numbers. This procedure establishes what is called a **rectangular co-ordinate system** in the plane; we shall frequently omit the word "rectangular."

Now consider any two real numbers given in a definite order. Find the point on the horizontal axis which corresponds to the first, and think of a line through this point parallel to the vertical axis (numbers being marked off on this line exactly as on the vertical axis). The second number of the pair corresponds to a point on this vertical line. Thus *every pair of real numbers in a given order corresponds to just one point in the plane, and these numbers are called the* **rectangular co-ordinates** *of the point. The first number is called the* **abscissa;** *it measures the distance and direction of the point from the vertical axis. The second number is called the* **ordinate;** *it measures the distance and direction of the point from the horizontal axis.* Evidently the axes of a co-ordinate system separate the remaining points of the plane into four sets which correspond to the four possible combinations of signs on the co-ordinates: upper right (called the **first quadrant**), both co-ordinates positive; upper left (called the **second quadrant**), first co-ordinate negative, second positive; lower left (called the **third quadrant**), both co-ordinates negative; lower right (called the **fourth quadrant**), first co-ordinate positive, second negative. If either co-ordinate is zero, then the point lies on one of the axes; if both co-ordinates are zero, then the point is the origin of co-ordinates.

To illustrate how this technique is applied in a particular case, suppose we consider the function given by the expression $x^2 + 1$. We write this $y = f(x)$, where $f(x) = x^2 + 1$, or $y = x^2 + 1$. Now for any value for x in the domain of f we may compute the corresponding element in the range. Let x' be some element in the domain of f, for example, $x' = \sqrt{2}$; let y' be that element in the range corresponding to x'. This idea is expressed in general by the equation $y' = f(x')$, and in our example by $y' = f(\sqrt{2}) = (\sqrt{2})^2 + 1 = 3$. In this way we have determined a pair of real numbers, $x' = \sqrt{2}$ and $y' = 3$, which correspond on a co-ordinate system to the point whose abscissa is x' and whose ordinate is y'. Similarly, such a pair may be determined for any number in the domain of f, each pair giving a point on the co-ordinate system. *The set of all such points (or the set of pairs) is called the* **graph** *of the function f.* By plotting a sufficient number of these points the general shape of the graph can be determined (see Fig. 2.3).

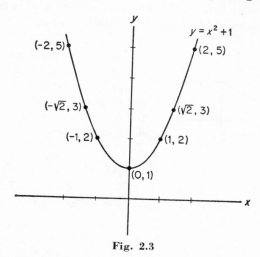

Fig. 2.3

It is customary to consider the horizontal axis as the axis of the independent variable (usually labeled the x-axis), the vertical axis as the axis of the dependent variable (usually labeled the y-axis). For this reason, the abscissa is sometimes called the **x-co-ordinate**, the ordinate is sometimes called the **y-co-ordinate**. If we wish to denote some arbitrary point on a co-ordinate system we make use of the symbol $P(x, y)$. This symbol means merely that the point P has as its abscissa the number x and as its ordinate the number y. The letters x and y may stand for any real numbers whatever, positive or negative, alike or not alike; which of these they are depends upon where in the plane we consider the point P to be located. For example, if $P(x, y)$ is to be a point in the second quadrant, then x must represent a negative number, while y must represent a positive number.

Two important concepts, distance and symmetry, are based on these ideas. For the discussion of these two concepts we assume a co-ordinate system to be established in the plane.

1. *Distance*. The distance between two points $P(x_1, y_1)$ and $Q(x_2, y_2)$ is the number of units measured along the straight line between the two points.

(a) If the line is parallel to the x-axis, then $y_1 = y_2$ and the distance is found by subtracting the smaller x-co-ordinate from the larger.

(b) If the line is parallel to the y-axis, then $x_1 = x_2$ and the distance is found by subtracting the smaller y-co-ordinate from the larger.

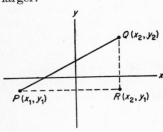

Fig. 2.4

(c) If the line is not parallel to either axis, then the distance can be found by application of the Pythagorean theorem, as in Fig. 2.4. Let the symbol dist (P, Q) represent the distance between the points P and Q. Then

$$[\text{dist } (P, Q)]^2 = [\text{dist } (P, R)]^2 + [\text{dist } (R, Q)]^2,$$

or $\quad$ dist $(P, Q) = \sqrt{(x_2 - x_1)^2 + (y_2 - y_1)^2}$,

where we agree to choose the positive sign on the radical.

2. *Symmetry*. *Two points P and Q are said to be* **symmetric with respect to a line** *l if the straight line interval joining P and Q is perpendicular to l and is bisected by it. Two points P and Q are said to be* **symmetric with respect to a third point** *R if R is the mid-point of the straight line interval joining P and Q.* Suppose $P(x, y)$ is a point on the co-ordinate system. The point Q is symmetric to P with respect to the

$\left.\begin{array}{l} x\text{-axis} \\ y\text{-axis} \\ \text{origin} \end{array}\right\}$ if the co-ordinates of Q are $\left\{\begin{array}{l} (x, -y) \\ (-x, y) \\ (-x, -y). \end{array}\right.$

------| **Problem Set 2.4** |------

1. Plot the following points on a co-ordinate system and tell which quadrant each is in: $(1, 4)$, $(4, 1)$, $(-2, 5)$, $(-5, 2)$, $(-3, 0)$, $(-2, -3)$, $(7, -1)$, $(3, -1)$, $(0, 3)$, $(-3, -4)$.

2. What characteristic is shared by all points on a vertical line passing through the point $(-5, 0)$?

3. What characteristic is shared by all points on a horizontal line 2 units above the x-axis?

4. What characteristic is shared by all points on the line bisecting Quadrants I and III? On the line perpendicular to this one?

5. Given the point $P(x, y)$.
   - (a) If y is positive, in which quadrants might P fall?
   - (b) If x is negative, in which quadrants might P fall?
   - (c) If x and y have the same sign, in which quadrants might P fall?

6. Given the point $P(x, y)$.
   - (a) If P is in Quadrant II, what signs must x and y have?
   - (b) If P is in Quadrant IV, what signs must x and y have?
   - (c) If P is on the y-axis, what can be said about its co-ordinates?
   - (d) If P is equidistant from the axes, what can be said about its co-ordinates?

7. Find the distance between the following pairs of points.
   - (a) $(1, 0)$ and $(4, 0)$,
   - (b) $(3, 5)$ and $(3, -2)$,
   - (c) $(-7, -2)$ and $(-2, -2)$,
   - (d) $(-1, 4)$ and $(-1, -4)$.

8. Find the distance between the following pairs of points.
   - (a) $(-1, -3)$ and $(1, 3)$,
   - (b) $(-5, 2)$ and $(7, 1)$,
   - (c) $(4, 0)$ and $(2, 1)$,
   - (d) $(0, 0)$ and $(4, -7)$.

9. Derive the formula for the distance between the origin and an arbitrary point $P(x, y)$.

10. Write the co-ordinates of the points which are symmetric to each point of Problem 1 with respect to (a) the x-axis, (b) the y-axis, (c) the origin.

—————————| **Miscellaneous Problems** |—————————

1. What words must x and y represent if $\{a, x, y\}$ is the set of articles in the English language?

2. List all distinct two-digit numbers formed from the elements of the set $\{1, 2, 3\}$.

3. List all different two-element sets formed from the digits 1, 2, and 3.

REMARK 1. *A natural number greater than* 1 *is called* **prime** *if it cannot be written as the product of two factors other than itself and* 1. For example, the first three prime numbers are 2, 3, and 5.

4. List the set of primes less than 30.

5. Specify the elements belonging to the set of odd prime numbers less than 15.

6. How many elements are there in the set of whole numbers
   - (a) between -4 and 10,

(b) between -11 and 0,

(c) between -15 and -3?

7. Suppose a and b are whole numbers and $a < b$. Devise a rule for obtaining the number of elements in the set of whole numbers between a and b.

8. Using the rule found in Problem 7, how many whole numbers are there

(a) between -21 and 203,

(b) between -728 and -325?

9. Is the following number rational or irrational?

(a) $0.1\ 01\ 001\ 0001\ 00001 \cdots$. (The number of zeros is increased by one at each step.)

(b) $0.1\ 11\ 111\ 1111 \cdots$. (The number of ones is increased by one at each step.)

10. Find a fraction representing the repeating decimal

(a) $0.123451234512345 \cdots$,

(b) $0.1010010\ 1010010\ 1010010 \cdots$.

11. Show that

$$0.49999 \cdots = \tfrac{1}{2}.$$

12. Show that the numbers in each pair are equal:

(a) 0.75 and $0.749999 \cdots$,

(b) 0.33 and $0.329999 \cdots$,

(c) 0.01 and $0.009999 \cdots$.

REMARK 2. As indicated in Problem 12, any terminating decimal can be expressed as an infinite repeating decimal of Period 1.

13. Write an equivalent infinite decimal for the fraction

(a) $\tfrac{1}{8}$,

(b) $\tfrac{1}{4}$,

(c) $\tfrac{9}{1000}$.

14. Suppose d is an unknown digit. If the denominator of a is $1,111$, find d when

(a) $a = 0.015d\ 015d \cdots$,

(b) $a = 0.017d\ 017d \cdots$.

15. Explain in your own words the distinction between a *relation* and a *function*.

16. Which of the following relations is also a function?

(a) To each son corresponds his mother.

(b) To each mother correspond her children.

(c) To each teacher correspond his (or her) students.

(d) To each student corresponds his (or her) first-period subject.

17. Explain in your own words the distinction between *domain* and *range*.

18. Describe carefully the domain and range for each relation listed in Problem 16.

19. If $f(x)$ is to be real valued, what are the inadmissible values of x in the expression

(a) $f(x) = \sqrt{x}$,
(b) $f(x) = 1/\sqrt{x}$,
(c) $f(x) = \sqrt{1 - x}$,
(d) $f(x) = 1/\sqrt{1 - x}$?

20. If the domain is $-3 \leq x \leq 5$, sketch the graph of

$$y = \begin{cases} 0 & \text{for } x \geq 0, \\ 1 & \text{for } x < 0. \end{cases}$$

21. Let z be a variable that ranges over the set of even whole numbers. For each even whole number the function $f(x)$ is given by

$$f(x) = x - z \quad \text{for} \quad z - 1 \leq x < z + 1.$$

Sketch the graph of this function.

22. Each of the pairs of points (1, 4) and (4, 1), $(-2, -5)$ and $(-5, -2)$, $(-3, 3)$ and $(3, -3)$ is symmetric with respect to the same line. What line is it, and how far is each point from it?

23. Let the three vertices of a triangle be the points $P(0, 0)$, $Q(5, 0)$, and $R(5, 4)$.

(a) What is the area of this triangle?
(b) If R is replaced by the point $(5, -4)$, is the area changed?
(c) If R is replaced by the point $(8, 4)$, is the area changed?
(d) If R is replaced by the point $(5, y)$, what positive value of y produces an area of 25 square units?

24. A line segment has the end points (1, 3) and (6, 3). Find the co-ordinates of any point (above the line segment) which will form with the given two points a triangle of area 20 square units. Is there more than one such point? If so, how are their co-ordinates related?

25. Plot the graph of each of the following functions by finding the values in the range corresponding to the values 0, ± 1 and ± 3 in the domain.

(a) $y = x/3$,
(b) $y = |x/3|$,
(c) $y = x/3 - 2$,
(d) $y = |x/3 - 2|$.

3

INTRODUCTION TO THE TRIGONOMETRIC FUNCTIONS

We shall make frequent use of a circle of positive radius r having its center at the origin of a rectangular co-ordinate system. We call such a circle a **standard circle** and denote it by the letter C.

Suppose we are given a standard circle C on which is marked off a central angle[1] as shown in Fig. 3.1. Let s be the length of arc on C subtending the central angle θ. From plane geometry we recall three results.

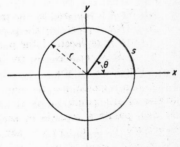

Fig. 3.1

1. *If a circle be divided into 360 equal central angles, any one of them is a unit in the **degree** system of measuring angles.* Thus the entire circumference subtends an angle of 360 degrees (360°).

One degree (1°) = 60 minutes (60′) = 3,600 seconds (3,600″).

2. *The circumference of a circle of radius r units is $2\pi r$ units.*

3. *In the same circle two central angles are in the same ratio as their intercepted arcs.*

---

[1] A central angle is formed by the intersection of two radii of the circle.

20

1. RADIAN MEASURE

Using the results of plane geometry related to C, the connections among s, r and θ are found quite easily. If θ is measured in degrees, then

$$\frac{s}{2\pi r} = \frac{\theta}{360},$$

from which

$$s = \frac{\pi}{180} \cdot r \cdot \theta,$$

and

$$\theta = \frac{180}{\pi r} \cdot s.$$

The number $\pi/180$ is called a *dimensional constant,* a phrase borrowed from physics in which the word "dimension" refers to the physical units of measurement. Different dimensional constants may occur depending upon the system of angle measurement used. In more advanced physics and mathematics it is inconvenient to express angular measure in terms of degrees, because doing so introduces into many formulas an unnecessary complication in the form of just such a constant. The simplest kind of angular measure that eliminates this complication is radian measure.

Let P be a point that moves continuously in one direction along C from a given initial position to a definite final position. As P moves, it generates an arc having length denoted by the number s. We shall agree to call this number positive if the motion is counter-clockwise and negative if the motion is clockwise. For example, the number $s = 2\pi r$ (or $s = -2\pi r$) corresponds to the situation in which P has moved counterclockwise (or clockwise) exactly one revolution. The arc generated by P subtends a central angle which we denote by θ. From result 3, stated above, we know that θ is proportional to arc length; that is, $\theta = k \cdot s$, where k is the factor of proportionality. This equation implies that the system used to measure the angle depends upon the value chosen for k. The choice of any real number for k (except $k = 0$) leads to a possible system for measuring the angle θ. For example, (1) we may choose $k = 180/\pi r$, obtaining the degree system of measuring angles used at the beginning of this section; or (2) we may choose $k = 1$, thus measuring θ by the arc length itself. The second of these systems has a disadvantage avoided in the first, for in it the measure of the angle θ is dependent upon the radius of C. This dependence follows from another plane geometry result.

4. *For a given central angle, its intercepted arc is proportional to the radius;* that is, $s = p \cdot r$, where p is the factor of proportionality.

On the other hand, the first system has the disadvantage of being more complicated than the second.

Our problem is to find a value for k that avoids as far as possible the disadvantages of each system; in other words, we want to find the simplest value for k that eliminates the dependence upon r. This criterion is satisfied if we choose $k = 1/r$, which in itself is quite simple and which avoids the dependence upon r by the effective expedient of canceling it out. Assigning this value to k, we determine a new system in which the measure of the angle θ is given by the equation $\theta = s/r$. Since the radius of C is positive, the number that measures the angle θ is positive or negative depending upon whether P has moved counterclockwise or clockwise.

The system that we have just selected for measuring angles is called the **radian method** of angle measurement. The unit in this system is determined by setting $\theta = 1$, from which it follows that $s = r$ for an angle of one unit. Thus *one* **radian** *is the measure of any angle subtended on C by an arc of length equal to the radius of C.* Since both s and r have the same physical dimension of length, it is evident that the number s/r is dimensionless from the point of view of physical applications. The radian measure of an angle is a real number; furthermore any real number may be considered the radian measure of some angle. Except where specifically indicated otherwise, we shall use the radian method of measuring angles, and in general we shall make no distinction between the angle itself and the number that measures the angle.

From the previous discussion we know that radian measure does not depend upon the radius of C. Similarly, degree measure also is independent of the radius of C. Since one complete revolution of P in the positive sense generates the number $2\pi r$, the number of radians contained in the angle described by that motion is 2π (because 2π is the number of times the radius r divides into the circumference $2\pi r$). This fact is sufficient to establish the correspondence in angular measurement between the degree and radian systems:

2π *radians is equivalent to* 360 *degrees,*
  1 *radian is equivalent to* $180/\pi$ *degrees (approximately* 57°17'45''),
  1 *degree is equivalent to* $\pi/180$ *radian (approximately* 0.017453 *radian).*

The first of these statements is to be interpreted as follows: 2π is the radian measure of an angle whose degree measure is 360; and similarly for the other statements.

In this section we have used the proportionality $\theta = k \cdot s$ to introduce the concept of radian measure. Our choice for k was $k = 1/r$, and one might object that we have chosen a variable for what obviously should be a constant. The point here is that in the use of the formula $\theta = k \cdot s$ we are considering a given circle C for which the radius, although arbitrarily chosen, is some definite number r. Hence $1/r$ actually is a constant with reference to the circle C.

──────────| **Problem Set 3.1** |──────────────

1. What is the radian equivalent of each of the angles: 42°, −16°, 1040°, −715°, 22°30'?

2. What is the degree equivalent of each of the angles (given in radians): $5\pi/6$, $7\pi/12$, $-11\pi/5$, $21\pi/4$, $-\sqrt{2}\pi$?

3. What can be said about the relation between the arc length and subtended angle on a circle of radius one unit, if the angle is measured in (a) radians, (b) degrees?

4. The earth revolves about the sun in a path that is very nearly a circle (actually it is closer to an ellipse). Suppose we let L represent a straight line joining the earth to the sun. If the path were actually a circle, through how many radians would L turn in (a) one year, (b) one day, (c) one week?

5. What angle in radians does an arc of length 12 units subtend on a circle having radius (a) 8 units, (b) π units, (c) 12 units, (d) $2/\pi$ units, (e) $3/\pi$ units? Express each of these angles also in degrees.

6. What must be the radius of the circle if an arc of length 10 units subtends an angle of (a) 1 radian, (b) π radians, (c) 10 radians, (d) $\frac{1}{4}$ radian?

7. What must be the radius of a circle in order that the measure of the subtended angle in radians shall be (a) $\frac{1}{2}$ the arc length, (b) π times the arc length, (c) $1/\pi$ times the arc length, (d) 4 times the arc length?

8. On page 22 we used the proportionality, $s = p \cdot r$. If θ is the angle subtended by s,
   (a) find p if θ is measured in radians,
   (b) find p if θ is measured in degrees.

2. APPLICATIONS OF RADIAN MEASURE

The discussion of radian measure indicates that a second formula for arc length is given by $s = r \cdot \theta$, where θ is measured in radians. This formula may be obtained by direct substitution in the original expression

$$s = \frac{\pi}{180} \cdot r \cdot \theta \text{(measured in degrees)}.$$

Since in one radian there are $180/\pi$ degrees, it follows that the number of degrees in a given angle is equal to the number of radians in that angle multiplied by $180/\pi$; that is

$$\theta \text{(measured in degrees)} = \frac{180}{\pi} \cdot \theta \text{(measured in radians)}.$$

Substituting this relationship above, we have

$$s = \frac{\pi}{180} \cdot r \cdot \frac{180}{\pi} \cdot \theta \text{(measured in radians)},$$

$$s = r \cdot \theta \text{(measured in radians)}.$$

Because of its simplicity, this is the formula for arc length most frequently used.

Another problem, closely allied to the one just discussed, illustrates also the convenience of radian measure. We wish to find the area A

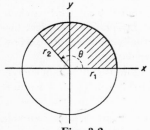

Fig. 3.2

of a **sector** of a circle; that is, the area cut out by two radii having a given angle θ between them (see Fig. 3.2). From plane geometry we know that the ratio of the area of the sector to the total area of the circle is the same as the ratio of the angle θ to the total angle in the circle. If θ is measured in radians, then

$$\frac{A}{\pi r^2} = \frac{\theta}{2\pi} \quad \text{or} \quad A = \frac{1}{2} \cdot r^2 \cdot \theta.$$

If θ were measured in degrees then the formula for area would have a more complicated appearance. In this particular application we think of θ as being measured in the positive direction since we wish A to be given by a positive number.

—————————| **Problem Set 3.2** |—————————

1. What is the area of the sector cut out of a circle of radius one unit by a central angle measuring (a) 1 radian, (b) 1 degree, (c) 30 degrees, (d) 1.25 radians, (e) 300 degrees?

2. In Problem 4 of Problem Set 3.1, if the distance from the earth to the sun is assumed to be 93,000,000 miles, what is the area of the sector swept out by L in one day; in one week?

3. The diameter of one pie is 12 inches and that of another pie is 10 inches. A slice is cut from the first having a vertex angle of 0.6 radian, and a slice is cut from the second having a vertex angle of 0.8 radian. Which slice is larger?

4. A circle of radius one unit rotates so that a point on the circumference makes two revolutions per second. How long does it take the point to cover each of the angles in Problem 1?

5. A wheel has five equally spaced spokes.
    (a) What is the angle in radians between two adjacent spokes?
    (b) What is the diameter of the wheel if the area between adjacent spokes is 100 square inches?
    (c) If the wheel rotates at the rate of two revolutions per minute, how long does it take a spoke to cover the angle in part (a)?

6. A bicycle with tires 28 inches in diameter is ridden at a speed of 10 miles per hour. Through what circular arc length does a point on the tire move in one second?

7. If the minute hand of a watch is one-half inch long,
    (a) how far does the tip of the hand move in 25 minutes?
    (b) how far does the tip of the hand move in one day?

3. ANGLE

In the preceding sections we have worked with an intuitive concept of angle, but for the future we shall need a more definite indication of how the word "angle" is to be interpreted.

We will consider a **geometric angle** $\angle AOB$ as being identified by
1. a vertex (usually the center of a standard circle C),
2. an initial side (usually the radius of C lying along the positive x-axis),
3. a terminal side (usually a radius of C),
4. a real number (associated with some given system of measurement; for example, radian or degree).

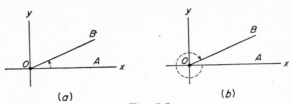

Fig. 3.3

In Figs. 3.3 (a) and (b) the angles are to be considered different even though their initial (OA) and terminal (OB) sides are in the same relative positions: the angle in (a) is measured by a positive number, the angle in (b) by a negative number.

We shall make frequent use of the statement, "the point P **generates** an angle θ," or of the statement, "θ is a **generated angle**," to describe the following idea: *from an initial position at $(r, 0)$ on C a point P moves in one direction continuously along C until it has covered an arc equal in length to the number $s = r \cdot \theta(\text{in radians})$.* When we speak of a point P having *generated* an angle, we mean that the vertex is at the origin, the initial side is along the positive x-axis, while the terminal side is along the half-line joining the origin to P.

Now suppose that θ and ϕ are two generated angles. This statement implies that the initial sides of θ and ϕ are identical. *If, in addition, the terminal sides of θ and ϕ are identical we say that the two angles are* **coterminal.** It is not hard to see that if any two numbers differ by a multiple of 2π, then the generated angles measured in radians by these numbers are coterminal. In a later chapter we will need to consider the sum (or difference) of two angles. *If two generated angles are measured by the numbers m and n, then the* **sum** *(or* **difference***) of these angles is that generated angle which is measured by the number $m + n$ (or $m - n$).*

The statement that a generated angle (if not a whole number multiple of a right angle) is in some one of the four quadrants means simply that the terminal side of the angle lies in the specified quadrant. The numerical value of the angle may or may not be between 0 and 2π. Thus the generated angle $\pi/4$ (45°) is a first-quadrant angle, but so also are the coterminal angles $9\pi/4$ (405°) and $-7\pi/4$ ($-315°$).

————————| **Problem Set 3.3** |————————

1. In which quadrant is each of the following generated angles:
(a) 45°,   (b) 135°   (c) $-3\pi/4$,   (d) $\pi/12$,

(e) $7\pi/3$,   (f) $305°$,   (g) $710°$,   (h) $9\pi/4$,

(i) $-30°$,   (j) $-4\pi/3$,   (k) $5\pi/4$,   (l) $-15\pi/4$?

2. Which of the angles in Problem 1 are coterminal?

3. Sketch each of the following generated angles:

(a) $45° + 30°$,   (b) $215° - 35°$,   (c) $11\pi/4 - \pi/4$,

(d) $\pi/3 + 4\pi/3$,   (e) $150° + 60°$,   (f) $7\pi/2 - \pi$.

4. Which, if any, of the angles in Problem 3 are coterminal?

REMARK. In the following problems recall that n represents a variable on the set of natural numbers.

5. Sketch the generated angles in each of the following infinite sets for $n = 0$, 1, and 2:

(a) $\{0 \pm n\pi\}$,   (b) $\{0 \pm 2n\pi\}$,   (c) $\{\pi/2 \pm n\pi\}$,

(d) $\{\pi/2 \pm 2n\pi\}$,   (e) $\{\pi \pm n\pi/2\}$,   (f) $\{\pi \pm 3n\pi/2\}$.

6. For each of the six infinite sets of angles in Problem 5, what characteristic is common to all angles in a given set?

7. In Problem 5, which (if any) of the sets are equal, that is, contain the same angles?

8. Give an expression for an infinite set of generated angles each having its terminal side along the negative y-axis.

9. Give an expression for an infinite set of generated angles each having its terminal side along the negative x-axis.

4. TRIGONOMETRIC DEFINITIONS

Let C be a standard circle of radius r, and let the point $P(x, y)$ on C generate an angle θ. With this angle there are associated three num-

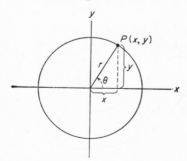

Fig. 3.4

bers, x, y, and r, from which we may form exactly six ratios called the trigonometric ratios:

sine of θ	$= sin\ \theta$	$= y/r$	$= ordinate/radius,$
cosine of θ	$= cos\ \theta$	$= x/r$	$= abscissa/radius,$
tangent of θ	$= tan\ \theta$	$= y/x$	$= ordinate/abscissa,$
cotangent of θ	$= cot\ \theta$	$= x/y$	$= abscissa/ordinate,$
secant of θ	$= sec\ \theta$	$= r/x$	$= radius/abscissa,$
cosecant of θ	$= csc\ \theta$	$= r/y$	$= radius/ordinate.$

As always when dealing with quotients, these definitions are subject to the condition that the expression is undefined at any value of θ for which the denominator is zero.

The second column gives the usual abbreviations of these ratios. A point to be stressed here is that for a specific value of θ the symbol $sin\ \theta$ (or any other of the trigonometric symbols) represents simply a real number and must not be thought of as a product of the two symbols sin and θ.

In Section 1 the radian measure of an angle θ was defined so as to be independent of the radius of the standard circle C. We have defined the trigonometric ratios in terms of a standard circle, and the question naturally arises: are these ratios also independent of the radius of C? The following argument shows that the answer is affirmative.

Let C be a standard circle and suppose that the angle θ is generated

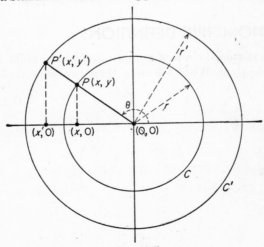

Fig. 3.5

by the point $P(x, y)$. Now let C' be any other circle concentric with C but of different radius. If the angle θ is generated by the point $P'(x', y')$ on C', then the points P and P' are collinear. From plane geometry we know that the right triangles $[(0, 0), (x, y), (x, 0)]$ and $[(0, 0), (x', y'), (x', 0)]$ are similar; therefore the ratios of corresponding side lengths are equal. Since corresponding co-ordinates of both points must have the same sign, it follows that the trigonometric ratios formed on C' are identical with those formed on C.

Thus the trigonometric ratios are indeed functions having θ as independent variable. Sin θ, for a given angle, is the same number regardless of what positive value is chosen for r. For this reason, we are at liberty to choose a defining circle of any convenient radius. In Section 6 we will have examples of the use of several different radii.

Because the trigonometric ratios are defined in terms of the co-ordinates of a point on a circle, they are sometimes referred to as **circular functions.**

5. ELEMENTARY RELATIONSHIPS

Because we have assumed that the radius of C is a positive quantity, the signs of the trigonometric functions are determined by the signs of the co-ordinates of P. For example, sin θ is positive for θ in Quadrants I and II and is negative for θ in Quadrants III and IV (because y has those signs). In this connection, we notice that the sign of each function in the following pairs must be the same for any admissible angle θ: sin θ and csc θ, cos θ and sec θ, tan θ and cot θ. This is because these functions, by definition, are reciprocals of one another; that is,

$$\csc\ \theta = 1/\sin\ \theta \quad \text{or} \quad \sin\ \theta \cdot \csc\ \theta = 1$$
$$\sec\ \theta = 1/\cos\ \theta \quad \text{or} \quad \cos\ \theta \cdot \sec\ \theta = 1$$
$$\cot\ \theta = 1/\tan\ \theta \quad \text{or} \quad \tan\ \theta \cdot \cot\ \theta = 1.$$

Another important relationship is:

$$\tan\ \theta = \sin\ \theta/\cos\ \theta, \text{ for admissible values of } \theta$$

(that is, values for which cos θ is not zero). This result follows immediately from the definitions since

$$\frac{\sin\ \theta}{\cos\ \theta} = \frac{(y/r)}{(x/r)} = (y/r) \cdot (r/x) = \frac{y}{x} = \tan\ \theta.$$

A consequence of this is the relationship

$$\cot \theta = \cos \theta / \sin \theta, \text{ for admissible values of } \theta.$$

──────────────| **Problem Set 3.4** |──────────────────

1. List the trigonometric functions, if any, that are undefined at the following generated angles.

(a) $\pi/2$,   (b) 0,   (c) $-\pi$,

(d) $-3\pi/2$,   (e) $7\pi/4$,   (f) $-\pi/4$,

(g) $3\pi/2$,   (h) -2π,   (i) π.

In each of the following problems evaluate the six trigonometric functions of the angle θ under the given conditions.

2. $r = 2$ and θ is generated by the point $P(1, \sqrt{3})$.

3. $r = 2$ and θ is generated by the point $P(\sqrt{3}, -1)$.

4. $r = 2$ and θ is generated by the point $P(0, 2)$.

5. $r = 5$ and θ is generated by the point $P(-4, 3)$.

6. $r = 5$ and θ is generated by the point $P(-3, -4)$.

7. $r = \sqrt{2}$ and θ is generated by the point $P(1, -1)$.

8. $r = \sqrt{2}$ and θ is generated by the point $P(-\sqrt{2}, 0)$.

6. EXAMPLES

There is an interesting type of trigonometric problem which can be solved directly from the definitions and elementary relationships. The solution does not even require that we know the value of the angle under consideration. The problem in general can be stated as follows: given a value for one of the trigonometric functions of an angle θ together with enough additional information to fix the quadrant of θ, how then may we evaluate the other trigonometric functions of that angle? As the first step, sketch a standard circle C and let P generate θ in the proper quadrant. From P draw a line segment perpendicular to the horizontal axis and note that this forms a right triangle with its base on the x-axis. From the given ratio we may assign values to two of the quantities x, y, and r. The third may be computed from the Pythagorean theorem and can be given the proper sign according to the quadrant of θ. Knowing these three quantities, we may then evaluate the other functions at θ.

EXAMPLE 1. If $\tan \theta = \frac{3}{4}$ and if $\sin \theta$ is positive, evaluate the trigonometric functions of θ.

Solution. Sin θ is positive only if y is positive; therefore $P(x,y)$ lies above the x-axis. Tan θ is positive only if θ is in Quadrants I or III; hence θ must be in Quadrant I (if θ were in Quadrant III, y would be negative). Sketch C and the terminal side of the angle θ.

Because $\tan \theta = y/x = \frac{3}{4}$, we assign, for convenience, the values $x = 4$ and $y = 3$ as the co-ordinates of P. The value of r is then computed by the equation $r^2 = x^2 + y^2 = 16 + 9 = 25$. Thus $r = \pm 5$, and we choose $r = 5$, since the radius is assumed positive. The required values are

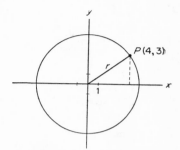

$$\sin \theta = \tfrac{3}{5}, \quad \cot \theta = \tfrac{4}{3},$$
$$\cos \theta = \tfrac{4}{5}, \quad \sec \theta = \tfrac{5}{4},$$
$$\tan \theta = \tfrac{3}{4}, \quad \csc \theta = \tfrac{5}{3}.$$

Fig. 3.6

EXAMPLE 2. If $\cos \theta = -1/\sqrt{2}$ and if $\csc \theta$ is negative, evaluate the trigonometric functions of θ.

Solution. Both $\cos \theta$ and $\csc \theta$ are negative only if θ is in Quadrant III. Sketch C and the terminal side of the angle θ.

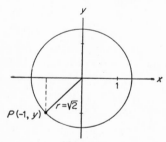

Fig. 3.7

Because $\cos \theta = x/r = -1/\sqrt{2}$, we assign the values $r = \sqrt{2}$ and $x = -1$ and then compute y by the equation

$$y^2 = r^2 - x^2 = 2 - 1 = 1.$$

Thus $y = \pm 1$, and we choose $y = -1$ since θ is in Quadrant III. The required values are

$$\sin \theta = -1/\sqrt{2}, \quad \cot \theta = 1,$$
$$\cos \theta = -1/\sqrt{2}, \quad \sec \theta = -\sqrt{2},$$
$$\tan \theta = -1/-1 = 1, \quad \csc \theta = -\sqrt{2}.$$

——————| **Problem Set 3.5** |——————

1. In which quadrants might θ lie if:
    (a) $\sin \theta = -\frac{1}{2}$, (b) $\sin \theta = \sqrt{2}/2$, (c) $\cos \theta = \frac{1}{3}$,
    (d) $\sec \theta = 3$, (e) $\csc \theta = -2$, (f) $\tan \theta = -1$,
    (g) $\cos \theta = -\sqrt{2}/3$, (h) $\tan \theta = 2$, (i) $\cot \theta = -1$?

2. In which quadrant must θ lie if:
    (a) $\sin \theta$ and $\cos \theta$ are positive;
    (b) $\tan \theta$ is positive and $\sec \theta$ is negative;
    (c) $\cos \theta$ is negative and $\cot \theta$ is positive;
    (d) $\cot \theta$ and $\csc \theta$ are negative;
    (e) $\sin \theta$ is negative and $\sec \theta$ is positive?

In each of the following problems evaluate the trigonometric functions of the angle θ under the given conditions.

3. $\sin \theta = \frac{3}{4}$ and θ is in Quadrant II.

4. $\cos \theta = -\frac{1}{3}$ and $\sin \theta$ is negative.

5. $\tan \theta = 5/2$ and $\sec \theta$ is positive.

6. $\sin \theta = 5/13$ and $\cos \theta = -12/13$.

7. $\sin \theta = -\frac{1}{2}$ and $\cos \theta = \sqrt{3}/2$.

8. $\tan \theta = -\frac{3}{4}$ and $\sec \theta = 5/4$.

9. $\sin \theta = \sqrt{5}/3$ and $\cos \theta = -4/6$.

10. $\sec \theta = 2/\sqrt{3}$ and $\csc \theta = -2$.

——————| **Miscellaneous Problems** |——————

1. Using a protractor, sketch the generated angles.
    (a) $25°$, (b) $-305°$, (c) $170°$,
    (d) $-130°$, (e) $195°$, (f) $-10°$.

2. Find the radian measure of each angle in Problem 1.

3. On the same co-ordinate system, plot the point P and also the point P' in which the abscissa and ordinate of P are interchanged.
    (a) $P(2, 5)$, (b) $P(-1, 6)$, (c) $P(4, 0)$,
    (d) $P(3, -7)$, (e) $P(-2, -2)$, (f) $P(0, 0)$.

4. In each part of Problem 3, P and P' are located in which quadrants?

5. (a) What common property is shared by all triangles having vertices $(0, 0)$, $(x, 0)$, (x, y)?
    (b) Sketch any three particular cases (for example, $x = 3$ and $y = 5$, etc.).
    (c) What additional property do the triangles share if $y = x$?

6. Draw the graph of the function
$$y = |x| + |x - 1|$$
Plot at least the points corresponding to $x = 0, 1, -1, 2, -2, 4, -4$.

REMARK 1. *If a radius rotates through an angle θ in a time interval t, then θ/t is called its* **average angular velocity**.

7. What is the average angular velocity of
(a) the minute hand of a watch?
(b) the hour hand of a watch?

8. What is the average angular velocity (in radians per second) of the earth as it rotates about its axis?

REMARK 2. In military terminology, *an angle of one* **mil** *is subtended by an arc of length one yard at a distance of* 1,000 *yards.*

9. How many mils are there in an angle of (a) one degree, (b) one radian?

10. In the proportionality, $\theta = k \cdot s$, find k if θ is measured in mils (assume radius and arc length measured in yards).

REMARK 3. *A plane which passes through the center of a sphere cuts the surface of the sphere in a path called a* **great circle**. For the following problems assume that the earth is a sphere of diameter 7,920 miles.

REMARK 4. *A* **nautical mile** *is approximately the length of arc along a great circle on the earth's surface which subtends at the center of the earth an angle of* 1 *minute.*

11. One nautical mile is equivalent to how many statute miles?

12. A ship sails along a great circle route from San Francisco to Honolulu. If the distance covered is 2,408 nautical miles, what angle (in radians) is subtended at the center of the earth by the path of the ship?

13. In the proportionality, $\theta = k \cdot s$, find k if θ is measured in radians, s in nautical miles, and r in statute miles.

14. In some cases it is convenient to use one right angle as the unit of angular measurement. In the equation, $\theta = k \cdot s$, determine k so that θ is measured in right-angle units.

15. Express the following angles in right-angle units:
(a) $180°$, (b) $-150°$, (c) $\pi/6$ radians,
(d) $-7\pi/5$ radians, (e) $5/2$ radians, (f) $75°$.

16. On page 22 we used the proportionality, $s = p \cdot r$. If θ is the angle subtended by s, find p
(a) if θ is measured in mils,
(b) if θ is measured in right-angle units.

17. Find which two of the following infinite sets of generated angles are equal:

$$\left\{\frac{\pi}{2}(1 \pm n)\right\}, \quad \left\{\frac{\pi}{4}(2 \pm n)\right\}, \quad \left\{0 \pm \frac{n\pi}{2}\right\}.$$

18. Express the following infinite set of generated angles in a different way

$$\left\{\pm(2n - 1)\frac{\pi}{2}\right\}.$$

19. Give an expression for an infinite set of generated angles each having terminal side coinciding with the line (from the origin) which bisects the first quadrant.

20. Give an expression for an infinite set of generated angles each having its terminal side on the line which bisects Quadrants II and IV.

21. Prove directly from the trigonometric definitions that:

(a) $\cot \theta = \dfrac{\cos \theta}{\sin \theta}$,

(b) $\csc \theta \cdot \cos \theta = \cot \theta$,

(c) $\sec \theta \cdot \sin \theta = \tan \theta$.

22. In Problem 21, what values of θ are inadmissible?

23. From the basic definitions, show that

(a) $\sin \theta$ is never greater than 1,

(b) $\cos \theta$ is never greater than 1.

24. From the basic definitions, show that

(a) $\sec \theta$ has no positive value less than 1,

(b) $\csc \theta$ has no positive value less than 1.

25. Is the following combination of signs possible? If so, in what quadrant must θ be?

(a) $\sin \theta$ positive, $\cos \theta$ negative, and $\tan \theta$ negative,

(b) $\sin \theta$ negative, $\cos \theta$ positive, and $\cot \theta$ positive,

(c) $\sin \theta$ positive, $\tan \theta$ positive, and $\sec \theta$ negative.

26. Which of the following combinations are possible?

(a) $\sin \theta > 0$, $\cos \theta = 0$, $\tan \theta$ undefined,

(b) $\cos \theta < 0$, $\tan \theta = 1$, $\sec \theta < -1$,

(c) $\sin \theta = 0$, $\cos \theta = 0$, $\tan \theta = 0$.

27. Find the six trigonometric values associated with the point $P(7, 24)$ [*Hint:* Use the Pythagorean theorem to find r.]

28. Find the six trigonometric values associated with the point $P(-5, \sqrt{11})$.

29. Find the remaining trigonometric values if

$$\sin \theta = -\tfrac{4}{5}, \text{ and } \sec \theta > 0.$$

30. Find the remaining trigonometric values if

$$(\sin \theta)(\cos \theta) = \tfrac{1}{2}, \text{ and } \tan \theta = 1.$$

4

NUMERICAL PROPERTIES OF THE TRIGONOMETRIC FUNCTIONS

The trigonometric definitions, given in the preceding chapter, make up the nucleus for all theoretical discussions and practical applications of trigonometry. In this chapter we shall be concerned with one of the basic problems of trigonometry, that of assigning numerical values to the trigonometric ratios.

1. DOMAIN AND RANGE

Each trigonometric ratio is a function having as its unrestricted domain the set of all real numbers except those for which the given ratio is undefined. The domain of the sine function is the set of all real numbers, because $\sin \theta$ is never undefined ($\sin \theta = y/r$ and $r > 0$). On the other hand, $\tan \theta$ ($= y/x$) is undefined for values of θ for which $x = 0$; that is, $\theta = \pi/2$ and all whole number multiples of π added to that number. Hence these numbers must be excluded from the domain of the tangent function. Geometrically, of course, we think of a number in the domain as measuring a generated angle.

The following tabulation gives both domain and range of each trigonometric function.

Function	Domain	Range
$\sin \theta$	R (all real numbers)	$-1 \leqq \sin \theta \leqq 1$
$\cos \theta$	R	$-1 \leqq \cos \theta \leqq 1$
$\tan \theta$	R except $\{\pi/2 \pm n\pi\}$	R
$\cot \theta$	R except $\{\pm n\pi\}$	R
$\sec \theta$	R except $\{\pi/2 \pm n\pi\}$	$\sec \theta \leqq -1, \sec \theta \geqq 1$
$\csc \theta$	R except $\{\pm n\pi\}$	$\csc \theta \leqq -1, \csc \theta \geqq 1.$

Problem Set 4.1

1. What is the range of each of the trigonometric functions if the domain is restricted as follows?

(a) $0 \leqq \theta \leqq \pi,$ (b) $0 \leqq \theta \leqq \pi/2.$

2. What is the range of each of the trigonometric functions if the domain is restricted to be $-\pi/2 < \theta < \pi/2$?

3. What is the unrestricted domain of the function $f(\theta)$ if

(a) $f(\theta) = \sin \theta + \tan \theta,$
(b) $f(\theta) = \tan \theta - \cot \theta,$
(c) $f(\theta) = 1/(\sin \theta + \cos \theta)$?

4. What is the unrestricted domain of the function $g(\theta)$ if

(a) $g(\theta) = 1/\sin \theta,$
(b) $g(\theta) = 1/\cos \theta,$
(c) $g(\theta) = \sec \theta - \csc \theta$?

REMARK. An entire expression is undefined if any one of its component parts is undefined.

5. Find the inadmissible angles on the interval $0 \leqq \theta < 2\pi$ for each of the following expressions.

(a) $\tan \theta + \cot \theta,$ (c) $\sin \theta + 1/\cos \theta,$
(b) $\tan \theta/\cos \theta,$ (d) $\sec \theta/\sin \theta.$

6. Find the inadmissible angles on the interval $0 \leqq \theta < 2\pi$ for each of the following expressions:

(a) $\cos \theta/(1 - \sin \theta),$ (b) $\sin \theta/(\tan \theta - \cot \theta).$

In each of the following problems, find the range of $f(\theta)$ if the domain is the set of all admissible values.

7. $f(\theta) = 2 \cos \theta,$ **9.** $f(\theta) = \sin \theta + 1,$
8. $f(\theta) = -2 \sin \theta,$ **10.** $f(\theta) = 1 - \cos \theta.$

2. QUADRANTAL ANGLES

If the point P on C generates an angle measured by one of the numbers $\{\pm n\pi/2\}$*, that angle is called a* **quadrantal angle.** In other words, a quadrantal angle is a generated angle having its terminal side on one of the co-ordinate axes. The first four non-negative quadrantal angles are 0, $\pi/2$, π, $3\pi/2$. These angles are not considered to lie in any quadrant.

For any non-quadrantal angle, each of the six trigonometric functions has a definite real number value. For quadrantal angles, however, certain of these functions are undefined because the defining ratio would involve division by zero. We can easily evaluate the defined trigonometric functions of the quadrantal angles by noticing that the co-ordinate axes intersect a standard circle in the points $(r, 0)$, $(0, r)$, $(-r, 0)$, and $(0, -r)$. Thus the ratios can only be 1, -1, 0, or undefined. Table 2 in Section 4 lists the trigonometric values for all the quadrantal angles. As an example of how these values are determined, we consider the generated angle $\theta = \pi$. The angle π is generated by the point $P(-r, 0)$, hence the three numbers associated with this angle are $x = -r$, $y = 0$, and r. From the definitions we have

$$\sin \pi = (0/r) = 0, \qquad \cot \pi \text{ is undefined} = (-r/0),$$
$$\cos \pi = (-r/r) = -1, \qquad \sec \pi = (r/-r) = -1,$$
$$\tan \pi = (0/-r) = 0, \qquad \csc \pi \text{ is undefined} = (r/0).$$

------------| **Problem Set 4.2** |------------

1. List all quadrantal angles between
   (a) -3π and $3\pi/2$,
   (b) $\pi/2$ and $7\pi/2$.

2. List all quadrantal angles between
   (a) $-2\pi/3$ and $9\pi/4$,
   (b) -5 and 5 (radians).

3. How many quadrantal angles are there on the interval
   (a) $|\theta| < \pi/2$,
   (b) $|\theta| \leqq \pi/2$,
   (c) $-\pi < \theta \leqq 3\pi$?

In each of the following, sketch the angle and find the trigonometric values.

4. $\theta = 0$.   6. $\theta = -\pi/2$.   8. $\theta = -3\pi$.   10. $\theta = -\pi$.

5. $\theta = \pi/2$.   7. $\theta = 7\pi/2$.   9. $\theta = 2\pi$.

3. TRIGONOMETRIC VALUES FOR SPECIAL ANGLES

From the preceding section, we know the trigonometric values for any quadrantal angle. The problem is not so simple for a nonquadrantal angle, but it can be solved for the angles $\pi/3$ (60°), $\pi/4$ (45°), and $\pi/6$ (30°), by using only elementary results from plane geometry.

Case 1, $\theta = \pi/3$. We recall from plane geometry that if a triangle has three sides equal in length it is called *equilateral*, and each of its angles is 60°. In a standard circle C we inscribe an equilateral triangle as shown in Fig. 4.1(a). From symmetry it is easy to see that the side PQ is vertical and that the three medians intersect at the origin. As

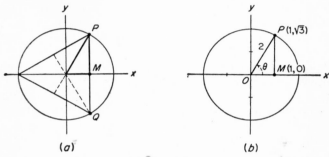

(a)   (b)

Fig. 4.1

we proved earlier, any convenient value may be selected for the radius. If we now choose a length of 2 units for the radius of C, then the length of each median is 3 units (since the medians trisect each other). As indicated in Fig. 4.1(b), the angle θ generated by P is 60° (since angle MPO is 30°). The co-ordinates of M are $(1, 0)$, and from the Pythagorean theorem we find that the co-ordinates of P are $(1, \sqrt{3})$. Hence the trigonometric values for the angle $\pi/3$ are

$$\sin \pi/3 = \sqrt{3}/2, \quad \cot \pi/3 = 1/\sqrt{3} = \sqrt{3}/3,$$
$$\cos \pi/3 = 1/2, \quad \sec \pi/3 = 2,$$
$$\tan \pi/3 = \sqrt{3}, \quad \csc \pi/3 = 2/\sqrt{3} = 2\sqrt{3}/3.$$

Case 2, $\theta = \pi/4$. In a standard circle we inscribe a square with sides parallel to the co-ordinate axes, as in Fig. 4.2(a). From symmetry it is easy to see that the diagonals intersect at the origin, and that triangle OPM is isosceles. As indicated in Fig. 4.2(b), the angle θ generated by P is 45° (the two angles on the radius are equal and add to 90°). Since

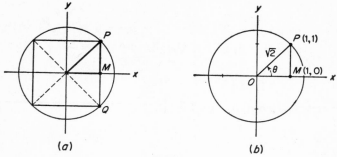

Fig. 4.2

the triangle is isosceles the horizontal and vertical legs are equal and we choose one unit as the length of each. Thus the co-ordinates of P are $(1, 1)$, and by the Pythagorean theorem we have $r = \sqrt{2}$. Hence the trigonometric values for the angle $\pi/4$ are

$$\sin \pi/4 = 1/\sqrt{2} = \sqrt{2}/2, \quad \cot \pi/4 = 1,$$
$$\cos \pi/4 = 1/\sqrt{2} = \sqrt{2}/2, \quad \sec \pi/4 = \sqrt{2},$$
$$\tan \pi/4 = 1, \quad \csc \pi/4 = \sqrt{2}.$$

Case 3, $\theta = \pi/6$. In a standard circle we inscribe a regular hexagon (six-sided polygon) as shown in Fig. 4.3(a). From symmetry it is easy to see that the side PQ is vertical and that it subtends a central angle

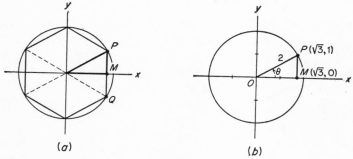

Fig. 4.3

of 60°. Thus the triangle OPQ is equilateral and the length of the segment MP is one half of the radius. As indicated in Fig. 4.3(b), the angle θ generated by P is 30°, and if we choose a radius of 2 units, then the co-ordinates of P are $(\sqrt{3}, 1)$. Hence the trigonometric values for the angle $\pi/6$ are

$$\sin \pi/6 = 1/2, \qquad \cot \pi/6 = \sqrt{3},$$
$$\cos \pi/6 = \sqrt{3}/2, \qquad \sec \pi/6 = 2/\sqrt{3} = 2\sqrt{3}/3,$$
$$\tan \pi/6 = 1/\sqrt{3} = \sqrt{3}/3, \quad \csc \pi/6 = 2.$$

———————| **Problem Set 4.3** |———————————

1. What are the co-ordinates of the point P if it generates an angle $\pi/4$ radians on a circle
  (a) of radius $\sqrt{8}$ units?
  (b) of radius 2 units?
  (c) of radius π units?

2. What are the co-ordinates of the point P on a circle of radius 6 units if P generates an angle
  (a) $\pi/3$ radians?
  (b) $\pi/4$ radian?
  (c) $\pi/6$ radian?

3. Simplify the following expressions.
  (a) $\sin \pi/3 \cdot \cos \pi/6$,
  (b) $\cos \pi/4 \cdot \tan \pi/3 - \sin \pi/6$,
  (c) $\dfrac{\sin \pi/3 \cdot \tan \pi/3}{\cot \pi/6}$.

4. Simplify the following expressions.
  (a) $\dfrac{\cos \pi/6}{\tan \pi/3} + \dfrac{1 - \sin \pi/3}{\sec \pi/6}$,
  (b) $\tan \pi/4 \cdot \cot \pi/3 \cdot \dfrac{1}{\cos \pi/3}$.

5. Show that
  (a) $\sin \pi/2 \neq \sin \pi/4 + \sin \pi/4$,
  (b) $\cos \pi/3 \neq \cos \pi/6 + \cos \pi/6$.

6. Show that
  (a) $\dfrac{\sin \pi/3 \cdot \sec \pi/3}{\cos \pi/4} = \sec \pi/4 \cdot \tan \pi/3$,
  (b) $\sin \pi/3 = \tan \pi/4 \cdot \cot \pi/6 \cdot \sin \pi/6$.

7. Fill out the following table of approximate values (use three decimal places).

TABLE 4.1

θ	$\sin \theta$	$\cos \theta$	$\tan \theta$	$\cot \theta$
0	0.000	1.000	0.000	Undefined
$\pi/6$	0.500	0.866	0.577	
$\pi/4$	0.707		1.000	
$\pi/3$				0.577
$\pi/2$				

8. Making use of the preceding table, estimate the numerical value of

(a) $2 \sin \pi/6 \cdot \cos \pi/6$,

(b) $2 \sin \pi/4 \cdot \cos \pi/4$,

(c) $(\cos \pi/6)^2 - (\sin \pi/6)^2$.

9. Referring to the table of Problem 7, what can you say about the relation of the expressions in Problem 8 to the values $\sin \pi/3$, $\sin \pi/2$, and $\cos \pi/3$? Do you think this connection is accidental?

4. TABLES OF SIGNS AND VALUES

The following tables are given for quick reference.

TABLE 4.2

Signs of the trigonometric functions of angles in the four quadrants

θ in	$\sin \theta$	$\cos \theta$	$\tan \theta$	$\cot \theta$	$\sec \theta$	$\csc \theta$
I	+	+	+	+	+	+
II	+	−	−	−	−	+
III	−	−	+	+	−	−
IV	−	+	−	−	+	−

TABLE 4.3

Values of the trigonometric functions for quadrantal angles

θ in	$\sin \theta$	$\cos \theta$	$\tan \theta$	$\cot \theta$	$\sec \theta$	$\csc \theta$
$\{0 \pm 2n\pi\}$	0	1	0	undefined	1	undefined
$\{\pi/2 \pm 2n\pi\}$	1	0	undefined	0	undefined	1
$\{\pi \pm 2n\pi\}$	0	−1	0	undefined	−1	undefined
$\{3\pi/2 \pm 2n\pi\}$	−1	0	undefined	0	undefined	−1

TABLE 4.4

Values of the trigonometric functions for special first quadrant angles

θ	$\sin \theta$	$\cos \theta$	$\tan \theta$	$\cot \theta$	$\sec \theta$	$\csc \theta$
$\pi/6$	$1/2$	$\sqrt{3}/2$	$\sqrt{3}/3$	$\sqrt{3}$	$2\sqrt{3}/3$	2
$\pi/4$	$\sqrt{2}/2$	$\sqrt{2}/2$	1	1	$\sqrt{2}$	$\sqrt{2}$
$\pi/3$	$\sqrt{3}/2$	$1/2$	$\sqrt{3}$	$\sqrt{3}/3$	2	$2\sqrt{3}/3$

5. REDUCTION FORMULAS[1]

A table of trigonometric values for all angles in degrees between $0°$ and $90°$, at one-minute intervals, is included in most mathematics handbooks and it finds frequent use in practical applications. A similar table for angles measured in radians over the same interval is found in most handbooks. Tables for angles in degrees are most useful in surveying and related fields, in which angles are actually measured in terms of degrees. The use of these tables is described in Appendix 4.

A generated angle which satisfies the inequality $0 \leqq \alpha \leqq \pi/2$ *is called a reference angle.* The reason that we may limit tabular angles to this particular interval is that the trigonometric values for any angle whatever can be reduced to terms of the trigonometric values for a reference angle. In this section we shall discuss the method by which this reduction is accomplished.

Suppose that the point $P(x, y)$ on C generates an arbitrary angle θ. The three numbers associated with θ are x, y, and r. If ϕ is any generated angle different from θ but coterminal with it, then the same three numbers x, y, and r are associated also with ϕ. This means that the trigonometric values for both θ and ϕ are identical. (Of course, in order for ϕ to be coterminal with θ it must be one of the angles $\{\theta \pm 2n\pi\}$.) Fixing the terminal side of a generated angle is sufficient to determine its trigonometric values uniquely. On the other hand, there are many different generated angles associated with the same terminal side. In fact, the set of generated angles having the same terminal side is infinite. Therefore, given any generated angle what-

---

[1]The discussion of reduction formulas given here depends strongly upon the concept of symmetry (see p. 16). Although the results are the same, the attack is different from that given in many textbooks.

ever, in order to find its trigonometric values we might determine, as a first step, the smallest non-negative generated angle coterminal with it.

Any angle outside the interval $0 \le \theta < 2\pi$ can easily be reduced to a coterminal angle on that interval. If the angle is negative we add 2π repeatedly until the result is somewhere in the desired interval; if the angle is positive we subtract 2π repeatedly until the result is somewhere in the desired interval. For example, $14\pi/3$ is coterminal with $2\pi/3$, and $-11\pi/4$ is coterminal with $5\pi/4$.

Now suppose that the point $P(x, y)$ generates a reference angle α. The point P is related by symmetry to three other points:

$Q(-x, y)$ symmetric to P with respect to the y-axis,
$R(-x, -y)$ symmetric to P with respect to the origin,
$S(x, -y)$ symmetric to P with respect to the x-axis.

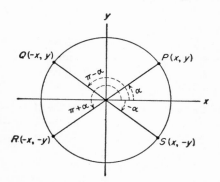

Fig. 4.4

We may assume that the angle generated by Q is $\pi - \alpha$, by R is $\pi + \alpha$, and by S is $2\pi - \alpha$. Since the angle $-\alpha$ has the same terminal side (and the same trigonometric values) as the angle $2\pi - \alpha$, we shall, for brevity, write $-\alpha$ instead of $2\pi - \alpha$. In geometric language, the points P and R, and Q and S determine the two lines which are exactly α angular units above and below the horizontal axis.

From the definitions we obtain immediately the following sets of equations:

(1)
$$\sin(\pi - \alpha) = y/r = \sin\alpha, \qquad \cot(\pi - \alpha) = -x/y = -\cot\alpha,$$
$$\cos(\pi - \alpha) = -x/r = -\cos\alpha, \qquad \sec(\pi - \alpha) = -r/x = -\sec\alpha,$$
$$\tan(\pi - \alpha) = -y/x = -\tan\alpha, \qquad \csc(\pi - \alpha) = r/y = \csc\alpha.$$

(2) $\sin(\pi + \alpha) = -y/r = -\sin\alpha,$ $\cot(\pi + \alpha) = x/y = \cot\alpha,$
    $\cos(\pi + \alpha) = -x/r = -\cos\alpha,$ $\sec(\pi + \alpha) = -r/x = -\sec\alpha,$
    $\tan(\pi + \alpha) = y/x = \tan\alpha,$ $\csc(\pi + \alpha) = -r/y = -\csc\alpha.$

(3) $\sin(-\alpha) = -y/r = -\sin\alpha,$ $\cot(-\alpha) = -x/y = -\cot\alpha,$
    $\cos(-\alpha) = x/r = \cos\alpha,$ $\sec(-\alpha) = r/x = \sec\alpha,$
    $\tan(-\alpha) = -y/x = -\tan\alpha,$ $\csc(-\alpha) = -r/y = -\csc\alpha.$

Trigonometric equations of the kind just given are called **reduction formulas.** With these three sets of equations we can express the trigonometric values for *any* angle in terms of those for a *reference* angle. For example, suppose we wish to find the trigonometric values for the angle $2\pi/3$.

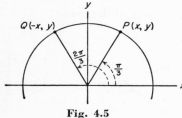

Fig. 4.5

This being a second-quadrant angle, we use the first set of formulas. Put $\pi - \alpha = 2\pi/3$, then $\alpha = \pi/3$ (a reference angle). By the formulas we have

$\sin 2\pi/3 = \sin \pi/3,$ $\cot 2\pi/3 = -\cot \pi/3,$
$\cos 2\pi/3 = -\cos \pi/3,$ $\sec 2\pi/3 = -\sec \pi/3,$
$\tan 2\pi/3 = -\tan \pi/3,$ $\csc 2\pi/3 = \csc \pi/3.$

The second set of formulas is used for a third-quadrant angle, while the third set is used for a fourth-quadrant angle. As another example, suppose we wish to find the trigonometric values for the angle $23\pi/6$.

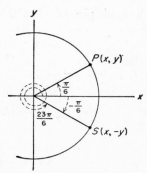

Fig. 4.6

Its trigonometric values are the same as those for the angle $-\pi/6$, and we have

$$\sin 23\pi/6 = \sin (-\pi/6) = -\sin \pi/6,$$
$$\cos 23\pi/6 = \cos (-\pi/6) = \cos \pi/6,$$
$$\tan 23\pi/6 = \tan (-\pi/6) = -\tan \pi/6,$$
$$\cot 23\pi/6 = \cot (-\pi/6) = -\cot \pi/6,$$
$$\sec 23\pi/6 = \sec (-\pi/6) = \sec \pi/6,$$
$$\csc 23\pi/6 = \csc (-\pi/6) = -\csc \pi/6.$$

We shall derive one other set of formulas which plays an important role in various practical applications. (In the following, bear in mind that $\pi/2$ is the radian measure of a right angle.) Let α be a reference angle generated by the point P having co-ordinates $x = a$ and $y = b$. From geometric theorems on similar triangles it is easy to see that the angle generated by the point Q having co-ordinates $x = b$ and $y = a$ is exactly $\pi/2 - \alpha$. Thus we have the formulas:

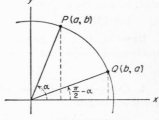

Fig. 4.7

(4) $\sin (\pi/2 - \alpha) = a/r = \cos \alpha,$ $\cot (\pi/2 - \alpha) = b/a = \tan \alpha,$
   $\cos (\pi/2 - \alpha) = b/r = \sin \alpha,$ $\sec (\pi/2 - \alpha) = r/b = \csc \alpha,$
   $\tan (\pi/2 - \alpha) = a/b = \cot \alpha,$ $\csc (\pi/2 - \alpha) = r/a = \sec \alpha.$

This set of reduction formulas describes the relationship between trigonometric values for the two smaller angles of a right triangle.

The derivation of all the above reduction formulas is based on the assumption that α represents a reference angle; but this restriction is unnecessary. It can be shown that the reduction formulas are valid for any angle whatever. For example, in the case of Formulas (1), it is necessary only to note that for any angle θ generated by the point $P(x, y)$ the angle $\pi - \theta$ is then generated by the point which is symmetric to P with respect to the y-axis; that is, by the point having co-ordinates $(-x, y)$. The reduction formulas are then derived as before. A similar argument can be supplied for each of the other sets of reduction formulas.

It should be noted also that the sets of reduction formulas given here are not the only possible ones. For example, one might easily discover reduction formulas for such angles as $\pi/2 + \theta$, $3\pi/2 + \theta$, or $3\pi/2 - \theta$.

———————| **Problem Set 4.4** |———————

1. Find an angle in one of the forms α, $\pi - \alpha$, $\pi + \alpha$, or $-\alpha$ (where α is a reference angle) which has its terminal side identical with that of the angle:

  (a) $16\pi/3$,   (b) $-21\pi/6$,   (c) $12\pi/5$,
  (d) $37\pi/3$,   (e) $-19\pi/3$.

2. Find an angle in one of the forms α, $\pi - \alpha$, $\pi + \alpha$, or $-\alpha$ (where α is a reference angle measured in radians) which has its terminal side identical with that of the angle:

  (a) $1215°$,   (b) $-410°$,   (c) $614°$.

REMARK. If α is measured in degrees the reduction formulas remain unchanged except that π is replaced by 180°. For example,

$$\sin 614° = \sin (180° + 74°) = -\sin 74°.$$

3. Express each of the following as some trigonometric function of a reference angle.

  (a) $\sin 375°$,   (b) $\cos 310°$,   (c) $\sec 7\pi/12$,
  (d) $\tan (-100°)$,   (e) $\csc (-\pi/3)$,   (f) $\sin 5\pi/3$,
  (g) $\cos 13\pi/11$.

4. List all angles on the interval $0 \le \theta \le \pi$ for which

  (a) $\sin \theta = \cos \pi/4$,   (b) $\cos \theta = \sin \pi/4$,
  (c) $\tan (-\theta) = -\cot \pi/3$,   (d) $\cos (-\theta) = \sin \pi/6$.

5. List all angles on the interval $0 \le \theta \le 2\pi$ for which

  (a) $\sin \theta = \sin \pi/3$,   (b) $\tan (-\pi/6) = \tan \theta$,
  (c) $\cos \theta = -\cos \pi/4$,   (d) $\cot (-\pi/4) = -\cot \theta$.

6. Find the infinite set of angles for which

  (a) $\sin \theta = \cos \pi/6$,   (b) $\sin (-\theta) = \sin \pi/6$,
  (c) $\tan \theta = -\cot \pi/4$,   (d) $-\cos (-\theta) = \cos (-\pi/3)$.

7. Evaluate (if possible) the following expressions.

  (a) $\sin \pi/2 + \cos \pi + \csc 3\pi/2$,
  (b) $\sec 3\pi/2 + \sin 3\pi/2$,
  (c) $(\cos 0°)(\csc 90°)(\sin 450°)$,
  (d) $(\sin 45°)\left(\dfrac{\sqrt{2}}{\cos 300°}\right)(\sec 150°)$,
  (e) $\dfrac{(\tan 5\pi/4)(\cot 2\pi/3)}{\sec (-\pi/3)}$.

8. Simplify the following.

(a) $\dfrac{\tan (180° - \theta)}{\tan (180° + \theta)} \cdot \dfrac{\cot (180° + \theta)}{\cot (180° - \theta)} \cdot \dfrac{\tan (-\theta)}{\cot \theta}$,

(b) $\dfrac{\sin (-\theta)}{\sec (\pi - \theta)} \cdot \dfrac{\csc (\pi + \theta)}{\cos \theta} \cdot \dfrac{\cos (\pi + \theta)}{\sin (\pi - \theta)}$,

(c) $\dfrac{\sin (\pi/2 - \theta)}{\cos \theta} \cdot \dfrac{\tan (\pi/2 - \theta)}{\sec (\pi/2 - \theta)}$,

(d) $\dfrac{\tan (\pi - \theta)}{\sin (\pi + \theta)} \cdot [\cos (\pi/2 - \theta)]$.

6. COMPLETE SPECIAL ANGLE VALUES

By means of reduction formulas and the earlier work in this chapter we may now determine the trigonometric values for three angles in each quadrant as well as for the quadrantal angles. For example, in the second quadrant we can find the trigonometric values for the angles $2\pi/3$, $3\pi/4$, and $5\pi/6$. These angles may be written: $2\pi/3 = \pi - \pi/3$, $3\pi/4 = \pi - \pi/4$, and $5\pi/6 = \pi - \pi/6$. Hence, by the reduction formulas (omitting the reciprocals),

$$\sin 2\pi/3 = \sin (\pi - \pi/3) = \sin \pi/3 = \sqrt{3}/2,$$
$$\cos 2\pi/3 = \cos (\pi - \pi/3) = -\cos \pi/3 = -\tfrac{1}{2},$$
$$\tan 2\pi/3 = \tan (\pi - \pi/3) = -\tan \pi/3 = -\sqrt{3},$$

$$\sin 3\pi/4 = \sin (\pi - \pi/4) = \sin \pi/4 = \sqrt{2}/2,$$
$$\cos 3\pi/4 = \cos (\pi - \pi/4) = -\cos \pi/4 = -\sqrt{2}/2,$$
$$\tan 3\pi/4 = \tan (\pi - \pi/4) = -\tan \pi/4 = -1,$$

$$\sin 5\pi/6 = \sin (\pi - \pi/6) = \sin \pi/6 = \tfrac{1}{2},$$
$$\cos 5\pi/6 = \cos (\pi - \pi/6) = -\cos \pi/6 = -\sqrt{3}/2,$$
$$\tan 5\pi/6 = \tan (\pi - \pi/6) = -\tan \pi/6 = -\sqrt{3}/3.$$

In a similar way the trigonometric values may be determined for angles in the third and fourth quadrants. Table 4.5 is a list of all angles on the interval $0 \leq \theta \leq 2\pi$ having trigonometric functions that we are able to evaluate.

TABLE 4.5

Radian	0	$\pi/6$	$\pi/4$	$\pi/3$	$\pi/2$
Degree	0°	30°	45°	60°	90°
Radian	$2\pi/3$	$3\pi/4$	$5\pi/6$	π	
Degree	120°	135°	150°	180°	
Radian	$7\pi/6$	$5\pi/4$	$4\pi/3$	$3\pi/2$	
Degree	210°	225°	240°	270°	
Radian	$5\pi/3$	$7\pi/4$	$11\pi/6$	2π	
Degree	300°	315°	330°	360°	

7. SPECIAL TOPIC: PTOLEMY'S TABLE OF CHORDS

Ptolemy's reputation rests mainly upon a treatise called (by its Arabian translators) the *Almagest*, which is one of the most important among the ancient manuscripts on mathematics and astronomy. It is believed that many of the results contained in this book were based on earlier work, particularly that of Hipparchus. Actually, it is difficult to determine just how much is original with Ptolemy, but in any case, the combined efforts of Hipparchus and Ptolemy produced an extensive body of mathematics. Both men were concerned primarily with problems in astronomy, and the mathematics they used and created might be classed as a tool for use in their practical researches.

The measurement of angles led to the creation of trigonometry, but the form in which the subject was first used differed from that of modern times. For example, instead of our trigonometric functions, the basic concept was the chord of an angle. The straight line interval joining two points on a circle is called a **chord** of the circle, or a chord of the central angle subtended by the interval. A diameter is a chord of 180°. The relationship between the original and the modern terminology is found from Fig. 4.8 to be

$$\text{crd } \theta = 2 \cdot r \cdot \sin \theta/2 \, .$$

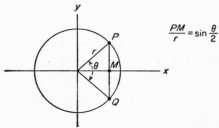

$$\frac{PM}{r} = \sin \frac{\theta}{2}$$

Fig. 4.8

A table in the *Almagest* gives values of the chords of all angles from 0° to 180° at one-half degree intervals. When converted to modern terms, the entries in general are correct to five or six decimal places. Although "chord" is not a basic concept in modern trigonometry, the ingenious method by which the table of chords was constructed is interesting and instructive enough to warrant a brief survey. The following discussion is a modernized version of the main ideas.

Consider a circle of radius one unit with center at the origin of a co-ordinate system. By well-known methods of plane geometry, it is possible to inscribe in the circle regular polygons of 3, 4, 5, 6, and 10 sides. One side of each polygon subtends a central angle of 120°, 90°, 72°, 60°, and 36°, respectively, and the lengths of the corresponding chords are crd 120° = $\sqrt{3}$, crd 90° = $\sqrt{2}$, crd 72° = $\sqrt{(5 - \sqrt{5})/2}$, crd 60° = 1, and crd 36° = $(\sqrt{5} - 1)/2$. The computation of these chord lengths is illustrated in Section 3; the computations involving the pentagon (5 sides) and the decagon (10 sides) are somewhat more complicated but can be found in most plane geometry textbooks.

Now we make use of a theorem which Ptolemy proved by geometric methods, and which is called by his name. Ptolemy's theorem states: *If a quadrilateral be inscribed in a circle, then the product of the diagonals equals the sum of the products of the opposite sides.* We shall consider the special case of this theorem in which one side of the quadrilateral is a diameter. As illustrated in Fig. 4.9, Ptolemy's theorem yields the equation

$$(1) \qquad PS \cdot QR = PR \cdot QS + PQ \cdot RS.$$

From the figure we find

$$PQ = \text{crd } 180° = 2,$$
$$QR = \text{crd } \theta, \quad PR = \text{crd } (180° - \theta),$$
$$QS = \text{crd } \phi, \quad PS = \text{crd } (180° - \phi).$$

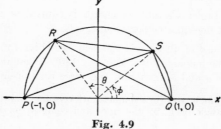

Fig. 4.9

From Eq. (1) we may derive three important relationships:

(2) $\quad \text{crd} (\alpha - \beta) = \frac{1}{2}[\text{crd} (180° - \beta) \cdot \text{crd}\, \alpha - \text{crd} (180° - \alpha) \cdot \text{crd}\, \beta]$;

(3) $\quad (\text{crd}\, \alpha/2)^2 = 2 - \text{crd} (180° - \alpha)$;

(4) $\quad \text{crd} [180° - (\alpha + \beta)] = \frac{1}{2}[\text{crd} (180° - \alpha) \cdot \text{crd} (180° - \beta)$
$$- \text{crd}\, \alpha \cdot \text{crd}\, \beta].$$

Equations (2) and (4) follow immediately from Eq. (1), and the proofs are left as exercises. [*Hint:* For (2) put $\alpha = \theta$ and $\beta = \phi$; for (4) put $\alpha = \phi$ and $\beta = 180° - \theta$, from which $\theta - \phi = 180° - (\alpha + \beta)$.] The proof of (3) is as follows.

Put $\alpha/2 = \phi$ and $\alpha/2 = 180° - \theta$; then $\theta - \phi = 180° - \alpha$. Because PQS is a right triangle we have $[\text{crd} (180° - \alpha/2)]^2 = 4 - (\text{crd}\, \alpha/2)^2$. From (1) we have

$$(\text{crd}\, \alpha/2)^2 = [\text{crd} (180° - \alpha/2)]^2 - 2 \cdot \text{crd} (180° - \alpha), \text{and}$$
$$(\text{crd}\, \alpha/2)^2 = 4 - (\text{crd}\, \alpha/2)^2 - 2 \cdot \text{crd} (180° - \alpha),$$
$$(\text{crd}\, \alpha/2)^2 = 2 - \text{crd} (180° - \alpha).$$

Ptolemy proved these three results by using methods of plane geometry. By (2) he computed the chord of 12° [72° − 60°], and by (3) obtained the chords of 6°, 3°, $1\frac{1}{2}$°, and $\frac{3}{4}$° successively. At this stage he was unable to find the chord of 1° exactly[2], but he was able to estimate its value to a very close approximation. Then by (3) he could approximate the chord of $\frac{1}{2}$°, and using the three results he was able to complete the table of chords from 0° to 180° at one-half degree intervals.

───────| **Suggested Exercises** |───────

1. Prove result (2).

2. Prove result (4).

3. Show that Ptolemy's table of chords is equivalent to a table of sines from 0° to 90° at one-quarter degree intervals.

4. In making use of Ptolemy's theorem (see Fig. 4.9), we assume that θ and ϕ satisfy the inequality $0 < \phi < \theta < 180°$. What restriction does this impose on angles α and β in each of the three relationships?

---

[2]It was proved much later (in the nineteenth century) that it is impossible even to construct an angle of 1° by the ruler and compass methods of elementary geometry.

Miscellaneous Problems

1. What is the maximum value that $\sin \theta$ may have if the domain is restricted to $3\pi/4 \leqq \theta \leqq 2\pi$? Where does this maximum value occur?

2. What is the maximum value that $\cos \theta$ may have if the domain is restricted to $3\pi/4 \leqq \theta \leqq 2\pi$? Where does this maximum value occur?

3. If the domain is restricted to $-\pi/4 \leqq \theta < \pi/2$, what is the minimum value of (a) $\tan \theta$, (b) $\sec \theta$?

4. If the domain is restricted to $\pi/4 \leqq \theta \leqq 3\pi/4$, what is the minimum value of (a) $\cot \theta$, (b) $\csc \theta$?

5. Find the inadmissible angles on the interval $0 \leqq \theta \leqq 2\pi$ for each of the expressions

    (a) $1/(1 + \sin \theta)$,   (b) $\tan \theta/(1 + \cos \theta)$.

6. Find the inadmissible angles on the interval $0 \leqq \theta \leqq 2\pi$ for the expression, $\tan \theta/(\sqrt{3} - \cot \theta)$.

7. What is the range of the function $\frac{1}{2} \sin \theta$?

8. What is the range of the function $2 - \frac{1}{2} \cos \theta$?

9. Evaluate the function $f(\theta) = \sin \theta + \cos \theta$ at each quadrantal angle on the interval $-\pi/4 \leqq \theta < 2\pi$.

10. Find all possible distinct values of the function

    (a) $f(n) = \sin n\pi$,   (b) $f(n) = 2 \sin n\pi/2$.

11. Find all possible distinct values of the function $f(n) = 2 \cos (\pm n\pi/2)$.

12. Find all possible distinct values of the function

    (a) $f(n) = \tan n\pi/2$;

    (b) $f(n) = 1 - \tan n\pi + \cot n\pi/2$.

13. On a circle of radius r, the point P generates an angle $-\pi/3$. Find x and r if the co-ordinates of P are

    (a) $P(x, -\sqrt{12})$,

    (b) $P(x, -\sqrt{300})$.

14. A point $P(x, y)$ generates an angle θ on a circle of radius 3 units. Find x and y if

    (a) $\theta = -10\pi/3$,   (c) $\theta = 100\pi/6$,

    (b) $\theta = 11\pi/4$,   (d) $\theta = -105\pi/3$.

Simplify each of the following six expressions.

15. $\dfrac{\tan \pi/3 \cdot \sec \pi/6}{\csc \pi/4} + \dfrac{\cot \pi/3 \cdot \cos \pi/6}{\sin \pi/4}$.

16. $\dfrac{\sec \pi/4}{\sin \pi/2} \cdot \left(1 - \dfrac{\cos \pi/4}{\tan \pi/6}\right)$.

17. $\dfrac{\sin 7\pi/6 \cdot \tan (\pi/2 - \pi/3) \cdot \cos (\pi - 8\pi/3)}{\sec (\pi + 13\pi/4)}$.

18. $\dfrac{\cos (\pi - \pi/3) \cdot \cot (\pi + \pi/4)}{1 + \sec (\pi + \pi/3)}$.

19. $\tan 7\pi/6 \cdot \cos (-7\pi/6) \cdot \csc (-7\pi/6)$.

20. $\sin (\pi + \pi/3) \cdot \cos (\pi/2 - \pi/6) \cdot \dfrac{1}{\tan (\pi - \pi/4)}$.

21. By considering the four possible cases, show that for θ in any quadrant,
   (a) $\sin (\pi/2 + \theta) = \cos \theta$.
   (b) $\tan (\pi/2 - \theta) = \cot \theta$.

22. If α is a reference angle, derive the reduction formulas for the angle $\pi/2 + \alpha$.

23. Evaluate by the reduction formulas of Problem 22:
   (a) $\sin (\pi/2 + \pi/4)$,   (b) $\cos (\pi/2 + \pi/3)$,
   (c) $\tan (90° + 30°)$,   (d) $\cot (\pi/2 + \pi/6)$.

24. Euclid proved that if $0 < \theta < \phi < \pi/2$, then $\dfrac{\sin \phi}{\sin \theta} < \dfrac{\phi}{\theta}$. Show that this inequality is satisfied if
   (a) $\theta = \pi/4$ and $\phi = \pi/3$;
   (b) $\theta = \pi/6$ and $\phi = \pi/4$.

25. Referring to Problem 24, prove Euclid's result if we assume the following theorem: *Let chords of the same length be drawn in two circles of radii r and r', where r < r'. If the smaller arcs intercepted by these two chords are s and s', respectively, then s' < s.*

5

PERIODICITY
AND
BASIC GRAPHS

One of the characteristic properties that distinguish trigonometric functions from the functions of elementary algebra is "periodicity." Because of its importance we shall discuss periodicity in general before showing the aptness of trigonometry in its description. The final sections of the chapter are devoted to graphs, and these will clearly illustrate the periodic behavior of the trigonometric functions.

1. THE UNIT CIRCLE

*A circle of radius one unit having its center at the origin of co-ordinates is called a **unit circle**.*

In referring to the unit circle we shall use the symbol U.

Let $P(x, y)$ be a point on U and suppose that P generates an angle θ. In this situation the trigonometric ratios are particularly simple in form. Referring to the original definitions, and remembering that $r = 1$, we see that

$$\begin{aligned} \sin \theta &= y, & \cot \theta &= x/y, \\ \cos \theta &= x, & \sec \theta &= 1/x, \\ \tan \theta &= y/x, & \csc \theta &= 1/y. \end{aligned}$$

Thus the co-ordinates of P on U are simply the cosine and sine values for the angle generated by P. No matter what the quadrant of θ may

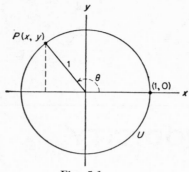

Fig. 5.1

be, the proper signs of the co-ordinates of P appear automatically in the appropriate trigonometric functions. In Fig. 5.1, for example, θ is drawn as a second-quadrant angle, hence $\cos \theta (= x)$ is negative while $\sin \theta (= y)$ is positive.

―――――| **Problem Set 5.1** |―――――

1. Give the co-ordinates of the point on U that generates the angle:
 (a) 30°   (b) $\pi/4$,   (c) 240°   (d) $2\pi/3$,
 (e) $-\pi/6$, (f) $7\pi/2$, (g) $-21\pi/4$, (h) $11\pi/3$.

2. Find the length of arc on U subtending the angle:
 (a) 60°,   (b) 15°,   (c) 110°,   (d) 135°,
 (e) 22° 30′, (f) 258°.

3. Show that all of the following are points on a unit circle.
 (a) $P(1/2, \sqrt{3}/2)$,   (b) $P(-4/5, -3/5)$,
 (c) $P(-\sqrt{3}/4, \sqrt{13}/4)$, (d) $P(2/3, \sqrt{5}/3)$.

By assigning special angle values to the variable θ, compute corresponding values for x and y and then sketch.

4. $\begin{cases} x = 5\cos\theta, \\ y = 5\sin\theta. \end{cases}$ **5.** $\begin{cases} x = 5\cos\theta, \\ y = -5\sin\theta. \end{cases}$ **6.** $\begin{cases} x = 5\cos\theta, \\ y = 2\sin\theta. \end{cases}$

2. LINE VALUES

Let the point P on U generate an angle θ in the first quadrant as shown in Fig. 5.2.

In this figure note that each of the trigonometric functions appears as one of the co-ordinates of a point on an axis:

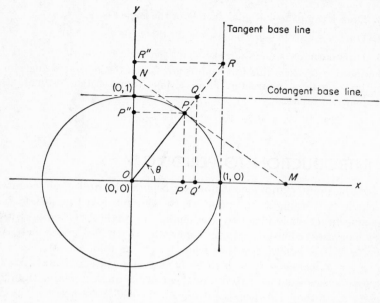

Fig. 5.2

$P''(0, \sin \theta),$ $Q'(\cot \theta, 0),$
$P'(\cos \theta, 0)$ $M(\sec \theta, 0),$
$R''(0, \tan \theta),$ $N(0, \csc \theta).$

For an angle in any quadrant the trigonometric functions of that angle are the nonzero co-ordinates of corresponding points located by a construction similar to the one given. For quadrantal angles some of these co-ordinates are impossible to determine because of parallel lines in the construction. Such cases occur when and only when the corresponding trigonometric functions are undefined. Regardless of the quadrant of θ, the base lines for tangent and cotangent determination must pass, respectively, through the points $(1, 0)$ and $(0, 1)$, not through the corresponding points $(-1, 0)$ and $(0, -1)$.

——————| **Problem Set 5.2** |————————————

1. On a large sketch locate points corresponding to P'', P', R'', Q', M, and N, for the angle $\theta = 30°$. Beside each point put its co-ordinates.

2. Draw a complete line value sketch for the angle $\theta = 135°$.

3. Draw a complete line value sketch for the angle $\theta = \pi$.

4. Draw a complete line value sketch for the angle $\theta = -150°$.

5. Draw a complete line value sketch for the angle $\theta = 5\pi/3$.

For each of the following three problems, sketch the generated angle on a unit circle with a protractor. From a line value sketch, estimate the trigonometric values.

6. $\theta = 220°$.　　7. $\theta = 7\pi/10$.　　8. $\theta = -3\pi/8$.

3. INTRODUCTION TO PERIODICITY

Let the point P move continuously around the unit circle counterclockwise beginning at the point $(1, 0)$, and consider the variation in the sine function induced by the change in angle θ generated by P. As θ increases from 0 to $\pi/2$, $\sin \theta$ increases from 0 to 1; as θ increases from $\pi/2$ to π, $\sin \theta$ decreases from 1 to 0; as θ increases from π to $3\pi/2$, $\sin \theta$ decreases from 0 to -1; as θ increases from $3\pi/2$ to 2π, $\sin \theta$ increases from -1 to 0. As P generates angles greater than 2π, we see that the values of $\sin \theta$ repeat themselves exactly as in the interval from 0 to 2π. This repetition occurs because $\sin \theta$ is defined in terms of the co-ordinates of the point P, which repeat themselves over and over again as P moves around U with either positive or negative rotation.

To be more precise, let θ be the angle generated by a point P, and consider the following angles: $\theta + 2\pi$, $\theta - 2\pi$, $\theta + 4\pi$, $\theta - 4\pi$, and in general $\{\theta \pm 2n\pi\}$. The terminal sides of these angles coincide with the terminal side of θ, hence the sine value is the same for each one of this infinite set of angles. These repetitions in value of the sine function occur regularly as the independent variable θ changes by 2π units. We will prove in Section 5 that this "regularity of repetition" in value is a characteristic of each of the trigonometric functions.

4. GENERAL DISCUSSION OF PERIODIC FUNCTIONS

The concept of regular repetition was introduced in the preceding section, relying on intuitive arguments about the behavior of the sine function. This concept is far too important, in both theoretical and practical aspect, to be left in such incomplete form. In the following discussion the essential ideas in the concept of regular repetition will receive clear-cut mathematical definitions and treatment. This general theory will lead to a broader understanding of the trigonometric functions and their applications.

Let $f(x)$ be a function having as its domain a set of real numbers denoted by D. Let k be a real number different from zero for which it is true that $x \pm k$ is in D whenever x is in D. The function $f(x)$ is called **periodic with period k** *if $f(x) = f(x + k)$ for every value of x in D[1]. The number k is called a **period** of $f(x)$.*

EXAMPLE 1. The function $f(x) = 2$ provides a trivial example of a periodic function. The graph of this function is the horizontal line two units above the x-axis. Any nonzero constant [say $k = 1$] is a period of this function [since $f(x + 1) = f(x) = 2$ for all x].

EXAMPLE 2. Following is a simple periodic function which is constant over alternate intervals. Let z be a variable on the set of even whole numbers, that is, the domain of the variable z is $\{\pm 2n\}$. We define a function for each even whole number as

$$f(x) = \begin{cases} 1 & \text{for} \quad z - 1 \leqq x < z, \\ 0 & \text{for} \quad z \leqq x < z + 1. \end{cases}$$

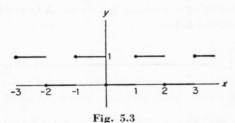

Fig. 5.3

This function is periodic and of period 2 [or 4, or -2, etc.] since for any value of $x, f(x) = f(x + 2)$ [or $f(\text{x}) = f(x + 4)$, or $f(x) = f(x - 2)$ etc].

EXAMPLE 3. A somewhat more interesting example is the following. Again let z be a variable on the set of even whole numbers. We define a function for each even whole number as

$$f(x) = x - z \quad \text{for} \quad z - 1 \leqq x < z + 1.$$

---

[1]The definition given here is appropriate for the trigonometric functions, but it is somewhat less general than the usual definition of periodicity.

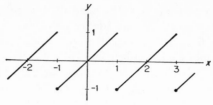

Fig..45

This function is periodic and likewise of period 2 [or 4, or -2, etc.]. For any value of x, $f(x) = f(x + 2)$ [or $f(x) = f(x + 4)$, or $f(x) = f(x - 2)$, etc.]. These equations mean, graphically, that the ordinates at x, $x + 2$, $x + 4$, $x - 2$, etc. have the same value.

The examples just given suggest the following question. *Among all possible periods of a periodic function $f(x)$, is there a smallest positive period? If so, it is called the* **primitive period** *of $f(x)$ or frequently* **the period** *of $f(x)$.* In Example 1 there is no primitive period since there is no smallest positive real number; the concept is not defined in that example. On the other hand, it is evident that $k = 2$ is the primitive period in each of the other two examples.

For later reference it is important that we become familiar with some of the properties of periodic functions. A few of the most useful results are discussed below.

THEOREM 1.

> *Suppose $f(x)$ is periodic with period k. Then any non-zero whole number multiple of k is also a period of $f(x)$.*

Example 2 provides a good illustration of this theorem. The number $k = 4$ is a period of this function and the theorem states that 8, -8, 12, -12, $\cdots$, are all periods of the function. It is easy to show that for any x, $f(x) = f(x + 8)$, or $f(x) = f(x - 8)$, or $f(x) = f(x + 12)$, $\cdots$, as required by the theorem.

Proof. We shall prove Theorem 1 for positive whole numbers by mathematical induction; a similar proof is easily made for the negative whole numbers. Suppose that k is a period of $f(x)$. Since $f(x)$ is periodic with period k, we know that $f(x) = f(x + 1 \cdot k)$. Let n be any positive whole number. As the second step in the induction we assume that $n \cdot k$ is a period of $f(x)$, which means that

$f(x) = f(x + n \cdot k)$. From this assumption it follows that whenever x is in the domain of $f(x)$ so also is $x + n \cdot k$; thus we have

$$f(x + n \cdot k) = f[(x + nk) + k].$$

Based on the assumption contained in the second step we see that

$$f(x) = f[x + (n + 1)k].$$

But this last equation shows that if nk is a period of $f(x)$ then $(n + 1)k$ is also a period of $f(x)$, which completes the proof by induction for positive whole numbers.

As a corollary to this theorem we note that *any periodic function must have a positive period.*

THEOREM 2. ──────────────────────────────────

> *If the function $f(x)$ is periodic with period k then for any number $c \neq 0$ the function $f(cx)$ is periodic with period k/c where x is the independent variable in each case.*

To illustrate this theorem consider Example 3 and assume $c = \frac{1}{2}$. The function $y = f(cx)$ is given by

$$y = x/2 - z \quad \text{for} \quad z - 1 \leq x/2 < z + 1.$$

The inequality on the right can also be written

$$2z - 2 \leq x < 2z + 2.$$

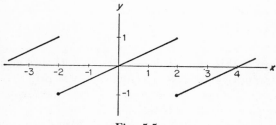

Fig. 5.5

From the graph it is evident that multiplying x by $\frac{1}{2}$ has had the effect of doubling the period, which is now $2k$, where k is a period of the original function.

Proof. Let x be a real number such that cx is in the domain of $f(x)$. Then

$$f(cx) = f(cx + k) = f[c(x + k/c)].$$

Thus in the function $f(cx)$, if we change x to $x + k/c$ the value of the function remains the same. Therefore, relative to the x-axis, k/c is a period of the function $f(cx)$.

To complete our introduction to periodic functions, the following two theorems are stated without proofs.

THEOREM 3. ───

> *Suppose that $f(x)$ and $g(x)$ are periodic functions and that both have k as a period. Then each of the following functions is periodic with period k:*
>
> $$h_1(x) = f(x) + g(x), \quad h_2(x) = f(x) - g(x),$$
>
> $$h_3(x) = f(x) \cdot g(x), \quad h_4(x) = \frac{f(x)}{g(x)}, \text{ where } g(x) \neq 0.$$

EXAMPLE 4. We illustrate h_3 by multiplying the functions given in Examples 2 and 3. We obtain the function

$$h_3(x) = \begin{cases} 1\,(x - z) = x - z & \text{for} \quad z - 1 \leqq x < z, \\ 0\,(x - z) = 0 & \text{for} \quad z \leqq x < z + 1. \end{cases}$$

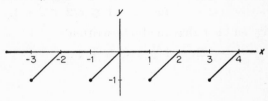

Fig. 5.6

With regard to this result, it is essential to note that nothing is said here about primitive periods. Even if k is the primitive period of both $f(x)$ and $g(x)$ it does *not* necessarily follow that k is the primitive period of any one of the h functions. The next example illustrates this; its primitive period is $k = 1$, while the primitive period of each original function is $k = 2$.

EXAMPLE 5. Suppose for this example we find h_1 by adding the functions given in Examples 2 and 3. We obtain the function

$$h_1(x) = \begin{cases} 1 + x - z & \text{for} \quad z - 1 \leqq x < z, \\ 0 + x - z & \text{for} \quad z \leqq x < z + 1. \end{cases}$$

But this function can be written more simply
$$h_1(x) = x - w \quad \text{for} \quad w \leqq x < w + 1,$$
where w is a variable on the set of whole numbers.

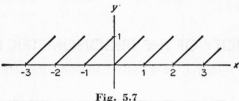

Fig. 5.7

THEOREM 4.

Suppose $f(x)$ and $g(x)$ are periodic functions having primitive periods which form a rational ratio. Then there exists a period which is common to both of them, and the h functions above are periodic.

———————| **Problem Set 5.3** |———————

1. By plotting at least four points each for z having the values $-2, 0, 2,$ and 4, sketch the graphs of Examples 2 and 3.

2. With reference to the illustration of Theorem 2 sketch similar graphs for (a) $c = 2$, (b) $c = 1/3$. State the primitive periods in each case.

3. If $f(x)$ is defined as in Example 2, sketch the graphs of (a) $f(x/2)$, (b) $f(2x)$. State the primitive periods in each case.

4. With reference to Theorem 3, let f be the function in Example 2 and let g be the function in Example 3. Sketch the graphs of (a) $h_2(x)$, (b) $g(x) - f(x)$.

5. Suppose z ranges over the set of even whole numbers. Put
$$f(x) = \begin{cases} 1 \text{ for } z \cdot \pi \leqq x < (z+1) \cdot \pi, \\ -1 \text{ for } (z-1) \cdot \pi \leqq x < z \cdot \pi, \end{cases}$$
$$g(x) = \begin{cases} \tfrac{1}{2} \text{ for } z \leqq x < z + 1, \\ -\tfrac{1}{2} \text{ for } z - 1 \leqq x < z. \end{cases}$$
Sketch the graph of $h_1(x) = f(x) + g(x)$ between -2π and 2π.

6. Referring to the functions given in Problem 5, sketch the graph of $h_3(x)$ between -2π and 2π.

7. Suppose the primitive period of $f(x)$ is 3 and the primitive period of $g(x)$ is 2. What is *a period* of (a) $f(x) + g(x)$, (b) $f(x)g(x)$?

8. Given the function $f(x) = \sqrt{1 - x^2}$.

(a) What is the domain of this function if $f(x)$ is to be real valued?

(b) Sketch the curve.

(c) Why does this function fail to satisfy the definition of a periodic function?

5. PERIODICITY OF THE TRIGONOMETRIC FUNCTIONS

It is now a relatively easy matter to prove the following theorem.

THEOREM. _____

| *The trigonometric functions are periodic with period* 2π.

Proof. Let θ be an arbitrary real number and suppose that $P(x, y)$ is a point on U generating the angle θ(in radians). Let θ' be the number $\theta + 2\pi$ generated on U by the point P'. The terminal sides of θ and θ' coincide (since 2π represents exactly one complete revolution of the generating point); hence the co-ordinates of P and P' are identical. Since the trigonometric functions of θ and θ' are defined in terms of the same numbers x, y, and r, it follows that the trigonometric functions of θ' are the same as those of θ. Hence the trigonometric functions satisfy the definition of periodicity with $k = 2\pi$.

Having established that the trigonometric functions are periodic, we next wish to find the primitive periods. From the discussion in Section 3, it appears that $\sin \theta$ cannot have a positive period less than 2π; thus its primitive period is 2π. By a similar argument it can be shown that each of the functions $\cos \theta$, $\sec \theta$, and $\csc \theta$ has 2π as primitive period also. The functions $\tan \theta$ and $\cot \theta$ are different in this respect. If θ is an angle generated by the point $P(x, y)$ then $\theta + \pi$ is generated by the point $P(-x, -y)$. From this we have

$$\tan \theta = y/x \quad \text{and} \quad \tan (\theta + \pi) = -y/-x = y/x.$$

The function $\tan \theta$ has π as its primitive period; but notice that 2π is also a period, as stated in the theorem. Similarly it can be shown that $\cot \theta$ has π as primitive period.

The periodicity of the trigonometric functions is one of the principal reasons for their fundamental importance in physical applications. Periodic motions (vibrations of a string, alternating currents, etc.) can be most easily described in terms of these functions.

Elsa Neustermann Sept. 1963

───────────| **Problem Set 5.4** |───────────────

1. What angle on the interval $0 \le \theta \le 2\pi$ has exactly the same six trigonometric values as (a) $9\pi/4$, (b) $-2\pi/3$, (c) $690°$, (d) $1210°$, (e) $34\pi/3$, (f) $-13\pi/6$?

2. Find all angles on the interval $0 \le \theta \le 2\pi$ having the same sine values as (a) $9\pi/4$, (b) $690°$.

3. Find all angles on the interval $0 \le \theta \le 2\pi$ having the same cosine values as (a) $-2\pi/3$, (b) $34\pi/3$.

4. Find all angles on the interval $0 \le \theta \le \pi$ having the same tangent values as (a) $1210°$, (b) $-13\pi/6$.

5. What is the set of all angles having the same:
   (a) sine values as $-\pi/2$?
   (b) cosine values as π?
   (c) tangent values as $\pi/4$?

6. What is the set of all angles having the same sine and cosine values as (a) $\theta = \pi/4$, (b) $\theta = 5\pi/6$, (c) $\theta = \pi/2$?

7. (a) Show that over an interval of one primitive period (for example, $0 \le \theta < 2\pi$) the sine function assumes each of its values twice (with two exceptions).
   (b) What are the two exceptions?

8. Show that over an interval of one primitive period the tangent function assumes each of its values exactly once.

6. GRAPHS OF THE TRIGONOMETRIC FUNCTIONS

To assist us in drawing graphs of the trigonometric functions we now have available three powerful tools: special angle values, line values, and the primitive periods. At first we shall use a co-ordinate system in which the horizontal and vertical scales are the same. This is merely a matter of convenience, and later on when we have become familiar with the general form of each graph, the scales may be altered to fit individual problems. For each graph we set up a co-ordinate system in the following way. Sketch the axes and mark unit distances on each. On the positive x-axis lay off a distance from the origin equal to the circumference of the unit circle (approximately 6.28 units) and mark the end-point 2π. This interval from $x = 0$ to $x = 2\pi$ is then subdivided by the numbers π, $\pi/2$, $\pi/3$, etc., as shown in Fig. 5.8 (these numbers correspond to the special angles). As a matter of convenience it is customary to designate numerically only

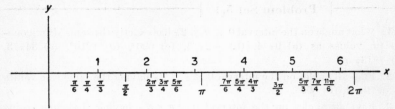

Fig. 5.8

the major subdivisions. It is also customary in drawing graphs to let x represent the angle measured in radians; that is, points marked on the horizontal axis are real numbers representing angles. The axis of the independent variable then has its usual label, x.

6.1 THE GRAPH OF $y = \sin x$

Since the primitive period of $\sin x$ is 2π, we need only plot values on that interval. Table 5.1 lists special angle values on this interval.

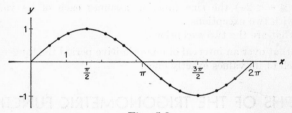

Fig. 5.9

These few points are sufficient to indicate fairly accurately the shape of the curve. If it were necessary to supply ordinates at values of x different from those given, we might make use of line values in the following way. Draw a circle having the given unit as radius. With a protractor sketch in an angle $\theta = x$(in radians). The distance OP'' (as in Section 2) is automatically the ordinate of $\sin x$, which may then be transferred to the graph.

6.2 THE GRAPH OF $y = \csc x$

The graph of the function $\csc x$ can be most easily sketched by making use of the relationship $\csc x = 1/\sin x$. Thus we may find its graph from that of $\sin x$ by plotting at any admissible value x the reciprocal of $\sin x$. Note that $\csc x$ is undefined at angles x for

TABLE 5.1

$x =$	either	0	$\pi/6$	$\pi/4$	$\pi/3$	$\pi/2$	$7\pi/6$	$5\pi/4$	$4\pi/3$	$3\pi/2$	2π
	or	π	$5\pi/6$	$3\pi/4$	$2\pi/3$		$11\pi/6$	$7\pi/4$	$5\pi/3$		
$\sin x =$	exactly	0	$1/2$	$\sqrt{2}/2$	$\sqrt{3}/2$	1	$-1/2$	$-\sqrt{2}/2$	$-\sqrt{3}/2$	-1	0
	decimal approx.	0.00	0.50	0.71	0.87	1.00	-0.50	-0.71	-0.87	-1.00	0.00

TABLE 5.2

x		0	$\pi/6$	$\pi/4$	$\pi/3$	$\pi/2$	$2\pi/3$	$3\pi/4$	$5\pi/6$	π
$\tan x =$	exactly	0	$\sqrt{3}/3$	1	$\sqrt{3}$	Undefined	$-\sqrt{3}$	-1	$-\sqrt{3}/3$	0
	decimal approx.	0.00	0.58	1.00	1.73	Undefined	-1.73	-1.00	-0.58	0.00

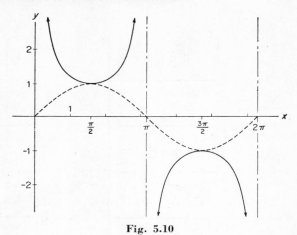

Fig. 5.10

which sin $x = 0$ (that is, $x = 0$, $x = \pi$, or $x = 2\pi$); thus the cosecant curve has no corresponding values at these numbers.

6.3 THE GRAPH OF $y = \cos x$

The graph of the function $\cos x$ may be sketched in any one of several ways. [Perhaps the easiest method is based on the equation[2] $\cos x = \sin (\pi/2 + x)$, which means that the shape of the cosine curve is identical to that of a sine curve with the origin shifted to $x = -\pi/2$. That is, when $x = -\pi/2$, $\cos x = \sin 0 = 0$; when $x = 0$, $\cos x = \sin \pi/2 = 1$; when $x = \pi/2$, $\cos x = \sin \pi = 0$; and so on.] In sketching this graph, however, suppose we illustrate the line value technique mentioned at the end of Paragraph 6.1. Lay off the co-ordinate axes as before, but to the left of the origin

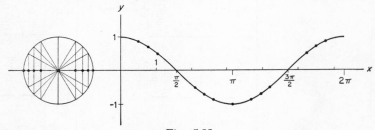

Fig. 5.11

———————
[2]See Problem 22, page 52.

construct a circle of radius 1 unit as shown in Fig. 5.11. Then for any angle $\theta = x$, we measure the horizontal distance OP' (as in Section 2) and mark it as the ordinate corresponding to x on our coordinate system. (A compass is useful for this purpose.)

In illustrating this method we have chosen the special angles in order that comparison with the method in Paragraph 6.1 might be made directly. The graphs of cos x and sin x are seen to be identical in shape and to differ only in that one graph appears to be shifted $\pi/2$ units along the axis from the other.

6.4 THE GRAPH OF $y = \sec x$

We sketch the graph of the function sec x by making use of the relationship sec $x = 1/\cos x$. At any admissible value x we plot the reciprocal of cos x. Note that sec x is undefined at $x = \pi/2$ and $x = 3\pi/2$; thus the secant curve has no corresponding values at these numbers.

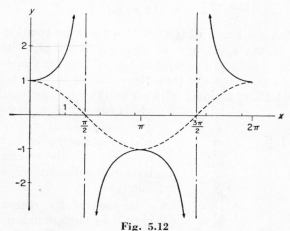

Fig. 5.12

6.5 THE GRAPH OF $y = \tan x$

To sketch this graph we illustrate again (as in Paragraph 6.1) the usual method, which consists of plotting points from a table of values. Since tan x has π as its primitive period, we need plot values only on the interval from $x = 0$ to $x = \pi$, as in Table 5.2. Note that since tan x is undefined for $x = \pi/2$ there is no value on the tangent curve corresponding to that number.

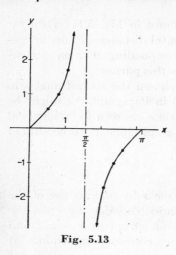

Fig. 5.13

We might also have sketched the graph of tan x from the graphs of sin x and cos x, using the relation tan x = sin x/cos x. The graph of tan x, sketched in this way, provides a good illustration of the remark under Theorem 3 of Section 4. Although sin x and cos x each has a primitive period of 2π, the quotient function (h_4 = tan x) has a different primitive period. However, we do know by Theorem 3 that 2π is *a* period of tan x.

6.6 THE GRAPH OF $y = \cot x$

We sketch the graph of the function cot x by treating it as the reciprocal of tan x. At any admissible value x plot the ordinate $1/\tan x$. Since tan x is undefined at $x = \pi/2$, we are unable to determine the value of cot $\pi/2$ from the equation cot $x = 1/\tan x$. To evaluate cot x here we must fall back on the original definition which

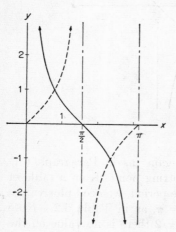

Fig. 5.14

yields cot $\pi/2 = 0$. Note that cot x is undefined at values of x for which tan $x = 0$ (that is, $x = 0$ and $x = \pi$); thus the cotangent curve has no corresponding values at these numbers.

In each of the preceding paragraphs we have sketched the trigonometric function for only one primitive period. We may extend the graph of each function indefinitely on either side of the given interval by a simple repetition of the functional values. The sine, cosine, and tangent functions for several periods have graphs as shown in Fig. 5.15.

In this figure, sin x and cos x are drawn for $2\frac{1}{4}$ primitive periods, while tan x is drawn for $4\frac{1}{2}$ primitive periods.

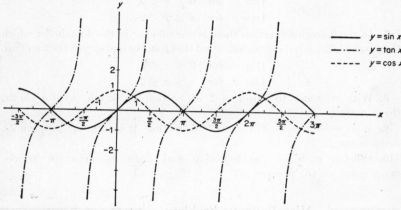

Fig. 5.15

Of the six trigonometric functions only sine and cosine are defined for all values of the independent variable. Partly for this reason these functions appear more frequently than the others in applications relating to periodic phenomena.

——————| **Problem Set 5.5** |——————————————

1. Draw the graph for exactly $2\frac{3}{4}$ primitive periods of (a) $y = \sin x$, (b) $y = \cos x$, (c) $y = \tan x$.

2. Draw the graph for exactly $2\frac{3}{4}$ primitive periods of (a) $y = \sec x$, (b) $y = \csc x$, (c) $y = \cot x$.

3. On the same co-ordinate system sketch the graphs of sin x and cos x; then draw the graph of tan x by estimating values from the relationship tan x = sin x/cos x.

4. Sketch the following function.

$$f(x) = \begin{cases} \cos x & \text{for} \quad -\pi/2 \leqq x < \pi/4, \\ \sin x & \text{for} \quad \pi/4 \leqq x \leqq \pi. \end{cases}$$

5. Sketch the following function.

$$f(x) = \begin{cases} \tan x & \text{for} \quad -\pi/2 < x \leqq 0, \\ \sin x & \text{for} \quad 0 < x \leqq \pi, \\ -\tan x & \text{for} \quad \pi < x < 3\pi/2. \end{cases}$$

6. In the following function there is one number in the domain for which the graph of $f(x)$ is not connected. Find that number and sketch the function.

$$f(x) = \begin{cases} \sin x & \text{for } 0 \leq x < \pi, \\ \cos x & \text{for } \pi \leq x < 2\pi. \end{cases}$$

7. In the following function there is one number in the domain for which the graph of $f(x)$ is not connected. Find that number and sketch the function.

$$f(x) = \begin{cases} \tan x & \text{for } 0 \leq x < \pi, \\ \sin x & \text{for } \pi \leq x \leq 2\pi. \end{cases}$$

8. With reference to Theorem 2 of Section 4, sketch (a) $y = \sin 2x$, (b) $y = \sin (x/2)$.

9. With reference to Theorem 2 of Section 4, sketch (a) $y = \tan 2x$, (b) $y = \tan (x/2)$.

10. Sketch each of the following and state its primitive period: (a) $y = \sin \pi x$, (b) $y = \cos \pi x$.

——————————| **Miscellaneous Problems** |——————————

1. Find the unknown co-ordinate if P is to be on the unit circle (two possibilities).

    (a) $P(x, 24/25)$,   (b) $P(-5/13, y)$,   (c) $P(x, 0)$.

2. Find the shorter arc length between the following pairs of points on a unit circle.

    (a) $P(1, 0)$ and $Q(0, 1)$,

    (b) $P(\sqrt{2}/2, \sqrt{2}/2)$ and $Q(-\sqrt{2}/2, \sqrt{2}/2)$,

    (c) $P(\sqrt{3}/2, 1/2)$ and $Q(-\sqrt{3}/2, 1/2)$.

3. Sketch the graph.

$$\begin{cases} x = 3 \cos \theta, \\ y = 6 \sin \theta. \end{cases}$$

4. On the same co-ordinate system draw a complete line value sketch for each of the angles $\theta = \pi/4$ and $\phi = \pi/3$. Show geometrically that $\sin (\theta + \phi) \neq \sin \theta + \sin \phi$.

5. Referring to Problem 4, show geometrically that $\tan (\theta + \phi) \neq \tan \theta + \tan \phi$.

6. By mathematical induction, prove Theorem 1 of Section 4 for negative whole numbers.

7. Prove that $f(\theta) = \sin \theta + \cos \theta$ is periodic with period 2π.

8. Prove, in general, that if $f(x)$ and $g(x)$ are both periodic with period k, then $f(x) + g(x)$ and $f(x) \cdot g(x)$ are also periodic with period k.

9. Describe the geometric significance of Theorem 3 of Section 4.

10. Sketch the graph of $f(\theta) = \sin \theta - \cos \theta$. What is the primitive period?

11. Sketch the graph of $f(x) = 2 \sin x \cdot \cos x$. From the graph, estimate the primitive period.

12. What is the primitive period of:
   (a) $\sin 2x$,   (b) $\tan x/2$,   (c) $\cos x/4$,
   (d) $\sin \pi x$,   (e) $\cot \pi x$?

13. Show that the function $\sin 2x + \cos \pi x$ is not periodic.

REMARK. *If every element of a given set of numbers A is less than or equal to some number b, then the set A is said to be **bounded above** by the number b; and b is called an **upper bound** of the set A. If the number c is less than or equal to each element of A then c is a **lower bound** of A, and A is **bounded below** by c.* For example, the set of values of $\sin x$ is bounded above by any number $b \geqq 1$, since $\sin \theta$ is never larger than 1.

14. Show that $c = -1$ is a lower bound for the set of values of $\cos \theta$.

15. Show that $\tan \theta$ has neither upper bound nor lower bound.

16. According to the definition given in Section 4, show that a function $f(x)$ cannot be periodic if its domain is bounded above.

17. If $f(x)$ is a real-valued function, find an upper bound for:
   (a) the domain of $f(x) = \sqrt{1 - x}$,
   (b) the range of $f(x) = 1 + \sin x$,
   (c) the domain of $f(x) = \sqrt{4 - x^2}$,
   (d) the range of $f(x) = \cos x - 1$.

18. With reference to Theorem 2 of Section 4, sketch on the same co-ordinate system, $y = \cos (x/2)$ and $y = \cos 2x$. What is a period of $\cos (x/2) + \cos 2x$?

19. On the same co-ordinate system, sketch $y = \tan 2x$ and $y = \tan x/2$. What is the primitive period of the sum?

20. Sketch the function and state its primitive period: $y = \cos \pi x$.

21. Sketch the function and state its primitive period: $y = \sin \pi x/2$.

22. Sketch the function and state its primitive period: $y = \tan \pi x$.

23. What is the primitive period of the function
   (a) $f(x) = \sin \pi x + \cos \pi x/2$?
   (b) $f(x) = \tan \pi x/2 - \sin 2\pi x$?

24. Sketch the following pair of functions on the same co-ordinate system. Are both periodic?

$$y = \sin \pi x, \quad y = \sin (\pi x^2).$$

25. Sketch the following pair of functions on the same co-ordinate system. Is either function periodic?

$$y = \cos \pi x, \quad y = \cos (\pi x^2).$$

6

TRIGONOMETRIC
IDENTITIES
AND
EQUATIONS

Formally, at least, a mathematical equation is a statement that two mathematical expressions are equal. A trigonometric equation results when one or both of the expressions involves a trigonometric function. Trigonometric equations occur frequently, and it is our objective now to distinguish between several types of equation and to discover techniques for handling each.

1. INTRODUCTION

In a trigonometric expression, inadmissible values of the variable, say x, may occur in one of several ways. Any value of x is inadmissible if (a) it causes a zero factor in any denominator, or (b) it causes any single trigonometric function in the expression to be undefined, or (c) it causes an even root of a negative number. For example, the expression $\sin x + \cos x/\sin x$ has inadmissible values $\{0 \pm n\pi\}$, the expression $1/(\tan x - 1)$ has inadmissible values $\{\pi/4 \pm n\pi\}$ and also $\{\pi/2 \pm n\pi\}$, and $\sqrt{1 - \tan x}$ has inadmissible values $\{\pi/2 \pm n\pi\}$ and also those numbers on the interval $\pi/4 < x < \pi/2$, plus or minus multiples of π. In this chapter we shall be concerned with equations containing a single variable, and we agree to omit from consideration all inadmissible values of the variable.

The admissible values of an equation are divided into two sets: those values that are solutions of the equation, and those values that are not solutions. The word "equation" is subject to an ambiguity which depends upon these two sets. *Suppose, for a given equation, we let S represent the set of admissible values that are solutions, and we let N represent the set of admissible values that are not solutions. If S is void then the equation is called* **null;** *if N is void then the equation is called an* **identity;** *if neither S nor N is void then the equation is called* **conditional.** For example, consider the following:

(1) $\qquad\qquad\qquad \sin x = 2,$
(2) $\qquad\qquad\qquad \tan x = \sin x/\cos x,$
(3) $\qquad\qquad\qquad \cos x = -1.$

Equation (1) is satisfied by no value of x, hence S is void and this is a null equation. Equation (2) is satisfied by all admissible values of x, hence N is void and this is an identity. Equation (3) is satisfied by the set of values $\{\pi \pm 2n\pi\}$ and by no others, hence neither S nor N is void and this is a conditional equation.

In general, it is not easy to determine how a particular equation should be classified. As in so many other instances, experience is the best guide; but the following is a useful rule: *if an admissible value can be found that is not a solution, then the equation is not an identity.* Consider, for example, the equation, $\sin x = \tan x \cdot \cot x$. The number $x = \pi/4$ is admissible, and since it is not a solution $(\sqrt{2}/2 \neq 1)$ we know that the equation is not an identity. It is important that the limitations of the rule be remembered. The rule does *not* tell us when an equation *is* an identity; to prove that an equation is an identity an entirely different scheme must be employed, as illustrated in Section 4.

Problem Set 6.1

1. What are the inadmissible values of the variable in each of the expressions: (a) sec θ, (b) sec $\theta/\sin \theta$, (c) cot $\theta/(\cos \theta + 1)$?

2. What are the inadmissible values of the variable in each of the expressions: (a) tan $\theta \cdot$ csc θ, (b) sin $\theta/(\tan \theta - 1)$, (c) $1/(\tan \theta - \cot \theta)$?

3. Is $\theta = \pi/2$ a root of the equation, $\sin \theta = \tan \theta \cdot \cot \theta$?

4. Classify the equation, cot $\theta = \cot \theta \cdot \cos \theta$.

5. Classify the following algebraic equations if x is limited to real number values.

(a) $x^2 + x + 1 = 0,$ $\qquad\qquad$ (b) $\dfrac{x^3 - 8}{x - 2} = x^2 + 2x + 4.$

6. Classify the following algebraic equations if x is limited to real number values.

(a) $1 - \dfrac{1}{x} = 1 + \dfrac{1}{x}$, (b) $\dfrac{x - \frac{1}{2}}{x(x - 1)} = \dfrac{1}{2x}$.

7. Prove that the following equations are not identities.

(a) $\sec x = \sin x + 1$,

(b) $\cot x + \tan x = 2$,

(c) $\sin x - \tan x = \cos x - 1$.

8. Prove that the following equations are not identities.

(a) $(\tan x + 1)/\sin x = \sec x$,

(b) $\tan 2x - \cot 2x = 0$,

(c) $\sin 2x - \cos x + 1 = 0$.

2. GRAPHS OF EQUATIONS

The characteristics of an equation, depending upon its classification, show up clearly in a graphical analysis. We may study a given equation $f(x) = g(x)$ by sketching on the same co-ordinate system the two graphs $y = f(x)$ and $y' = g(x)$. The intersections of these two graphs occur at the roots (or solutions) of the original equation. In slightly different language, the set S (the admissible values that are solutions) consists of all points on the x-axis corresponding to intersections of the two graphs. The equations of Section 1 have the following graphs.

(1) $\sin x = 2.$

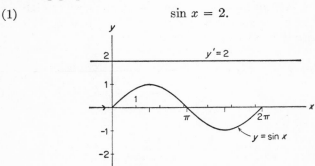

Fig. 6.1

Put $y = \sin x$ and $y' = 2$. The fact that there is no value of x for which the two graphs intersect indicates that S is void and that $y = y'$ is a null equation.

(2)    $\tan x = \sin x/\cos x.$

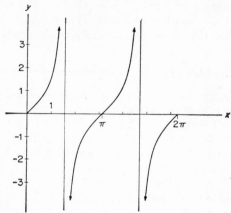

Fig. 6.2

Put $y = \tan x$ and $y' = \sin x/\cos x$. The graphs of these two functions appear superimposed one on the other, showing that N is void and that $y = y'$ for every admissible value of x (x not in the set $\{\pi/2 \pm n\pi\}$).

It is evident graphically that the expressions $g(x)$ and $f(x)$ in an identity, $f(x) = g(x)$, are simply two ways of saying exactly the same thing over the set of all admissible values. But it sometimes happens that an inadmissible value in one of the expressions might not be inadmissible in the other. For example, in the equation $\sin x = 1/\csc x$ we must exclude those values of x for which $\csc x$ is undefined, making this an identity over the set of all real numbers except $\{0 \pm n\pi\}$.

(3) $\cos x = -1.$

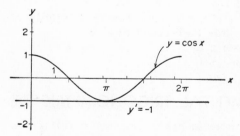

Fig. 6.3

Put $y = \cos x$ and $y' = -1$. The intersections of the two graphs occur at the values $\{\pi \pm 2n\pi\}$. Notice that for any other value of x the functions are defined but unequal. This indicates that neither S nor N is void and that $y = y'$ is a conditional equation.

─────────────| **Problem Set 6.2** |─────────────

1. Show graphically that the following equations are null, assuming that x may have only real number values.

    (a) $x^2 + x + 1 = 0$,

    (b) $x^2 - 3x + 2 = -1$.

2. Show graphically that the following equation is null, assuming that x may have only real number values.

$$1 + 1/x = 1 - 1/x.$$

3. Analyze graphically the following equations.

    (a) $\sqrt{2} - \cos \theta = 0$,

    (b) $\tan x + 1 = 0$.

4. Analyze graphically the following equations.

    (a) $\tan x = \cot x$,

    (b) $\sin \theta = \cos \theta$.

5. Analyze graphically the following equations.

    (a) $\cot \theta = \cos \theta / \sin \theta$,

    (b) $\sin \theta = 1 + \cos \theta$.

6. On the interval $0 \leqq x \leqq 2\pi$, show graphically by a heavy line, and express by inequalities, the domain for which

    (a) $\sin x \leqq \cos x$,

    (b) $\tan x \leqq \sin x$.

7. On the interval $0 \leqq x \leqq 2\pi$, show graphically by a heavy line, and express by inequalities, the domain for which

    (a) $\tan x \leqq 1$,

    (b) $\cot x \leqq 1$.

8. On the interval $0 \leqq x \leqq 2\pi$, show graphically by a heavy line, and express by inequalities, the domain for which

    (a) $0 \leqq \cos x \leqq 1$,

    (b) $0 \leqq \tan x \leqq 1$.

3. FUNDAMENTAL TRIGONOMETRIC IDENTITIES

The trigonometric identities discussed in this section are so important that they should be memorized, and the development of each should be carefully studied. In Section 5 of Chapter 3 we introduced five identities which followed directly from the basic definitions.

(1) $\qquad \sin\ \theta \cdot \csc\ \theta = 1,$

(2) $\qquad \cos\ \theta \cdot \sec\ \theta = 1,$

(3) $\qquad \tan\ \theta \cdot \cot\ \theta = 1,$

(4) $\qquad \tan\ \theta = \sin\ \theta / \cos\ \theta,$

(5) $\qquad \cot\ \theta = \cos\ \theta / \sin\ \theta.$

Now let P be a point fixed arbitrarily on U and let θ be the angle

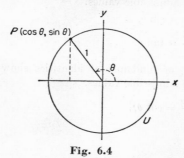

Fig. 6.4

generated by P. The Pythagorean theorem applied to the right triangle whose vertices are $(0, 0)$, $(\cos\ \theta, 0)$, and $(\cos\ \theta, \sin\ \theta)$ yields the equation

(6) $\qquad \sin^2 \theta + \cos^2 \theta = 1.$

At this point we must explain a convention in notation. The square of $\sin\ \theta$ is sometimes denoted by $(\sin\ \theta)^2$, but more frequently by $\sin^2 \theta$. In general, for $n \neq -1$, $\sin^n \theta$ illustrates the way of denoting the nth power of any trigonometric function. There are two pitfalls to beware of: (i) $\sin\ \theta^2$ is not considered to be the same as $\sin^2 \theta$, it is taken to mean $\sin\ (\theta^2)$; (ii) the reciprocal of $\sin\ \theta$ is denoted by $(\sin\ \theta)^{-1}$ or by $1/\sin\ \theta$, the symbol $\sin^{-1}\ \theta$ denotes an entirely different idea, which will be discussed in Chapter 8.

Equation (6) is satisfied by all values of the variable θ since P was chosen arbitrarily; thus it is an identity. From it we find on dividing through by $\sin^2 \theta$:

(7) $\qquad 1 + \cot^2 \theta = \csc^2 \theta;$

and dividing through by $\cos^2 \theta$:

(8) $\qquad \tan^2 \theta + 1 = \sec^2 \theta.$

Each of Equations (7) and (8) is an identity since the operation of division that was performed on the original identity eliminates no admissible values of the new equation. These two identities can also be derived directly from a line value diagram.

─────────────| **Problem Set 6.3** |─────────────────────

1. By making use of fundamental identities show that the following equations hold for all admissible values.

(a) $\tan \theta \cdot \cos \theta = \sin \theta,$

(b) $\dfrac{\sin^2 \theta \cdot \csc \theta}{\cos \theta} = \tan \theta.$

2. By making use of fundamental identities show that the following equations hold for all admissible values.

(a) $\dfrac{\cos^2 \theta \cdot \sec \theta}{\sin \theta} = \cot \theta,$

(b) $\dfrac{\csc \theta}{\sec \theta} = \cot \theta.$

3. From a line value diagram give a geometric proof (based on the Pythagorean theorem) of Fundamental Identity (7).

4. From a line value diagram give a geometric proof (based on the Pythagorean theorem) of Fundamental Identity (8).

5. Show that the following equations hold for all admissible values.

(a) $\sin^3 x + \sin x \cdot \cos^2 x = \sin x,$

(b) $\dfrac{\sin^3 \theta + \sin \theta \cdot \cos^2 \theta}{\cos \theta} = \tan \theta.$

6. Show that the following equations hold for all admissible values.
(a) $\sin^2 \theta \cdot (1 + \cot^2 \theta) = 1,$
(b) $\sin^2 \theta + \sin^2 \theta \cdot \tan^2 \theta = \tan^2 \theta.$

7. Prove that the following are not identities.
(a) $\sin^2 \theta = 1 + \cos^2 \theta,$
(b) $\tan^2 x = \sec^2 x + 1,$
(c) $\csc^2 x = 1 - \cot^2 x,$
(d) $\tan^2 x + \cot^2 x = 1,$
(e) $\sin^2 \theta \cdot \cos^2 \theta = 1.$

8. Is it possible to find an angle θ for which
(a) $\sin \theta = \sqrt{5}/3$ and $\cos \theta = \frac{1}{3}$?
(b) $\tan \theta = \frac{1}{2}$ and $\sec \theta = 2$?

9. Find all real numbers satisfying the inequalities
  (a) $2x - 5 \geq x$,
  (b) $x(x - 1) \geq 0$,
  (c) $(x + 1)(x - 1) \leq 0$,
  (d) $2x^2 - 3x - 2 \leq 0$.

10. In the following problems find the values of θ on the interval $0 \leq \theta \leq 2\pi$ which satisfy the inequality. [*Hint.* Express the left-hand side in factored form.]
  (a) $\sin^2 \theta - 1 \leq 0$,
  (b) $\sin^2 \theta - \cos^2 \theta \leq 0$,
  (c) $\tan^2 \theta - 1 \geq 0$,
  (d) $\csc \theta - \cot \theta \geq 0$.

4. THE PROOF OF IDENTITIES

Unless it is obvious by the rule stated in Section 1 that a given trigonometric equation is not an identity, we may first try to prove that it is an identity. Such a proof, by the definition, must demonstrate that the equation is true for all admissible values of the variable. Our first attempt might be to show by actual computation that the equation is true for a number of admissible values of the variable. Although the equation may be true for all values tried, it is easy to see that this procedure cannot lead to a proof, for it is always possible that some untried value might not be a solution. The general technique that we shall use to prove an identity has two main steps. First, check each side of the equation to determine all inadmissible values of the variable. Second, beginning with a known identity, change the form of one of the expressions in the equation to exactly the form of the other expression through a succession of steps each one of which is an identity. If in any step an operation is performed which introduces a new inadmissible value, it must be added to the original list of inadmissible values.

EXAMPLE 1. Prove that the equation $\sec^2 \theta + \csc^2 \theta = \sec^2 \theta \cdot \csc^2 \theta$ is an identity.

Proof. As the first step we indicate the inadmissible values of θ (these are the angles which θ must *not* equal)

$$\{0 \pm 2n\pi\}, \quad \{\pi/2 \pm 2n\pi\}, \quad \{\pi \pm 2n\pi\}, \quad \{3\pi/2 \pm 2n\pi\}.$$

This set of inadmissible values can be expressed more concisely as $\{0 \pm n\pi/2\}$. In the future it will be sufficient to indicate only angles in the interval $0 \leqq \theta < 2\pi$, provided we remember that all coterminal angles are likewise inadmissible.

The second step can be presented in the following succession of identities. The numbers in brackets refer to the fundamental identities used in that step.

$$\sec^2 \theta + \csc^2 \theta = \frac{1}{\cos^2 \theta} + \frac{1}{\sin^2 \theta} \quad [(1) \text{ and } (2)],$$

$$= \frac{\sin^2 \theta + \cos^2 \theta}{\cos^2 \theta \cdot \sin^2 \theta},$$

$$= \frac{1}{\cos^2 \theta \cdot \sin^2 \theta} \quad [(6)],$$

$$= \frac{1}{\cos^2 \theta} \cdot \frac{1}{\sin^2 \theta},$$

$$= \sec^2 \theta \cdot \csc^2 \theta \quad [(1) \text{ and } (2)].$$

Notice that in none of the five identities above have we introduced a new inadmissible value. Thus the given equation is an identity over the set of all real numbers except those listed at the beginning of the proof.

The next example illustrates a practical form for use in writing out the proof of an identity.

EXAMPLE 2. Prove the identity $\dfrac{\cos \theta}{1 + \sin \theta} + \dfrac{\cos \theta}{1 - \sin \theta} = 2 \sec \theta.$

Proof. $\theta \neq \pi/2, \quad \theta \neq 3\pi/2.$

$$\frac{\cos \theta}{1 + \sin \theta} + \frac{\cos \theta}{1 - \sin \theta} = \frac{\cos \theta \left[(1 - \sin \theta) + (1 + \sin \theta) \right]}{1 - \sin^2 \theta},$$

$$= \frac{2 \cos \theta}{\cos^2 \theta},$$

$$= 2 (1/\cos \theta),$$

$$= 2 \sec \theta.$$

It might be called an unwritten law of mathematics that when working with radicals one must exercise extreme caution. The next example shows that this is good advice.

EXAMPLE 3. Decide whether the following equation is an identity

$$\sqrt{\frac{1 - \cos x}{1 + \cos x}} = \csc x - \cot x.$$

Solution. $x \neq 0, \quad x \neq \pi$.

$$\sqrt{\frac{1-\cos x}{1+\cos x}} = \sqrt{\frac{1-\cos x}{1+\cos x} \cdot \frac{1-\cos x}{1-\cos x}},$$

$$= \sqrt{\frac{(1-\cos x)^2}{1-\cos^2 x}},$$

$$= \sqrt{\frac{(1-\cos x)^2}{\sin^2 x}},$$

$$= \frac{1-\cos x}{\sin x},$$

$$= \frac{1}{\sin x} - \frac{\cos x}{\sin x},$$

$$= \csc x - \cot x.$$

This appears to be a complete and valid proof, with nothing wrong except that the original equation is not an identity over the set of all admissible values. As a check let us put $x = 3\pi/2$, from which

$$\sqrt{\frac{1-0}{1+0}} = -1 + 0 \quad \text{or} \quad 1 = -1, \text{ which is nonsense.}$$

It should not be difficult to discover where the "proof" has gone astray. Suppose we examine the original statement to determine in which quadrants the equation can possibly be true. Since the left-hand side is never negative, we must limit the domain of the variable x to those values for which the right-hand side is not negative. The example is an identity as long as the variable is kept within the allowable domain. That is, along with the inadmissible values we must exclude also the entire interval $\pi < x < 2\pi$, because on it the right-hand side is negative.

The following list of suggestions may be useful in proving identities:

1. Begin the proof on the more complicated appearing side of the identity.

2. Look for the possibility of factoring one of the expressions, or of changing a denominator (as in Example 3).

3. Sometimes a preliminary simplification of both sides will suggest a method of attack.

4. If a method of proof does not suggest itself immediately, it frequently helps to reduce all trigonometric expressions to terms of sine and cosine.

5. Always check to be certain that each operation performed is valid for all angles in the domain under consideration.

─────────| **Problem Set 6.4** |─────────

Prove the following identities.

1. $\sin^2 \theta \cdot \sec^2 \theta + \sin^2 \theta \cdot \csc^2 \theta = \sec^2 \theta.$

2. $(\sec^2 \theta + \csc^2 \theta)/\tan^2 \theta = \csc^4 \theta.$

3. $\dfrac{\cos^2 \theta}{1 + \sin \theta} + \dfrac{\cos^2 \theta}{1 - \sin \theta} = 2.$

4. $\tan x + \cot x = \sec x \cdot \csc x.$

5. $\dfrac{1 - \cos x}{1 + \cos x} = (\cot x - \csc x)^2.$

6. $\dfrac{1 + \sin x}{\cos x} = \dfrac{\cos x}{1 - \sin x}.$

7. $\dfrac{\sec x + \tan x}{1/(1 - \sin x)} = \cos x.$

8. $\tan^2 \theta + \cot^2 \theta = \dfrac{1 - 2 \sin^2 \theta \cdot \cos^2 \theta}{\sin^2 \theta \cdot \cos^2 \theta}.$

9. $\dfrac{1}{\sec \theta - \tan \theta} = \sec \theta + \tan \theta.$

10. $\sin^4 \theta - \cos^4 \theta = 2 \sin^2 \theta - 1.$

11. $\dfrac{1 - \cos^6 \theta}{\sin^2 \theta} = 1 + \cos^2 \theta + \cos^4 \theta.$

12. $\dfrac{\tan^2 x + 1}{2 \cos (-x) - \sin (\pi/2 - x)} = \sec^3 x.$

13. $\dfrac{\cos^2 x - \sin (\pi + x) \cdot \sin (\pi - x)}{\csc (\pi - x)} = \sin x.$

14. $\dfrac{\sin (\pi - \theta)}{1 + \cos \theta} - \cot (\pi - \theta) = \csc \theta.$

5. CONDITIONAL EQUATIONS

*A **complete solution** of a conditional equation is the set, denoted by S, of all admissible values of the variable which satisfy the equation.*

As in algebra, any single value belonging to S is called a **root** *(or a* **solution**) *of the equation.*

If a given trigonometric equation is not null, then there may or may not be an infinite number of roots, depending upon the composition of the equation. If the variable enters the equation only in trigonometric functions, then there will be infinitely many roots, for if x_1 is a root, so also are the values $\{x_1 \pm 2n\pi\}$. But if the variable enters the equation also in algebraic form (for example, $\sin x + x = 1$), then the number of roots may be finite. In the following discussion we shall be concerned mainly with equations of the former kind. Equations of the latter kind usually can be solved only approximately; solutions of limited accuracy may be obtained by graphical methods.

Trigonometric equations appear in a wide variety of forms, and the techniques of solution are almost as varied. No practical rule, applicable in all instances, can be given. In general, we attempt to express the equation in terms of a single trigonometric function. Then, if possible, ordinary algebraic techniques are used to simplify or factor the expression before attempting to resolve the trigonometric questions. A careful study of examples is a good guide in learning to solve trigonometric equations.

EXAMPLE 1. Find the complete solution of $\sin^2 \theta + \cos \theta = -1$.

Solution. Replacing $\sin^2\theta$ by an equivalent leads to a quadratic equation in the variable ($\cos \theta$) which can be solved by the usual algebraic methods.

$$(1 - \cos^2 \theta) + \cos \theta + 1 = 0,$$
$$\cos^2 \theta - \cos \theta - 2 = 0,$$
$$(\cos \theta - 2)(\cos \theta + 1) = 0.$$

From this product there are two possibilities: (i) $\cos \theta = 2$, and (ii) $\cos \theta = -1$. Case (i) is a null equation, thus the only possible roots come from Case (ii). But $\cos \theta = -1$ only when θ is π or any coterminal angle, hence the complete solution is $S = \{\pi \pm 2n\pi\}$.

EXAMPLE 2. Find the complete solution of $\tan 2x + 1 = 0$.

Solution. If we put $2x = \theta$ then this equation can be written in the simple form $\tan \theta = -1$. But $\tan \theta = -1$ only when θ is one of the angles $\{3\pi/4 \pm 2n\pi\}$ or $\{7\pi/4 \pm 2n\pi\}$. As the figure indicates, these two sets of values can be combined into the single state-

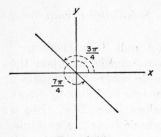

Fig. 6.5

ment $\theta = 3\pi/4 \pm n\pi$.[1] From this we have $2x = 3\pi/4 \pm n\pi$, and the complete solution is $S = \{3\pi/8 \pm n\pi/2\}$. Numerically, the first few positive roots of this equation are $3\pi/8, 7\pi/8, 11\pi/8, 15\pi/8$.

EXAMPLE 3. Find the complete solution of sec $x + \tan x = 2$.

Solution.

$$\sec x = 2 - \tan x,$$
$$\sec^2 x = 4 - 4 \tan x + \tan^2 x,$$
$$\tan^2 x + 1 = 4 - 4 \tan x + \tan^2 x,$$
$$4 \tan x = 3,$$
$$\tan x = \tfrac{3}{4} = 0.75.$$

Since tan x is positive, x may be in either Quadrant I or Quadrant III. From the tables it appears that the solution is $x = 36°52' \pm n \cdot 180°$ (where the angle $36°52'$ is approximate).[2] In finding the solution, however, we may have introduced extraneous roots by squaring both sides, hence the solution must be checked in the original equation. There are two possible roots between $0°$ and $360°$, each of which must be checked.

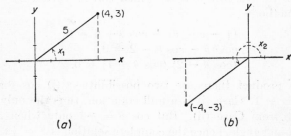

(a) (b)

Fig. 6.6

---

[1] As a matter of convenience, we shall sometimes write (for example) $\theta = 3\pi/4 \pm n\pi$ to mean that θ may be any one of the angles in the set $\{3\pi/4 \pm n\pi\}$. The complete solution, however, will always be recorded as a set.

[2] See Appendix 4 for use of tables.

QUADRANT I	QUADRANT III
$\sec x_1 = \frac{5}{4}$	$\sec x_2 = -\frac{5}{4}$
$\tan x_1 = \frac{3}{4}$	$\tan x_2 = \frac{3}{4}$
$\sec x_1 + \tan x_1 = 2$	$\sec x_2 + \tan x_2 \neq 2$

The third-quadrant angle is not a root of the equation, hence the complete solution is $S = \{36°52' \pm n \cdot 360°\}$.

Sometimes a trigonometric equation may be reduced to an equality of the same function of two different angles, for example $\sin x = \sin y$. The solution of an equation of this type requires a detailed discussion.

It is obvious that if $x = y$, then $\sin x = \sin y$. From the periodicity of the sine function it also follows that if x and y differ by a multiple of 2π (that is, if $y = x \pm 2n\pi$) then $\sin x = \sin y$. (Taking $n = 0$ shows that the equality $x = y$ is included as a special case in the more general statement $y = x \pm 2n\pi$, therefore we shall omit further reference to the special case $x = y$.)

Now suppose we are given the equality $\sin x = \sin y$. What conclusion can be drawn about the relationship between x and y? From the discussion above, it is possible that x and y may differ by a multiple of 2π. But this is not the only possibility. There may be an entirely different relationship, illustrated by the special case $x = \pi/4$ and $y = 3\pi/4$. Here the angles do not differ by a multiple of 2π, although $\sin \pi/4 = \sin 3\pi/4$. In spite of this apparently complicated situation, there is a definite and easily discoverable relationship between x and y.

Given an arbitrary angle x, the related angles in the four quadrants are x, $\pi - x$, $\pi + x$, and $- x$. By the reduction formulas we have

$$\sin x = \sin x,$$
$$\sin x = \sin (\pi - x),$$
$$\sin x = - \sin (\pi + x),$$
$$\sin x = - \sin (- x).$$

Thus from the given equality, $\sin x = \sin y$, we know that the angles are related as in one of the first two equations (because the sign on each side of the equation is plus). That is, either $y = x \pm 2n\pi$ or $y = (\pi - x) \pm 2n\pi$, where the term $2n\pi$ is added to make the solution completely general. Also, if we are given the equality $\sin x = - \sin y$, then by using the last two equations above (because the signs are opposite) we find that either $y = (\pi + x) \pm 2n\pi$ or $y = (- x) \pm 2n\pi$.

These conclusions may be diagrammed in the following way:

$$\sin x = \sin y$$

implies

either   or

$$y = x \pm 2n\pi \qquad\qquad y = (\pi - x) \pm 2n\pi$$

$$\sin x = -\sin y$$

implies

either   or

$$y = (\pi + x) \pm 2n\pi \qquad\qquad y = (-x) \pm 2n\pi$$

The equation $\cos x = \cos y$ may be analyzed in the same way. The four reduction formulas are

$$\cos x = \cos x,$$
$$\cos x = -\cos (\pi - x),$$
$$\cos x = -\cos (\pi + x),$$
$$\cos x = \cos (-x).$$

In this case the first and last formulas are applicable (because of the signs), hence $y = x \pm 2n\pi$ or $y = (-x) \pm 2n\pi$. Of course, if the given equation is $\cos x = -\cos y$, then the relationship is either $y = (\pi - x) \pm 2n\pi$ or $y = (\pi + x) \pm 2n\pi$.

Equations involving the other trigonometric functions may be analyzed in a similar way.

EXAMPLE 4. Solve the equation $\cos 2\theta = \sin 5\theta$.

First solution. By a reduction formula the sine function may be changed to a cosine function, and the equation may be written

$$\cos 2\theta = \cos (\pi/2 - 5\theta).$$

From the previous discussion there are two possibilities, and the complete solution is a combination of the two.

$$\pi/2 - 5\theta = 2\theta \pm 2n\pi, \qquad \pi/2 - 5\theta = -2\theta \pm 2n\pi,$$
$$7\theta = \pi/2 \pm 2n\pi, \qquad 3\theta = \pi/2 \pm 2n\pi,$$
$$\theta = \pi/14 \pm 2n\pi/7, \qquad \theta = \pi/6 \pm 2n\pi/3.$$

Second solution. By a reduction formula the cosine function may be changed to a sine function, and the equation may be written $\sin (\pi/2 - 2\theta) = \sin 5\theta$.

Hence

$$\pi/2 - 2\theta = 5\theta \pm 2n\pi, \qquad \pi/2 - 2\theta = (\pi - 5\theta) \pm 2n\pi,$$
$$7\theta = \pi/2 \pm 2n\pi, \qquad 3\theta = \pi/2 \pm 2n\pi,$$
$$\theta = \pi/14 \pm 2n\pi/7, \qquad \theta = \pi/6 \pm 2n\pi/3.$$

The solution may be expressed a little more concisely as

$$S = \left\{ \frac{\pi \pm 4n\pi}{14} \right\} \quad \text{and} \quad \left\{ \frac{\pi \pm 4n\pi}{6} \right\}.$$

-------------| **Problem Set 6.5** |-------------

In each of the following eight equations find the complete solution:

1. $\cos^2 \theta = \frac{1}{2}$,   2. $\cos^2 \theta + \sin \theta = -1$,

3. $\sin^2 \theta - \cos^2 \theta = 0$,   4. $\cot 2x = 1$,

5. $\sin 2x + \csc 2x = -2$,   6. $3 \tan^2 2x = 1$,

7. $\sin (\theta - \pi) = \cos (\pi - \theta)$,   8. $2 \sin \theta = -\tan \theta$.

9. Show graphically the solutions of the equation $\sin \theta = \sin \pi/6$. [*Hint.* Sketch the two functions $y = \sin \theta$ and $y' = \sin \pi/6$.]

10. Find the complete solution of the equation
   (a) $\sin x = \cos x/2$,   (b) $\sin \pi x = -\cos \pi x/2$,
   (c) $\sin 3\theta = \cos \theta$,   (d) $-\sin \theta = \cos 3\theta$.

11. From the equality $\tan x = \tan y$, what is implied regarding the relationship between x and y?

12. Find the complete solution of the equation
   (a) $\tan \theta = \tan 2\theta$,   (b) $\tan 3x = \cot 5x$,
   (c) $\tan \pi x = \cot \pi x/2$.

-------------| **Miscellaneous Problems** |-------------

1. Classify the equation:
   (a) $\csc \theta = \csc \theta \cdot \cot \theta$,
   (b) $\tan x = \tan x \cdot \csc x$.

2. (a) Classify the equation, $\cos x = \tan x \cdot \cot x$.
   (b) What are the roots, if any, of $\tan \theta = \tan \theta \cdot \cot \theta$?

3. Prove that the following are conditional equations.
   (a) $\sin x + \cos x = -1$;
   (b) $\cos \pi x + x = \sin \pi x$;
   (c) $\sin x - \cos x + \tan x = \cot x$.

4. Which of the following equations has $\pi/2$ as a root?

(a) $\sin \theta \cdot \csc \theta = 1$,

(b) $\cos \theta \cdot \sec \theta = 0$,

(c) $\sin \theta + \cot \theta = 1$.

5. Prove that the following equations are not identities:

(a) $\sin x = \sqrt{1 - \cos^2 x}$,

(b) $\tan x = \sqrt{\sec^2 x - 1}$.

6. Analyze graphically the equation $\sin \theta = 2 + \cos \theta$.

7. Suppose $f(x)$ and $g(x)$ are two periodic functions defined on the same domain.

(a) If the primitive periods of f and g are different, is it possible that the equation $f(x) = g(x)$ is an identity?

(b) If the primitive periods of f and g are the same, is it necessary that the equation $f(x) = g(x)$ be an identity?

8. Simplify $\dfrac{\tan^2 x + 1}{\sin (-x) + \cos (-x)} \cdot \dfrac{\cos^2 x + \sin (\pi + x) \sin (\pi - x)}{-\csc (\pi/2 - x)}$.

9. Simplify $\dfrac{\tan (\pi/2 + \theta)}{\sin^2 \theta - \cos^2 \theta} \cdot [\tan (\pi - \theta) + 1]$.

10. Simplify $\dfrac{\sin^2 x - 1}{\cos (\pi + x)} \cdot \dfrac{\sec (-x)}{1 + \tan^2 (-x)}$.

11. On the interval $0 \leq x \leq 2\pi$ find the values of x for which

(a) $\tan x - \cot x \geq 0$,

(b) $\sec x - \tan x \geq 0$.

12. On the interval $0 \leq x \leq 2\pi$ find the values of x for which

(a) $\csc x - \cot x \leq 0$,

(b) $\sin x - \cos x \leq 0$.

13. On the interval $0 \leq \theta \leq \pi$ find the values of θ for which

(a) $\tan^2 \theta - 1 \geq 0$,

(b) $\tan^2 \theta - \cot^2 \theta \geq 0$.

Prove the following six identities.

14. $\dfrac{\sec (-x)}{\csc x} \cot (\pi + x) = 1$.

15. $\dfrac{1 + \cot^2 \theta}{\tan^2 \theta + 1} = \csc^2 \theta - 1$.

16. $\sin^4 \theta + \sin^2 \theta \cdot \cos^2 \theta + \cos^4 \theta = 1 - \sin^2 \theta \cdot \cos^2 \theta$.

17. $\sin \theta \cos \theta \tan \theta = 1/(1 + \cot^2 \theta)$.

18. $(1 - 2 \sin^2 \theta)(1 + \cot^2 \theta) = \cot^2 \theta - 1$.

19. $1 - 3 \sin^2 x \cos^2 x = \sin^6 x + \cos^6 x$.

20. Find the domain over which the following is an identity.

$$\tan x = \sqrt{(\sec x - 1)(\sec x + 1)}.$$

21. Find the domain over which the following is an identity.

$$\sqrt{\frac{1 - \sin x}{1 + \sin x}} = \sec x - \tan x.$$

22. Show that the product of the six trigonometric functions for any admissible angle is equal to 1.

23. Find the set of five trigonometric functions for which the product is identically equal to: (a) $\sin x$, (b) $\cot x$.

24. Prove the identity:
  (a) $\sin (\theta - \pi/2) = \cos (\pi - \theta)$,
  (b) $\tan (x - \pi) = -\cot (\pi/2 + x)$.

25. Find the complete solution:
  (a) $\sec^2 x - \tan x - 1 = 0$,
  (b) $\csc^4 x + \cot^2 x + 1 = 0$,
  (c) $\csc \theta = 2 - \cot \theta$,
  (d) $\sec \theta = 1 + \tan \theta$.

26. Find the complete solution:
  (a) $\sin 2x = \cos 5x$,
  (b) $\sin \pi x/2 = \cos \pi x$,
  (c) $\sin 2\theta = -\cos 5\theta$,
  (d) $-\sin \pi x = \cos \pi x/2$.

27. From the equality $\cot x = \cot y$, what is implied regarding the relationship between x and y?

28. Find the complete solution:
  (a) $\cot 3x = \cot x$,
  (b) $\tan \theta = -\cot 2\theta$,
  (c) $\tan \pi x/2 = -\cot \pi x$.

29. Solve the equation $\cos \theta + \theta = 1$.

30. Estimate (two decimal places) the solution of $\sin x + \cos x = x$.

7

MULTIPLE ANGLE FORMULAS

In the preceding chapters we have been able to assign actual values to the trigonometric functions for only a few special angles. It sometimes happens that an angle which is not a special angle can be expressed as a sum or difference of two special angles; for example, $75° = 45° + 30°$ or $105° = 150° - 45°$. It seems reasonable to assume that the trigonometric values of such an angle must be related in some way to those of the special angles. This is indeed the case, but the relationship is not at all obvious. From the fact that $\sin 45° + \sin 30° = \sqrt{2}/2 + 1/2 = (\sqrt{2} + 1)/2$, which is greater than 1, it follows that $\sin 75° = \sin (45° + 30°) \neq \sin 45° + \sin 30°$. Hence the relationship must be a little more complicated than we might at first suspect.

1. THE ADDITION FORMULAS FOR SINE AND COSINE

Let O denote the origin of co-ordinates, and let M denote the point $(1, 0)$ on the unit circle U. Let the angle β be generated by the point P $(\cos \beta, \sin \beta)$, let the angle γ be generated by the point Q $(\cos \gamma,$ $\sin \gamma)$, and let R be the point which generates the angle $\alpha = \beta + \gamma$ (see Fig. 7.1). From plane geometry it follows that triangles QOM and ROP are congruent, hence corresponding sides of each are equal in length. In particular, $d_1 = d_2$, where $d_1 = \text{dist } (Q, M)$ and

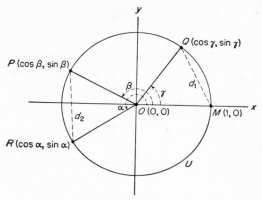

Fig. 7.1

$d_2 = $ dist (P, R). From the distance formula we have

$$d_1{}^2 = (\cos \gamma - 1)^2 + \sin^2 \gamma,$$
$$d_2{}^2 = (\cos \alpha - \cos \beta)^2 + (\sin \alpha - \sin \beta)^2.$$

Since $d_1 = d_2$, it follows that $d_1{}^2 = d_2{}^2$, therefore

$$\cos^2 \gamma - 2 \cos \gamma + 1 + \sin^2 \gamma = \cos^2 \alpha - 2 \cos \alpha \cos \beta + \cos^2 \beta$$
$$+ \sin^2 \alpha - 2 \sin \alpha \sin \beta + \sin^2 \beta$$

Simplifying we get

$$2 - 2 \cos \gamma = 2 - 2 \cos \alpha \cos \beta - 2 \sin \alpha \sin \beta,$$
$$\cos \gamma = \cos \alpha \cos \beta + \sin \alpha \sin \beta.$$

But $\gamma = \alpha - \beta$; hence

$$\cos (\alpha - \beta) = \cos \alpha \cdot \cos \beta + \sin \alpha \cdot \sin \beta.$$

In the derivation of this formula nothing exceptional has been assumed regarding the positions of the points P and Q. We may conclude, therefore, that the formula is valid for any pair of angles whatever. The following special cases are of the utmost importance. In each case let θ and ϕ be two arbitrary angles and let α and β be related to them as indicated.

(1.1) $\alpha = \pi/2 - \theta$, $\beta = \phi$.

$$\cos (\pi/2 - \theta - \phi) = \cos (\pi/2 - \theta) \cdot \cos \phi +$$
$$\sin (\pi/2 - \theta) \cdot \sin \phi,$$
$$\cos [\pi/2 - (\theta + \phi)] = \sin \theta \cdot \cos \phi + \cos \theta \cdot \sin \phi,$$
$$\sin (\theta + \phi) = \sin \theta \cdot \cos \phi + \cos \theta \cdot \sin \phi.$$

(1.2) $\alpha = \pi/2 - \theta$, $\beta = -\phi$.

$\cos(\pi/2 - \theta + \phi) = \cos(\pi/2 - \theta) \cdot \cos(-\phi) +$
$\qquad\qquad\qquad\qquad\qquad \sin(\pi/2 - \theta) \cdot \sin(-\phi)$,

$\cos[\pi/2 - (\theta - \phi)] = \sin\theta \cdot \cos\phi + \cos\theta \cdot (-\sin\phi)$,

$\sin(\theta - \phi) = \sin\theta \cdot \cos\phi - \cos\theta \cdot \sin\phi$.

(1.3) $\alpha = \theta$, $\beta = -\phi$.

$\cos[\theta - (-\phi)] = \cos\theta \cdot \cos(-\phi) + \sin\theta \cdot \sin(-\phi)$,

$\cos(\theta + \phi) = \cos\theta \cdot \cos\phi - \sin\theta \cdot \sin\phi$.

(1.4) $\alpha = \theta$, $\beta = \phi$.

$\cos(\theta - \phi) = \cos\theta \cdot \cos\phi + \sin\theta \cdot \sin\phi$.

From the derivation it follows that each of these equations is an identity. Furthermore, there are no inadmissible values of the variables. These addition and subtraction formulas are of such importance and occur so frequently in later work that it is advisable to memorize them and to study carefully the derivations. All subsequent identities derived in this chapter depend upon these four; they are the basic tools. For convenience the equations are frequently combined (signs in corresponding positions are to be taken together):

(1.5)
$$\sin(\theta \pm \phi) = \sin\theta \cdot \cos\phi \pm \cos\theta \cdot \sin\phi,$$
$$\cos(\theta \pm \phi) = \cos\theta \cdot \cos\phi \mp \sin\theta \cdot \sin\phi.$$

2. OTHER ADDITION FORMULAS

Using the fundamental identity, $\tan\theta = \sin\theta/\cos\theta$, it is easy to derive an addition formula for the tangent function.

$$\tan(\theta + \phi) = \frac{\sin(\theta + \phi)}{\cos(\theta + \phi)} = \frac{\sin\theta \cdot \cos\phi + \cos\theta \cdot \sin\phi}{\cos\theta \cdot \cos\phi - \sin\theta \cdot \sin\phi}.$$

We are interested in expressing $\tan(\theta + \phi)$ in terms of $\tan\theta$ and $\tan\phi$ if possible. This can be done if we divide both numerator and denominator by $\cos\theta \cdot \cos\phi$.

$$\tan(\theta + \phi) = \frac{\dfrac{\sin\theta \cdot \cos\phi + \cos\theta \cdot \sin\phi}{\cos\theta \cdot \cos\phi}}{\dfrac{\cos\theta \cdot \cos\phi - \sin\theta \cdot \sin\phi}{\cos\theta \cdot \cos\phi}},$$

$$= \frac{\dfrac{\sin \theta}{\cos \theta} + \dfrac{\sin \phi}{\cos \phi}}{1 - \dfrac{\sin \theta \cdot \sin \phi}{\cos \theta \cdot \cos \phi}}.$$

(2.1) $\qquad \tan (\theta + \phi) = \dfrac{\tan \theta + \tan \phi}{1 - \tan \theta \cdot \tan \phi}.$

This equation is an identity having as inadmissible values all angles and combinations of angles described as follows: $\theta = \phi = \pi/2 \pm n\pi$, $\theta + \phi = \pi/2 \pm n\pi$, and θ and ϕ such angles that $\tan \theta \cdot \tan \phi - 1 = 0$. By solving the latter equation, it can be seen that these angles are already among those excluded.

The formula for $\cot (\theta + \phi)$ can be derived in a similar way.

(2.2) $\qquad \cot (\theta + \phi) = \dfrac{\cot \theta \cdot \cot \phi - 1}{\cot \phi + \cot \theta}.$

Formulas for $\tan (\theta - \phi)$ and $\cot (\theta - \phi)$ can be found from the formulas above by writing $\theta - \phi = \theta + (-\phi)$. Formulas for sec $(\theta \pm \phi)$ and csc $(\theta \pm \phi)$ are seldom required.

Returning to the angles mentioned at the beginning of this chapter, it is now an easy matter to determine the trigonometric values.

$$\sin \; 75° = \sin (45° + 30°) = \sin 45° \cdot \cos 30° + \cos 45° \cdot \sin 30°$$

$$= \frac{\sqrt{2}}{2} \cdot \frac{\sqrt{3}}{2} + \frac{\sqrt{2}}{2} \cdot \frac{1}{2} = \frac{\sqrt{6} + \sqrt{2}}{4} = 0.9659 \text{ (approx.).}$$

$$\sin 105° = \sin (150° - 45°) = \sin 150° \cdot \cos 45° - \cos 150° \cdot \sin 45°$$

$$= \frac{1}{2} \cdot \frac{\sqrt{2}}{2} - \left(-\frac{\sqrt{3}}{2}\right) \cdot \frac{\sqrt{2}}{2} = 0.9659 \text{ (approx.).}$$

$$\cos 75° \;\; = \cos (45° + 30°), = \cos 45° \cdot \cos 30° - \sin 45° \cdot \sin 30°$$

$$= \frac{\sqrt{2}}{2} \cdot \frac{\sqrt{3}}{2} - \frac{\sqrt{2}}{2} \cdot \frac{1}{2} = \frac{\sqrt{6} - \sqrt{2}}{4} = 0.2588 \text{ (approx.).}$$

$$\cos 105° = \cos (150° - 45°) = \cos 150° \cdot \cos 45° + \sin 150° \cdot \sin 45°$$

$$= -\frac{\sqrt{3}}{2} \cdot \frac{\sqrt{2}}{2} + \frac{1}{2} \cdot \frac{\sqrt{2}}{2} = -0.2588 \text{ (approx.).}$$

$$\tan 75° = \tan (45° + 30°) = \frac{\tan 45° + \tan 30°}{1 - \tan 45° \cdot \tan 30°}$$

$$= \frac{1 + (\sqrt{3}/3)}{1 - (\sqrt{3}/3)1} = 3.732 \text{ (approx.)}.$$

$$\tan 105° = \tan (150° - 45°) = \frac{\tan 150° - \tan 45°}{1 + \tan 150° \cdot \tan 45°}$$

$$= \frac{(-\sqrt{3}/3) - 1}{1 + (-\sqrt{3}/3)1} = -3.732 \text{ (approx.)}.$$

------| **Problem Set 7.1** |------

1. Using the addition formulas, find the following trigonometric values.
  (a) sin 15°, (b) tan $11\pi/12$,
  (c) cos 255°, (d) sin $(-\pi/12)$.

2. Using the addition formulas, find the following trigonometric values.
  (a) cot $(-75°)$, (b) cos $11\pi/12$,
  (c) cot $7\pi/12$, (d) sin $7\pi/12$.

3. Find the six trigonometric values for the angles (a) $\pi/12$, (b) $-\pi/12$.

4. Find the six trigonometric values for the angles (a) $11\pi/12$, (b) 195°.

5. What are the inadmissible values for θ and ϕ in Equation 2.2?

6. Derive a formula for tan $(\theta - \phi)$ by the method used in the derivation of Equation 2.1. What are the inadmissible values of θ and ϕ?

7. Derive a formula for cot $(\theta + \phi)$ in terms of tan θ and tan ϕ.

8. Derive the equation sec $(\theta + \phi) = \dfrac{\sec \theta \sec \phi}{1 - \tan \theta \tan \phi}$.

9. By first writing $A + B = \theta$ and $C = \phi$, show that
$$\sin (A + B + C) = \sin A \cos B \cos C + \cos A \sin B \cos C$$
$$+ \cos A \cos B \sin C - \sin A \sin B \sin C.$$

10. Find the formula for sin $(A + B - C)$.

3. DOUBLE-ANGLE FORMULAS

An angle of the form 2θ can be written as $\theta + \theta$, hence the trigonometric functions of such an angle can be found by application of the addition formulas.

(3.1) $\sin 2\theta = \sin (\theta + \theta) = \sin \theta \cdot \cos \theta + \cos \theta \cdot \sin \theta$;
    $\sin 2\theta = 2 \sin \theta \cdot \cos \theta$.

(3.2) $\cos 2\theta = \cos (\theta + \theta) = \cos \theta \cdot \cos \theta - \sin \theta \cdot \sin \theta$;
    (a) $\cos 2\theta = \cos^2 \theta - \sin^2 \theta$.

This formula can be expressed in two other useful forms:

(b) $\cos 2\theta = (1 - \sin^2 \theta) - \sin^2 \theta$,

$\cos 2\theta = 1 - 2\sin^2 \theta$.

(c) $\cos 2\theta = \cos^2 \theta - (1 - \cos^2 \theta)$,

$\cos 2\theta = 2\cos^2 \theta - 1$.

(3.3) $\tan 2\theta = \tan(\theta + \theta) = \dfrac{\tan \theta + \tan \theta}{1 - \tan \theta \cdot \tan \theta} = \dfrac{2\tan \theta}{1 - \tan^2 \theta}$.

Each of the cases above leads to an identity, the first two having no inadmissible values, the third having the sets $\{\pi/4 \pm n\pi/2\}$ and $\{\pi/2 \pm n\pi\}$ as inadmissible values.

─────────────| **Problem Set 7.2** |─────────────

1. Derive the formula $\cot 2\theta = \dfrac{\cot^2 \theta - 1}{2\cot \theta}$. What are the inadmissible values of θ?

2. Show that $\csc 2\theta = \dfrac{\sec \theta \cdot \csc \theta}{2}$.

3. Show that $\sec 2\theta = \dfrac{1 + \tan^2 \theta}{1 - \tan^2 \theta}$.

4. By writing $3\theta = 2\theta + \theta$, find $\sin 3\theta$ and $\cos 3\theta$ in terms of the angle θ.

5. Show that $\cos^4 \theta - \sin^4 \theta = \cos 2\theta$.

6. If $\sin \theta = \frac{1}{3}$, find $\cos 2\theta$. Notice that $\cos 2\theta$ has a single value but that $\tan 2\theta$ has two possible values. What are they?

7. If $\cos \theta = \frac{3}{5}$ and if $\sin \theta > 0$, find (a) $\sin 2\theta$, (b) $\cos 2\theta$, (c) $\tan 2\theta$.

8. If $\tan x = 4/3$, find $\tan 2x$.

9. If $\tan 2x = 2\sqrt{2}$, find $\tan x$.

4. HALF-ANGLE FORMULAS

Trigonometric functions of the angle $\theta/2$ may be found in terms of the angle θ by making use of formulas in the preceding section.

For any angle x, Equation 3.2b may be rewritten

$$\sin^2 x = \frac{1 - \cos 2x}{2}.$$

Now assuming $\theta = 2x$, we obtain the formula

(4.1)
$$\sin \frac{\theta}{2} = \pm \sqrt{\frac{1 - \cos\theta}{2}} \, .$$

The expression $1 - \cos \theta$ is never negative; therefore the radical always represents a real number. The sign before the radical depends upon the quadrant of the angle $\theta/2$, and it must be chosen accordingly.

For any angle x, Equation 3.2c may be rewritten

$$\cos^2 x = \frac{1 + \cos 2x}{2} \, .$$

Now assuming $\theta = 2x$ we obtain the formula

(4.2)
$$\cos \frac{\theta}{2} = \pm \sqrt{\frac{1 + \cos \theta}{2}} \, .$$

Again the radical always represents a real number, and the sign before the radical depends upon the quadrant of the angle $\theta/2$.

EXAMPLE 1. Suppose we wish to find the trigonometric values of the angle $165°$. This is a second-quadrant angle, hence the sine is positive and the cosine is negative. If we put $\theta = 330°$ then $\theta/2 = 165°$, and we find from the formulas above

$$\sin 165° = \sqrt{\frac{1 - \sqrt{3}/2}{2}} = \frac{\sqrt{2 - \sqrt{3}}}{2} = 0.2588 \text{ (approx.)};$$

$$\cos 165° = -\sqrt{\frac{1 + \sqrt{3}/2}{2}} = -\frac{\sqrt{2 + \sqrt{3}}}{2} = -0.9659 \text{ (approx.)}.$$

The remaining trigonometric values may be found from these two.

Two convenient formulas for $\tan (\theta/2)$, may be derived from the fundamental relationship,

$$\tan \frac{\theta}{2} = \frac{\sin (\theta/2)}{\cos (\theta/2)} \, .$$

Multiplying both numerator and denominator first by $2 \sin (\theta/2)$ and second by $2 \cos (\theta/2)$, leads to the two formulas

$$\tan \frac{\theta}{2} = \frac{2 \sin^2(\theta/2)}{2 \sin (\theta/2) \cos (\theta/2)} \quad \text{and} \quad \tan \frac{\theta}{2} = \frac{2 \sin (\theta/2) \cos (\theta/2)}{2 \cos^2(\theta/2)} \, .$$

By Formulas 3.1, 3.2b, and 3.2c, we obtain

(4.3)
$$\tan \frac{\theta}{2} = \frac{1 - \cos \theta}{\sin \theta} \, ,$$

(4.4)
$$\tan\frac{\theta}{2} = \frac{\sin \theta}{1 + \cos \theta}.$$

Since neither $1 - \cos \theta$ nor $1 + \cos \theta$ is ever negative, the sign of $\tan (\theta/2)$ is the same as the sign of $\sin \theta$ (compare Problem 17, Miscellaneous Problem Set).

EXAMPLE 2. If $\theta = 330°$ then from Formula 4.3 we have

$$\tan 165° = \frac{1 - (\sqrt{3}/2)}{-1/2} = -0.2679 \text{ (approx.).}$$

For certain quadrantal angles one of these formulas may yield a value while the other one does not. For example, if $\theta = 360°$ then $\tan (\theta/2)$, cannot be evaluated by Formula 4.3, whereas by Formula 4.4 we find $\tan 180° = 0/(1 + 1) = 0$.

───────────| **Problem Set 7.3** |───────────

1. If angle $A/2$ is in Quadrant I, prove that angle A is either in Quadrant I or II. [*Hint.* First express $A/2$ in the following way, then solve for A: $A/2 = \theta \pm 2n\pi$, where $0 < \theta < \pi/2$.]

2. If angle $A/2$ is in Quadrant II, prove that angle A is either in Quadrant III or IV.

3. If angle A is in Quadrant I, prove that angle $A/2$ is either in Quadrant I or III.

4. Derive the formula, $\tan (\theta/2) = \pm\sqrt{\dfrac{1 - \cos \theta}{1 + \cos \theta}}$.

5. Find the following trigonometric values by use of the half-angle formulas:
  (a) $\sin 22\frac{1}{2}°$,   (b) $\cos 165°$,   (c) $\tan \pi/12$,
  (d) $\cot 7\pi/12$,   (e) $\sin (-\pi/12)$,   (f) $\tan (-\pi/8)$.

6. Using the half-angle formulas, express in radical form:
  (a) $\cos (\pi/8)$ and $\cos (\pi/16)$;
  (b) $\sin (\pi/12)$ and $\sin (\pi/24)$.

7. Express $\sin^2 (\pi/48)$ in radical form.

8. Express $\tan^2 (\pi/48)$ in radical form.

5. IDENTITIES AND EQUATIONS

The formulas derived in the preceding sections are all identities, and they may be applied directly to more complicated problems than those considered in Chapter 6. The general techniques for proving the identities and solving the equations in this chapter are essentially the same as those described in the preceding chapter.

EXAMPLE 1. Prove the identity

$$\sin (x + y) \cdot \sin (x - y) = \sin^2 x - \sin^2 y.$$

Proof. There are no inadmissible values of x or y.

$$
\begin{aligned}
\sin (x + y) \cdot \sin (x - y) &= (\sin x \cdot \cos y + \cos x \cdot \sin y) \\
&\quad \cdot (\sin x \cdot \cos y - \cos x \cdot \sin y), \\
&= \sin^2 x \cdot \cos^2 y - \cos^2 x \cdot \sin^2 y, \\
&= \sin^2 x (1 - \sin^2 y) - (1 - \sin^2 x) \sin^2 y, \\
&= \sin^2 x - \sin^2 y .
\end{aligned}
$$

EXAMPLE 2. Prove the identity

$$\frac{\sin^3 2\theta}{1 + \cos 2\theta - \cos^2 2\theta - \cos^3 2\theta} = \tan \theta .$$

Proof. Tan θ has inadmissible values $\theta = \pi/2$ and $3\pi/2$. To find the remaining inadmissible values we set the left-hand denominator equal to zero.

$$1 + \cos 2\theta - \cos^2 2\theta - \cos^3 2\theta = 0.$$

Factoring, we have

$$
\begin{aligned}
(1 + \cos 2\theta) - \cos^2 2\theta \cdot (1 + \cos 2\theta) &= 0. \\
(1 + \cos 2\theta) \cdot (1 - \cos^2 2\theta) &= 0. \\
(1 + \cos 2\theta) \cdot \sin^2 2\theta &= 0. \\
\cos 2\theta = -1, \quad \text{and} \quad \sin^2 2\theta &= 0.
\end{aligned}
$$

Hence $\theta = \pi/2$ and $3\pi/2$, and $\theta = 0$, $\pi/2$, π, and $3\pi/2$. Thus we denote the inadmissible values by the statement, $\theta \neq 0$, $\pi/2$, π, $3\pi/2$. The next step in the proof makes use of the above factorization.

$$
\begin{aligned}
\frac{\sin^3 2\theta}{1 + \cos 2\theta - \cos^2 2\theta - \cos^3 2\theta} &= \frac{\sin^3 2\theta}{(1 + \cos 2\theta) \cdot \sin^2 2\theta} , \\
&= \frac{\sin 2\theta}{1 + \cos 2\theta} , \\
&= \frac{2 \sin \theta \cdot \cos \theta}{1 + 2 \cos^2 \theta - 1} , \\
&= \frac{\sin \theta}{\cos \theta} = \tan \theta .
\end{aligned}
$$

EXAMPLE 3. Solve the equation, $\sin 4\theta - \sin 2\theta + \sin \theta \cdot \cos \theta = 0$.
Solution.

$$2 \sin 2\theta \cdot \cos 2\theta - 2 \sin \theta \cdot \cos \theta + \sin \theta \cdot \cos \theta = 0,$$
$$2(2 \sin \theta \cdot \cos \theta) \cdot \cos 2\theta - \sin \theta \cdot \cos \theta = 0,$$
$$\sin \theta \cdot \cos \theta \cdot (4 \cos 2\theta - 1) = 0.$$

Setting each factor separately equal to zero we have

$$\sin \theta = 0, \quad \text{and} \quad \cos \theta = 0, \quad \text{and} \quad 4 \cos 2\theta = 1.$$
$$\theta = 0 \pm n\pi, \quad \theta = \pi/2 \pm n\pi, \quad \cos 2\theta = \tfrac{1}{4} = 0.25,$$
$$2\theta = \pm 1.3177 \pm 2n\pi \text{ (approx.)}, \quad \theta = \pm 0.6588 \pm n\pi.$$

Therefore the set S of solutions is

$$S = \{\pm n\pi/2\} \quad \text{and} \quad \{\pm 0.6588 \pm n\pi\}.$$

EXAMPLE 4. Solve the equation,

$$\sin x \cdot \cos (\pi/3) + \cos x \cdot \sin (\pi/3) = 1.$$

Solution. The left-hand side of this equation may be recognized as part of the basic formula:

$$\sin (x + \pi/3) = \sin x \cdot \cos (\pi/3) + \cos x \sin (\pi/3).$$

Hence we solve the simpler equation, $\sin (x + \pi/3) = 1$.
Thus $x + \pi/3 = \pi/2 \pm 2n\pi$, which gives the solution

$$S = \{\pi/6 \pm 2n\pi\}.$$

Problem Set 7.4

1. Express the following as single trigonometric functions:
   (a) $\cos \theta \cdot \cos 4\theta - \sin \theta \cdot \sin 4\theta$,
   (b) $\sin (\theta/2) \cdot \cos \theta - \cos (\theta/2) \cdot \sin \theta$,
   (c) $\cos (\pi/5) \cdot \cos \theta + \sin (\pi/5) \cdot \sin \theta$,
   (d) $\sin (\pi/8) \cdot \cos (\pi/10) + \cos (\pi/8) \cdot \sin (\pi/10)$.

2. Prove $2 \sin (x + y) \cdot \cos (x - y) = \sin 2x + \sin 2y$.

3. Prove $\cos (x + y) \cdot \cos (x - y) = 1 - \sin^2 x - \sin^2 y$.

4. Prove $\csc^2 2\theta - \sec^2 2\theta = 4 \cot 4\theta \csc 4\theta$.

5. Prove $8 \cos^4 \theta = 3 + 4 \cos 2\theta + \cos 4\theta$.

6. Prove $8 \sin^4 \theta = 3 - 4 \cos 2\theta + \cos 4\theta$.

7. Prove $4 \cos^3 \theta = \cos 3\theta + 3 \cos \theta$.

8. Prove $\cot^2 \theta - \tan^2 \theta = (4 \cos 2\theta)/\sin^2 2\theta$.

9. Solve $1 - \cos x = \sqrt{3} \sin x$.

10. Solve $\dfrac{1 - \cos x}{1 + \cos x} = \dfrac{1}{3}$.

11. Solve $\cos^2 x = \sin^2 x$.

12. Solve $\sin 2\theta = 2 - 2 \cos 2\theta$.

13. Solve $(\sqrt{3}/2) \cos \theta + \frac{1}{2} \sin \theta = 1$.

14. Solve $(\sqrt{2}/2) (\sin x - \cos x) = 1$.

15. Show that the following are null equations

    (a) $3 \sin^2 \theta + \cos^2 \theta = 0$;

    (b) $\tan^2 (x/2) + \csc^2 (x/2) = 1$;

    (c) $\sin x + \cos x = 2$.

6. THE PRODUCT AND SUM FORMULAS

The formulas listed in this section are used less frequently than those derived earlier. They may be proved by use of the fundamental addition and subtraction formulas.

(6.1) $$\sin \theta \cdot \cos \phi = \frac{\sin (\theta + \phi) + \sin (\theta - \phi)}{2},$$

(6.2) $$\cos \theta \cdot \sin \phi = \frac{\sin (\theta + \phi) - \sin (\theta - \phi)}{2},$$

(6.3) $$\cos \theta \cdot \cos \phi = \frac{\cos (\theta + \phi) + \cos (\theta - \phi)}{2},$$

(6.4) $$\sin \theta \cdot \sin \phi = \frac{\cos (\theta - \phi) - \cos (\theta + \phi)}{2},$$

(6.5) $$\sin x + \sin y = 2 \sin \left(\frac{x + y}{2}\right) \cdot \cos \left(\frac{x - y}{2}\right),$$

(6.6) $$\sin x - \sin y = 2 \cos \left(\frac{x + y}{2}\right) \cdot \sin \left(\frac{x - y}{2}\right),$$

(6.7) $$\cos x + \cos y = 2 \cos \left(\frac{x + y}{2}\right) \cdot \cos \left(\frac{x - y}{2}\right),$$

(6.8) $$\cos x - \cos y = - 2 \sin \left(\frac{x + y}{2}\right) \cdot \sin \left(\frac{x - y}{2}\right).$$

7. SPECIAL TOPIC: DERIVATIONS FROM PTOLEMY'S THEOREM

Consider a circle of radius $d/2$ with center O (see Fig. 7.2). Let the line segment AB be any diameter, and let C be any other point on the circle. Note that ABC is a right triangle, and that $\measuredangle \; BOC =$ $\measuredangle \; OAC + \measuredangle \; OCA$. The triangle AOC is isoceles and angle $\measuredangle \; BOC$ equals twice angle $\measuredangle \; OAC$, therefore we are justified in labeling these angles 2θ and θ. Since d is the diameter we have for BC and AC, respectively,

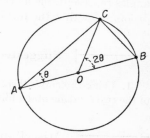

Fig. 7.2

(A)
$$\begin{cases} \operatorname{crd} 2\theta = d \sin \theta, \\ \operatorname{crd} (180° - 2\theta) = d \cos \theta. \end{cases}$$

It follows that any relation involving the chord of a central angle may be stated in terms of the sine or cosine of half the angle.

On the basis of Ptolemy's theorem we derived three equations in Section 7 of Chapter 4 which may be written, respectively:

(1) $\operatorname{crd} (2x - 2y) = \frac{1}{2}[\operatorname{crd} (180° - 2y) \cdot \operatorname{crd} 2x - \operatorname{crd} (180° - 2x)$
$\cdot \operatorname{crd} 2y],$

(2) $\operatorname{crd} [180° - (2x + 2y)] = \frac{1}{2}[\operatorname{crd} (180° - 2x) \cdot \operatorname{crd} (180° - 2y)$
$- \operatorname{crd} 2x \cdot \operatorname{crd} 2y],$

(3) $\operatorname{crd}^2 x = 2 - \operatorname{crd} (180° - 2x) .$

Recall that a circle of diameter 2 was used in the derivation of these formulas. We now make use of Equations (A) to show that these complicated formulas are actually three familiar identities in disguised form.

From Equation (1) we have
$$2 \sin (x - y) = \tfrac{1}{2}[2 \cos y \cdot 2 \sin x - 2 \cos x \cdot 2 \sin y],$$

(4) $\sin (x - y) = \sin x \cdot \cos y - \cos x \cdot \sin y.$

From Equation (2) we have
$$2 \cos (x + y) = \tfrac{1}{2}[2 \cos x \cdot 2 \cos y - 2 \sin x \cdot 2 \sin y],$$

(5) $\cos (x + y) = \cos x \cdot \cos y - \sin x \cdot \sin y.$

From Equation (3) we have
$$[2 \sin x/2]^2 = 2 - 2 \cos x,$$

(6)
$$\sin^2 \frac{x}{2} = \frac{1 - \cos x}{2}.$$

Thus the formulas used by Ptolemy 1800 years ago are closely related to three identities derived in this chapter. There is one point of difference, however. Ptolemy's formulas are proved valid only for angles representable as vertex angles of triangles, whereas the modern proofs show that the formulas are valid for all angles.

─────────| **Suggested Exercise** |───────────

1. Using Ptolemy's theorem, and an appropriate construction, prove each of the two fundamental addition formulas not proved here.

─────────| **Miscellaneous Problems** |───────────

1. Find the trigonometric values for the angle $5\pi/12$.

2. Find the trigonometric values for the angle $19\pi/12$.

3. Find a formula for $\cos (A + B + C)$.

4. Find a formula for $\cos (A - B - C)$.

5. Expand $\sin (A + B + C + D)$.

6. Derive formulas for $\tan (\theta - \phi)$ and $\cot (\theta - \phi)$ by the method used in the derivation of Equation 2.1. What are the inadmissible values of θ and ϕ?

7. Derive the equation $\csc (\theta + \phi) = \sec \phi \csc \theta/(1 + \tan \phi \cot \theta)$.

8. Find a formula for $\sec (\theta - \phi)$.

9. Find a formula for $\csc (\theta - \phi)$.

10. Find $\sin \theta$, $\cos \theta$, and $\tan \theta$ if (a) $\theta = \pi/8$, (b) $\theta = 3\pi/8$.

11. If $\sin \theta = 1/3$ and $\tan \theta > 0$, find (a) $\sin 2\theta$, (b) $\cos (\theta/2)$, (c) $\tan (-2\theta)$.

12. If $\cos \theta = -2/3$ and $\sin \theta < 0$, find (a) $\sin 4\theta$, (b) $\cos 4\theta$.

13. If $A/2$ is in Quadrant IV, find the possible quadrants of (a) A, (b) $2A$.

14. If A is in Quadrant I and B is in Quadrant II, find the possible quadrants of (a) $A + B$, (b) $A - B$.

15. If $\sin A > 0$, is it possible that (a) $\sin 2A < 0$, (b) $\tan \frac{1}{2}A < 0$?

16. If A is in Quadrant I and if $\sin B < 0$, which of the following is impossible?

(a) $\sin (A + B) < 0$,

(b) $A + B$ in Quadrant II,

(c) $\cos (A + B)$ and $\sin (A + B)$ have opposite signs.

17. By considering the possible cases, prove that for any angle θ, sin θ and tan $(\theta/2)$ have the same signs (provided the angles are admissible).

18. Derive the formula cot $(\theta/2) = (1 + \cos \theta)/\sin \theta$.

19. Using the double-angle formulas, prove that $\sin^2 2\theta + \cos^2 2\theta = 1$.

20. Using the half-angle formulas, prove that $\sin^2 (\theta/2) + \cos^2 (\theta/2) = 1$.

21. Prove sin $(x + y) \cdot \sin (x - y) + \cos (x + y) \cdot \cos (x - y) = \cos 2y$.

22. Prove $[\sin (x + y) - \cos (x + y)]^2 = 1 - \sin (2x + 2y)$.

23. Prove in two ways sin $3\theta \cdot \cos (-\theta) + \cos 3\theta \cdot \sin (-\theta) = \sin 2\theta$.

24. Prove in two ways sin $3\theta \cdot \cos 2\theta + \cos 3\theta \cdot \sin 2\theta = \sin 5\theta$.

25. Solve $3 \cos x - 2 \sin x = 0$.

26. Solve $\cos 2\theta = 2 - 2 \sin 2\theta$.

27. Solve $\frac{3}{5} \sin \theta - \frac{4}{5} \cos \theta = -1$.

28. Solve $12 \cos \theta = 13 \cdot \sqrt{2}/2 + 5 \sin \theta$.

29. If $\theta + \phi = \pi$ simplify:
   (a) sin $\theta +$ sin ϕ,
   (b) sin $\theta -$ sin ϕ,
   (c) cos $\theta +$ cos ϕ,
   (d) cos $\theta -$ cos ϕ.

30. If $\theta - \phi = \pi$ simplify:
   (a) sin $\theta +$ sin ϕ,
   (b) sin $\theta -$ sin ϕ,
   (c) cos $\theta +$ cos ϕ,
   (d) cos $\theta -$ cos ϕ.

8

THE INVERSES OF THE TRIGONOMETRIC FUNCTIONS

The ideas discussed in this chapter are based directly upon Section 3 of Chapter 2, on *Relation and Function*. Because of this close tie, a brief review of that section is prescribed as a good introduction to the study of inverse relations and functions. In this chapter, we shall use the symbol F to represent an arbitrary relation. Corresponding to the functional notation $y = f(x)$, we shall use $Y = F(x)$ to indicate that Y is the set of elements in the range of F which correspond under the relation to the element x in the domain.

1. THE INVERSE OF A RELATION

Let F represent a law of correspondence between two sets M and N. In order that F be a relation, it is necessary to designate one of the sets as the domain; in this instance let the domain be M. Suppose we represent the set M by the points in a circle and the set N by the

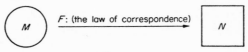

Fig. 8.1

points in a square. We then indicate, schematically, the relation F as in Fig. 8.1. The arrow from M to N indicates that, under F, each point of the domain M is made to correspond to some point, or set of points, of the range N. If x is some point in the circle, then $F(x)$ represents the point or points in the square that correspond to x under the relation F. The points x and $F(x)$ are said to be **related** by F.

Now suppose that G is another law of correspondence between the same two sets M and N. But in this case, suppose we convert the law G into a relation by choosing N as its domain. Schematically, this is indicated in Fig. 8.2. In the usual notation, if y is some point in the

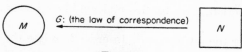

Fig. 8.2

square, then $G(y)$ represents the point or points in the circle that correspond to y under the relation G. The points y and $G(y)$ are said to be **related** by G.

Nothing has been assumed yet regarding a possible connection between G and F, beyond agreeing that both are laws of correspondence relating pairs of elements belonging to the two sets M and N. In fact, the two laws may relate entirely different pairs of elements. On the other hand, *if G should relate precisely the same pairs of elements that F relates, then G and F are called (**mutually**) **inverse relations**. In this situation the usual notation for G is F⁻¹, indicating that the relation G is the **inverse** of F.*

To summarize, if F is a relation and if F^{-1} is its inverse relation, then:

1. The domain (M) of F is the range of F^{-1}.
2. The domain (N) of F^{-1} is the range of F.
3. If x is a point of M, then $Y = F(x)$ is the set of all points of N related to x.
4. If y is a point of N, then $X = F^{-1}(y)$ is the set of all points of M related to y.
5. Even if F should be a function, F^{-1} is not necessarily a function (because there may be more than one element in the domain of F related to a particular element in the range).

EXAMPLE. Let M represent the set of all male children. We define a relation F, having M as its domain, in the following way: to each male child corresponds his father. That is, $Y = F(x)$ is to be read "Y is the father of x." Schematically, this is indicated in Fig. 8.3.

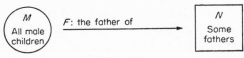

Fig. 8.3

About this relation we note that:

1. The domain of F is the set of all male children.

2. The range of F is not the set of all fathers, but is only the set of fathers each of whom has at least one male child (denoted by N).

3. F is a function, since to each male child corresponds exactly one father.

Now consider the inverse of F. In order to relate the same pairs of elements, the inverse law of correspondence must be stated in a way similar to the following: to each father (belonging to the set N) corresponds the set of all his sons. Schematically, this is indicated in Fig. 8.4. About the inverse relation we note that:

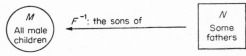

Fig. 8.4

1. The domain of F^{-1} is the set of all fathers of male children.

2. The range of F^{-1} is the set of all male children.

3. F^{-1} is not a function, because many fathers have more than one son; thus $F^{-1}(y)$ may contain more than one element.

─────────| Problem Set 8.1 |─────────

1. By the method used in the text diagram both the relation and its inverse.

    (a) F: to each automobile corresponds its manufacturer.

    (b) G: to each city corresponds its mayor.

2. By the method used in the text diagram both the relation and its inverse.

    (a) F: to each student corresponds his teachers.

    (b) G: to each country corresponds its inhabitants.

3. Which of the eight relations in the first two problems are functions?

4. Consider Example 1 in Section 3 of Chapter 2.

    (a) Diagram this function and its inverse.

    (b) Is the inverse relation a function?

5. Consider Example 2 in Section 3 of Chapter 2.
   (a) Diagram this relation and its inverse.
   (b) Is the inverse relation a function?

6. Make up an example of a function f which has a function as its inverse; that is, both f and f^{-1} are functions.

7. Consider the related pairs in the Example given in the text.
   (a) Is the domain of the function F the set of older or the set of younger individuals?
   (b) Is the range of the relation F^{-1} the set of older or the set of younger individuals?

8. Make up an example of a relation which is not a function, but which has a function as its inverse.

2. INVERSE GRAPHS

A point on a rectangular co-ordinate system is determined by a pair of numbers (x, y) given in a definite order. To sketch the graph of a relation F, we plot points the co-ordinates of which are pairs of numbers related by F. The first co-ordinate is a number from the domain of F, and the second co-ordinate is a related number from the range of F. By long-standing custom we let the number from the domain represent a horizontal distance, while the related number from the range represents a vertical distance.

Consider the function $y = x^2$, where the domain is the interval $-1 \leqq x \leqq 1$ (see Fig. 8.5). The pairs of numbers are all related by the law that the second is the square of the first. The range of this function is $0 \leqq y \leqq 1$.

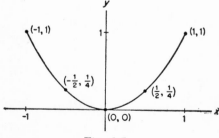

Fig. 8.5

Now, given a relation F, we should expect the graph of its inverse relation F^{-1} to obey the same laws and conventions that govern the graphing of any relation. But in defining the inverse relation, we interchanged the roles of the domain and the range. For example, the inverse relation to the function just given is found by solving the equation for x in terms of y. Instead of writing this in the form

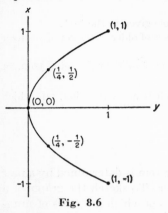

$x = \pm\sqrt{y}$ (as is sometimes done), we shall use the form $X = \pm\sqrt{y}$ in order to emphasize that for some element y there is more than one corresponding element x. For this relation the domain is $0 \leqq y \leqq 1$ and the range is $-1 \leqq x \leqq 1$. To sketch the graph of this relation, we assume, as usual, a number from the domain to represent a horizontal distance, while a related number from the range represents a vertical distance. For this reason, we should draw the y-axis hori-

Fig. 8.6

zontal and the x-axis vertical (see Fig. 8.6). Therefore, in order to retain the horizontal axis as the axis of the independent variable (domain) and the vertical axis as the axis of the dependent variable (range), it has been necessary to interchange the usual labels on the axes. To emphasize that the roles of domain and range have been interchanged, and to retain the x-axis as axis of the domain, we shall agree to the following convention:

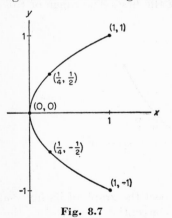

*Let $Y = F(x)$ be an arbitrary relation. Solve for x in terms of y to obtain $X = F^{-1}(y)$. Automatically interchange the variables to obtain the expression $Y = F^{-1}(x)$. Being careful to remember that x now represents an element from the domain of F^{-1}, we call $Y = F^{-1}(x)$ the **inverse relation** to the given relation.*

Fig. 8.7

Making use of this convention in the example above, we find a more agreeable situation. Given $y = x^2$, we solve for x in terms of y and interchange the variables, obtaining $Y = \pm\sqrt{x}$. The graph is shown in Fig. 8.7. We shall call this the **inverse graph** to Fig. 8.5.

Now consider again the graph of $y = x^2$. Think of the axes as remaining fixed, but rotate (in space) the graph itself about the straight line bisecting Quadrants I and III. The points $(0, 0)$ and $(1, 1)$ remain fixed, but the point $(-1, 1)$ becomes $(1, -1)$, $(\frac{1}{2}, \frac{1}{4})$ becomes $(\frac{1}{4}, \frac{1}{2})$, $(-\frac{1}{2}, \frac{1}{4})$ becomes $(\frac{1}{4}, -\frac{1}{2})$, and so on. The effect of this rotation is simply to interchange the co-ordinates while holding the axes fixed, and the new points are seen to be precisely the inverse graph (Fig. 8.7). In other words, a graph and its inverse graph are symmetric to each other about the line $y = x$. Thus we have found an easy method to obtain from a given graph its inverse graph. (In the special case of the function $y = x$, notice that the inverse is identical with the function.)

──────────| **Problem Set 8.2** |──────────────────

In the following problems consider only real number values of the variables.

1. Given the function $y = x$, domain $-1 \leq x \leq 1$.
   (a) What is the inverse relation? Is it a function?
   (b) On the same co-ordinate system sketch both the graph and the inverse graph.

2. Given the function $y = x^3$, domain $-1 \leq x \leq 1$.
   (a) What is the inverse relation? Is it a function?
   (b) On the same co-ordinate system sketch both the graph and the inverse graph.

3. Given a function $y = f(x)$. Every vertical line through an element of the domain intersects the graph of f in exactly one point. What statement made about the same graph indicates that the inverse relation is also a function?

4. Given the function $y = 1$, domain $0 \leq x \leq 2$.
   (a) What is the range of the function?
   (b) In words, this function can be described: to each value of x corresponds the number 1. Describe in words the inverse relation.
   (c) On the same co-ordinate system sketch both the graph and the inverse graph.

5. Sketch the inverse graph of the function $y = |x|$.

6. Given the relation $y^2 = x$, domain $0 \leq x \leq 1$.
   (a) What is the inverse relation? Is it a function?
   (b) On the same co-ordinate system sketch both the graph and the inverse graph.

7. Given the relation $y^2 = x^3$, domain $0 \leqq x \leqq 1$.
   (a) Sketch the graph.
   (b) What is the inverse relation? Is it a function?
8. Sketch the inverse graph of the relation $y^2 = x^2$.

3. PRINCIPAL VALUES

A relation that is not a function may assign more than one value in the range to a given element in the domain. The ambiguity implied here may be avoided by converting the relation into a function. This is done by arbitrarily selecting *one* value from the set of values in the range corresponding to a given element in the domain. Of course, this new function is only part of the original relation.

The graph of the relation $Y = \pm \sqrt{x}$ (see Fig. 8.7) indicates clearly that for any positive value of x there are two related values of y. From this relation we may define a function, called a **principal value function,** by eliminating (for example) all values of y except those on the interval $0 \leqq y \leqq 1$. Thus, by our definition, the principal value function corresponding to the relation $Y = \pm \sqrt{x}$ is $y = \sqrt{x}$. The graph of this principal value function is shown in Fig. 8.8, and it is called the **principal branch** of the graph shown in Fig. 8.7.

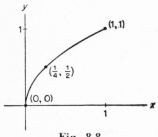

Fig. 8.8

About this concept in general we note that:

1. The principal value function of a relation is a function defined on the entire domain of the relation such that for a given element in the domain the function value is one of the relation values.

2. The range of the principal value function is a part of the range of the relation.

3. The way in which the principal value function is defined may be perfectly arbitrary, so long as it satisfies the two preceding statements.

EXAMPLE. The example of the fathers and sons, in Section 1, leads to ambiguity when we consider the inverse relation F^{-1}: the sons of. To avoid the ambiguity, we may define a principal value function in the following way: to each father (belonging to the set N) corresponds his eldest son. This function is seen to satisfy (1) and (2) above, since its domain is the domain of F^{-1} and its range is part of the range of F^{-1}.

---------------| **Problem Set 8.3** |------------------

1. The principal branch is the graph of a relation. Is it also the graph of a function?

2. In the example discussed in this section, define a different principal value function.

3. Given the function $y = x$, domain $-1 \leq x \leq 1$. Why is it, or is it not, necessary to define a principal value function for the inverse relation?

4. Given the function $y = x^2 + 1$, domain $-1 \leq x \leq 1$.

    (a) On the same co-ordinate system sketch both the graph and the inverse graph.

    (b) Define a principal value function for the inverse. Give both its domain and its range.

    (c) Explain why it is unnecessary to define a principal branch of the inverse graph if the domain is $0 \leq x \leq 1$.

In each of the following four relations define arbitrarily a principal value function, then sketch the principal branch.

5. $y^2 = x$, domain $0 \leq x \leq 2$.

6. $y^2 = x^2$, domain $-1 \leq x \leq 1$.

7. $y = \begin{cases} 1, x \leq 1, \\ -1, x \geq -1. \end{cases}$

8. $y = \begin{cases} x + 1, x \geq 0, \\ x - 1, x \leq 0. \end{cases}$

4. THE INVERSE SINE

The ideas discussed so far in this chapter apply to each of the trigonometric functions. The problem is threefold: for each function we wish to (A) describe its inverse relation, (B) determine its inverse graph, and (C) agree upon a principal branch of the inverse graph. We shall discuss this problem in detail for the function $y = \sin x$. In broad outline the discussion relating to each of the other trigonometric functions would be the same; therefore in those cases the conclusions only will be recorded.

(A) To find the inverse of an algebraic function we solve the equation for the independent variable in terms of the dependent variable.

This procedure applies equally well to the trigonometric functions; but here we are faced with a question of notation. If $y = \sin x$, how shall we express in symbols the solution for x in terms of y? In abstract language, if $y = f(x)$ then we denote the solution for x in terms of y by $X = f^{-1}(y)$ and the inverse relation by $Y = f^{-1}(x)$. Hence we are led to the following notation. *Given the function $y = \sin x$, we denote the inverse relation by $Y = \sin^{-1} x$, and we call it the **inverse sine** of x.* For each value of x, $\sin^{-1} x$ represents the set of all angles y for which $\sin y = x$. (Remember, the variables have been interchanged.)

In Section 3 of Chapter 6 we noted that there might be a tendency to misinterpret the symbol $sin^{-1} x$. In spite of the caution urged there, this tendency persists. To avoid confusion, it has become customary to use the symbol *arc sin* with the same meaning as sin^{-1}. For example, the solution of the equation $\sin x = -1$ is given by

$$\text{arc sin } (-1) = \{3\pi/2 \pm 2n\pi\}.$$

About the inverse sine relation we note that:

1. The usual notation is $Y = \text{arc sin } x$.

2. The domain of the arc sine relation is $-1 \leqq x \leqq 1$ (the range of the sine function).

3. The range of the arc sine relation is the set of all real numbers (the domain of the sine function).

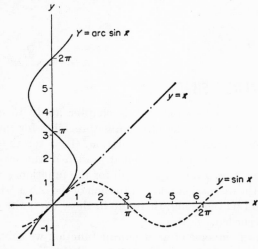

Fig. 8.9

4. The arc sine relation is not a function.

(B) The graph and the inverse graph are symmetric about the line $y = x$ as shown in Fig. 8.9. Notice that the horizontal and vertical scales must be the same in order to sketch the graph by this method.

(C) In many situations it is convenient to have some easily recognized system for distinguishing a principal value function from its corresponding relation. We shall adopt the following rule:

The principal value function of the arc sine relation is denoted by capitalizing the initial letter of arc, or by capitalizing the initial letter of sin if the symbol sin⁻¹ is used.

Thus Arc sin x (or Sin$^{-1} x$) denotes the principal value function of arc sin x (or sin$^{-1} x$). We shall arbitrarily select that principal branch which seems to be most useful in later work. Given the inverse relation $Y = $ arc sin x, the principal value function is determined as follows:

$$\begin{cases} 0 \leq \text{Arc sin } x \leq \pi/2, & \text{if} \quad 0 \leq x \leq 1, \\ -\pi/2 \leq \text{Arc sin } x < 0, & \text{if} \quad -1 \leq x < 0. \end{cases}$$

Notice that Arc sin x is actually a function and that its domain ($-1 \leq x \leq 1$) is exactly the domain of the inverse sine relation. The principal branch of the inverse graph is shown in Fig. 8.10.

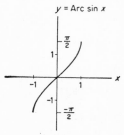

$y = $ Arc sin x

Fig. 8.10

5. OTHER TRIGONOMETRIC INVERSES

5.1 THE INVERSE COSINE

Given the function $y = \cos x$.

(A) About its inverse we note that:

1. The usual notation is $Y = $ arc cos x.
2. The domain is $-1 \leqq x \leqq 1$.
3. The range is the set of all real numbers.
4. The arc cosine relation is not a function.

(B) For the inverse graph see Fig. 8.11.

(C) The principal value function is defined as follows (see Fig. 8.12):
$$\begin{cases} 0 \leqq \text{Arc cos } x \leqq \pi/2, & \text{if} \quad 0 \leqq x \leqq 1, \\ \pi/2 \leqq \text{Arc cos } x \leqq \pi, & \text{if} \quad -1 \leqq x < 0. \end{cases}$$

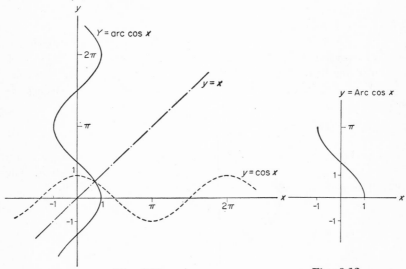

Fig. 8.11   **Fig. 8.12**

5.2 THE INVERSE TANGENT

Given the function $y = \tan x$.

(A) About its inverse we note that:
1. The usual notation is $Y = $ arc tan x.
2. The domain is the set of all real numbers.
3. The range is the set of all real numbers except $\{\pi/2 \pm n\pi\}$.
4. The arc tangent relation is not a function.

(B) For the inverse graph see Fig. 8.13.

(C) The principal value function is defined as follows (see Fig. 8.14):
$$\begin{cases} 0 \leqq \text{Arc tan } x < \pi/2, & \text{if} \quad x \geqq 0, \\ -\pi/2 < \text{Arc tan } x < 0, & \text{if} \quad x < 0. \end{cases}$$

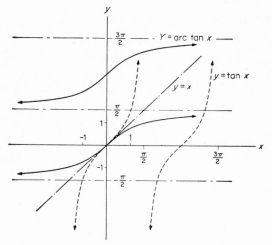

Fig. 8.13

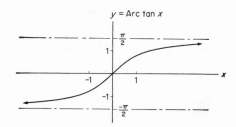

Fig. 8.14

---| **Problem Set 8.4** |---

1. Sketch the graph of $Y = \text{arc cot } x$.

2. Sketch the graph of $Y = \text{arc sec } x$.

3. Sketch the graph of $Y = \text{arc csc } x$.

4. Define and sketch a principal value function for the inverse cotangent relation.

5. Define and sketch a principal value function for the inverse secant relation.

6. Define and sketch a principal value function for the inverse cosecant relation.

6. EXAMPLES

EXAMPLE 1. What set of numbers is represented by the symbol. arc sin $(-\sqrt{3}/2)$?

Solution. An angle θ belongs to the required set provided $\sin\theta = -\sqrt{3}/2$. From the special angle values we know that

$$\text{arc sin } (-\sqrt{3}/2) = \begin{Bmatrix} \{ & 4\pi/3 \pm 2n\pi \}, \\ \{ & -\pi/3 \pm 2n\pi \}. \end{Bmatrix}$$

EXAMPLE 2. Evaluate Arc cos $(\cos 4\pi/3)$.

Solution. In words, this symbol represents: the principal angle whose cosine is (the cosine of $4\pi/3$). But the angle specified here is not $4\pi/3$. Since $\cos 4\pi/3 = -\frac{1}{2}$, and since $\pi/2 < \text{Arc cos }(-\frac{1}{2}) \leqq \pi$, we have

$$\text{Arc cos } (\cos 4\pi/3) = 2\pi/3.$$

EXAMPLE 3. Evaluate tan $[2 \text{ Arc cos } \frac{3}{5}]$.

Solution. Put $\theta = \text{Arc cos } \frac{3}{5}$. We wish to evaluate

$$\tan 2\theta = \frac{2\tan\theta}{1 - \tan^2\theta}.$$

We know $0 \leqq \text{Arc cos } \frac{3}{5} \leqq \pi/2$, and the angle is shown in Fig. 8.15

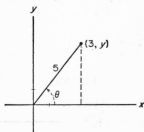

$(3, y)$

5

θ

Fig. 8.15

But $y = \sqrt{25 - 9} = 4$; therefore tan $\theta = 4/3$. From this we have

$$\tan [2 \text{ Arc cos } \tfrac{3}{5}] = \frac{2(\frac{4}{3})}{1 - (\frac{4}{3})^2} = -\frac{24}{7}.$$

EXAMPLE 4. Prove that the following equation is an identity if $u \geqq 0$, and is null if $u < 0$: Arc cos $u = $ Arc sin $\sqrt{1 - u^2}$.

Solution for $u \geqq 0$. As the first step, note that u cannot be greater than 1 (otherwise the angles are undefined). Put $\theta = \text{Arc cos } u$ and

$\phi = \text{Arc sin } \sqrt{1 - u^2}$. Note that both θ and ϕ are angles in Quadrant I. We must prove that $\theta = \phi$. Since $\cos \theta = u$ we may sketch the angle θ as in Fig. 8.16. But $y = \sqrt{1 - u^2}$ and $\sin \theta = y/1$; therefore $\theta = \text{Arc sin } \sqrt{1 - u^2}$. Thus we have proved that $\theta = \phi$.

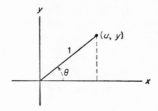

Fig. 8.16

Solution for $u < 0$. As the first step, note that u cannot be less than -1 (otherwise the angles are undefined). Put $\theta = \text{Arc cos } u$ and $\phi = \text{Arc sin } \sqrt{1 - u^2}$. Now for $-1 \leqq u < 0$, $\pi/2 < \theta \leqq \pi$ and $0 \leqq \phi \leqq \pi/2$. But these two angles are in different quadrants and therefore cannot be equal.

EXAMPLE 5. Solve the following equation:
$$\text{Arc cos } u + \text{Arc cos } 2u = \pi/2.$$

Solution. Put $\theta = \text{Arc cos } u$ and $\phi = \text{Arc cos } 2u$. The sketches are shown in Fig. 8.17. Since $\theta + \phi = \pi/2$ we know that $\cos (\theta + \phi)$

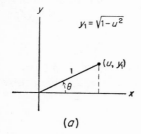

(a)   (b)

Fig. 8.17

$= \cos \pi/2$, hence $\cos \theta \cdot \cos \phi - \sin \theta \cdot \sin \phi = 0$.
$$u \cdot (2u) - \sqrt{1 - u^2} \cdot \sqrt{1 - 4u^2} = 0.$$

At this step we have reduced the problem to one of solving an algebraic equation.
$$2u^2 = \sqrt{(1 - u^2)(1 - 4u^2)},$$
$$4u^4 = 1 - 5u^2 + 4u^4,$$
$$u^2 = 1/5,$$
$$u = \pm 1/\sqrt{5}.$$

In the course of the solution we may have introduced an extraneous root, therefore both values should be checked in the original equation.

It is easy to see that $u = -1/\sqrt{5}$ cannot be a root, since for negative u both angles on the left are greater than $\pi/2$. The check for $u = 1/\sqrt{5}$ is given as the final example.

EXAMPLE 6. Prove that Arc cos $(1/\sqrt{5})$ + Arc cos $(2/\sqrt{5})$ = $\pi/2$.

Solution. Put θ = Arc cos $(1/\sqrt{5})$ and ϕ = Arc cos $(2/\sqrt{5})$. We must prove that $\theta + \phi = \pi/2$. The sketches are shown in Fig. 8.18. Now

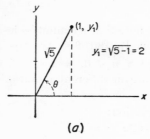

Fig. 8.18

$$\begin{aligned}
\cos(\theta + \phi) &= \cos\theta \cdot \cos\phi - \sin\theta \cdot \sin\phi, \\
&= (1/\sqrt{5})(2/\sqrt{5}) - (2/\sqrt{5})(1/\sqrt{5}), \\
&= 0.
\end{aligned}$$

Therefore $\theta + \phi$ is one of the angles $\{\pi/2 \pm n\pi\}$.

But $0 \leqq \theta \leqq \pi/2$ and $0 \leqq \phi \leqq \pi/2$; hence $0 \leqq \theta + \phi \leqq \pi$. The only solution on this interval is $\theta + \phi = \pi/2$, which proves the statement.

——————| **Problem Set 8.5** |——————

1. Sketch each function by plotting at least eight points.
   (a) y = Arc sin x, (b) y = Arc cos x,
   (c) y = Arc tan x.

2. What set of numbers does each of the symbols represent?
   (a) arc sin 1, (b) arc cos $(-1/\sqrt{2})$,
   (c) arc tan $\sqrt{3}$, (d) arc sec 2,
   (e) arc cot (-1), (f) arc csc (-2).

3. Evaluate:
   (a) Arc sin 1, (b) Arc sin (-1),
   (c) Arc cos $(1/\sqrt{2})$, (d) Arc cos $(-1/\sqrt{2})$,
   (e) Arc tan $\sqrt{3}$, (f) Arc tan $(-\sqrt{3})$.

4. Find the trigonometric values of θ if
   (a) $\theta = \text{Arc sin } \frac{1}{5}$,   (b) $\theta = \text{Arc cos } \frac{2}{3}$,
   (c) $\theta = \text{Arc tan } \frac{1}{2}$.

5. Evaluate, if possible:
   (a) $\sin (\text{Arc cos } 1)$,   (b) $\cos (\text{Arc sin } 1)$,
   (c) $\tan [\text{Arc sin } (-1)]$,   (d) $\cot (\text{Arc tan } 1)$.

6. Evaluate:
   (a) $\text{Arc sin } (\sin \pi/3)$,   (b) $\text{Arc cos } [\cos (-\pi/4)]$,
   (c) $\text{Arc tan } (\tan 2\pi/3)$.

7. Evaluate in terms of u:
   (a) $\sin [\text{Arc tan } u]$,
   (b) $\tan [\text{Arc sin } u]$,
   (c) $\cos [\text{Arc tan } (1 + u)]$.

8. Evaluate:
   (a) $\sin [\text{Arc sin } \frac{1}{2} + \text{Arc cos } \frac{1}{2}]$,
   (b) $\sin [\text{Arc sin } \frac{3}{5} - \text{Arc cos } \frac{3}{5}]$.

Prove that the following three equations are identities for suitable $u > 0$:

9. $\text{Arc tan } (-u) = \text{Arc sin } (-u/\sqrt{1 + u^2})$;

10. $\text{Arc cos } u + \text{Arc sin } u = \pi/2$;

11. $2 \cdot \text{Arc sin } u = \text{Arc cos } \sqrt{1 - u^2} + \text{Arc tan } (u/\sqrt{1 - u^2})$.

Solve the following three equations if possible.

12. $\text{Arc sin } 2u = \text{Arc cos } u$.

13. $\text{Arc sin } u = \text{Arc sin } (1/u)$.

14. $\text{Arc sin } u + \text{Arc cos } \sqrt{1 - u^2} = \text{Arc tan } 0$.

15. Prove that $\text{Arc cos } (-\frac{3}{5}) - \text{Arc sin } (\frac{3}{5}) = \text{Arc sin } 1$.

───────────| **Miscellaneous Problems** |───────────

1. Let F represent a relation. Make up mathematical illustrations for each of the cases.
   (a) F not a function and F^{-1} not a function.
   (b) F not a function and F^{-1} a function.
   (c) F a function and F^{-1} not a function.
   (d) F a function and F^{-1} a function.

2. In Problem 1 of Problem Set 2.3, diagram each of the given relations and its inverse.

3. Which of the ten relations in Problem 2 are functions?

4. Prove that the inverse of a periodic function is not a function.

5. Sketch the inverse graph of the function

    (a) $f(\theta) = \frac{1}{2}\sin\theta$,   (b) $f(x) = 2\cos x$.

6. Sketch the inverse graph of the function

    (a) $f(x) = 1 + 2\sin x$,   (b) $f(\theta) = \sin\theta - \cos\theta$.

7. Find the inverse relation (specify both domain and range) of each function given in Problem 5 of Problem Set 5.3.

8. Sketch the inverse graph of each function given in Problem 5 of Problem Set 5.3.

9. (a) Sketch the inverse graph of the function given in Problem 4 of Problem Set 5.5.

    (b) Is the inverse relation of the given function also a function?

10. (a) Find the inverse relation (specify both domain and range) of the function given in Problem 6 of Problem Set 5.5. Is it a function?

    (b) Sketch the inverse graph.

11. Find the inverse relation (specify both domain and range) of the function

    (a) $y = \sin(\theta/2)$, $(0 \leqq \theta \leqq 4\pi)$,

    (b) $y = 2\sin 2x$, $(0 \leqq x \leqq \pi)$.

12. Sketch the inverse graph of the function

$$f(\theta) = \theta + \cos\theta, \ (-\pi \leqq \theta \leqq 3\pi).$$

13. What set of numbers does each of the symbols represent?

    (a) arc sin $(\sqrt{3}/2)$,   (b) arc cos 0,   (c) arc sin (-1),

    (d) arc tan 1,   (e) arc tan 0,   (f) arc sin $\sqrt{2}$.

14. Find the trigonometric values of θ if

    (a) $\theta =$ Arc sin $(-1/3)$,

    (b) $\theta =$ Arc cos $(-5/13)$,

    (c) $\theta =$ Arc tan $(-4/3)$.

15. Evaluate, if possible

    (a) cos (Arc tan 1),   (b) sin $[$Arc cos $(-1/\sqrt{2})]$,

    (c) cot (Arc sin 0),   (d) tan $[$Arc sin $(-\sqrt{3}/2)]$.

16. Evaluate

    (a) Arc sin $[\sin(4\pi/3)]$,   (b) Arc cos $(\cos\pi)$,

    (c) Arc tan $[\tan(-\pi/3)]$.

17. Evaluate in terms of u (assume $u > 0$):

    (a) cot $[$Arc cos $u^2]$,   (b) sin $[2$ Arc sin $u]$,

    (c) cos $[2$ Arc cos $u]$,   (d) sin $[$Arc sin $u +$ Arc cos $u]$,

    (e) cos $[$Arc sin $u -$ Arc cos $u]$.

18. Evaluate:

  (a) $\cos \left[\text{Arc tan } 1 + \text{Arc cos } 1 \right]$,

  (b) $\cos \left[\text{Arc cos } (1/2) + \text{Arc tan } (-\sqrt{3}) \right]$.

Prove that the following are identities for suitable $u > 0$.

19. Arc sin $(1/u)$ = Arc tan $(1/\sqrt{u^2 - 1})$.

20. Arc tan $1/u$ = Arc cos $(u/\sqrt{1 + u^2})$.

21. Arc sin $(1 - u)$ = $\pi/2$ − Arc cos $(1 - u)$.

Solve the following equations, if possible.

22. Arc cos $1/u$ = Arc sin $1/u$.

23. Arc sin $(\sin^2 u)$ = $\pi/2$.

24. Arc cos $(\sin^2 u)$ = 0.

25. Arc cos $(\sqrt{3}/2)$ = $\pi/2$ − Arc sin $3u$.

REMARK. Referring to Remark 1 in Problem Set 2.1, a given function f defines a one-to-one correspondence between its domain and range if and only if f^{-1} is also a function.

Let f be a function, the domain and range being sets of real numbers, such that $f(x') < f(x'')$ whenever $x' < x''$; then f is called **monotonic increasing**. *Similarly, if $f(x') > f(x'')$ whenever $x' < x''$, then f is called* **monotonic decreasing**.

26. Prove that if a function f is either monotonic increasing or monotonic decreasing, then f^{-1} is a function.

27. Sketch the graph of the function $f(x) = -x^3$ and show that it is monotonic decreasing.

28. Show that the function $f(x)$ = Arc sin x is monotonic increasing; show that the function $g(x)$ = Arc cos x is monotonic decreasing.

9

SOLUTION
OF
TRIANGLES

This chapter and the next are devoted to a development of certain trigonometric tools and to a study of some few of the ways in which these tools are applied. We shall study the applications in historical sequence: first, triangle measurement; second, periodicity. Regardless of historical priority, when the word "sine," for example, is mentioned, the modern student thinks immediately of the graph given by $y = \sin x$ rather than of a ratio of sides of a triangle.

1. TRIANGLES IN GENERAL

Throughout this chapter we shall use the terms "triangle," "angle," "vertex," and so on, with the same intuitively acceptable meanings found in elementary geometry. We shall denote vertices by capital letters A, B, C; sides opposite by corresponding small letters a, b, c; vertex angles by corresponding Greek letters α, β, γ. For triangle applications vertex angles are usually given in degrees, and we shall think of the symbol α as denoting the *angle measured in degrees*. We shall denote the triangle itself by a triple of letters, for example ABC, representing the vertices in a counterclockwise order.

For the purposes of trigonometry, *triangles are divided into two types, those which contain a right angle (called **right triangles**) and* *those which do not* (*called* **oblique triangles**). In order to describe any triangle completely, we must know six parts: the length of each side and the measure of each angle. From plane geometry we know that not all six of these parts can be given independently. For example, if angles α and β are given, then the third angle must satisfy the equation $\gamma = 180° - (\alpha + \beta)$. The determination of the six parts is called a **solution** of the triangle, and our task is to discover the conditions under which a triangle may be solved and how the solution is to be effected. It is necessary to recall from plane geometry those parts which may be given independently and which then serve to fix the remaining parts of the triangle. For a right triangle:

Case 1. One side and one angle (other than the right angle).

Case 2. Two sides (if the hypotenuse is one of the sides given, it must be longer than the other, else the triangle fails to exist).

For an oblique triangle:

Case 3. Three sides (no side may be longer than the sum of the other two).

Case 4. Two sides and the included angle.

Case 5. Two angles and any side.

Each of these five cases leads to a unique triangle. There is an important sixth case which does not always lead to a unique triangle; it will be discussed separately in Section 6. Our immediate goal is to show how, in each of these five cases, the triangle solution may be obtained by the methods of trigonometry.

From a practical point of view, the value of this phase of trigonometry results precisely from the possibility of finding triangle solutions. By drawing an idealized picture of a certain physical triangle and by making several physical measurements, the remaining parts of the triangle can be computed, thus avoiding actual measurements on the unknown parts (frequently, one or more of the unknown parts is inaccessible).

Appendices 3 and 4 explain the use of logarithms and trigonometric tables. A grasp of this material is necessary in working with applications of trigonometry. In many of the illustrative examples throughout the chapter figures and computational details have been omitted. For practice, these figures and details should be supplied before the corresponding problems in each section are attempted.

2. TRIGONOMETRIC RATIOS FOR THE RIGHT TRIANGLE

Suppose we perform the following experiment. On a sheet of paper sketch a rectangular co-ordinate system. From a second piece of paper cut a small right triangle and label its vertices A, B ($= 90°$), and C in counterclockwise order. Now place the triangle in Quadrant I of the co-ordinate system with vertex A at the origin and side c along the positive x-axis (see Fig. 9.1). With reference to the angle α, a is the *side opposite*, b is the *hypotenuse*, and c is the *side adjacent*.

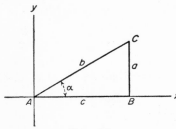

Fig. 9.1

The trigonometric ratios of α now appear as follows:

$$\sin \alpha = \frac{a}{b} = \frac{\text{side opposite}}{\text{hypotenuse}},$$

$$\cos \alpha = \frac{c}{b} = \frac{\text{side adjacent}}{\text{hypotenuse}},$$

$$\tan \alpha = \frac{a}{c} = \frac{\text{side opposite}}{\text{side adjacent}}.$$

The reciprocals are defined as usual.

Now we wish to find the trigonometric ratios of γ. Place the triangle in Quadrant I of the co-ordinate system so that vertex C is at the origin and side a is along the positive x-axis. From Fig. 9.2 we have

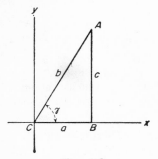

Fig. 9.2

$$\sin \gamma = \frac{c}{b} = \frac{\text{side opposite}}{\text{hypotenuse}},$$

$$\cos \gamma = \frac{a}{b} = \frac{\text{side adjacent}}{\text{hypotenuse}},$$

$$\tan \gamma = \frac{c}{a} = \frac{\text{side opposite}}{\text{side adjacent}}.$$

The reciprocals are defined as usual. Notice that

$$\sin \alpha = \cos \gamma,$$
$$\cos \alpha = \sin \gamma,$$
$$\tan \alpha = \cot \gamma;$$

thus agreeing with the final set of reduction formulas derived in Section 5 of Chapter 4. For the purposes of right triangle applications the trigonometric ratios are assumed to be related to the sides of the triangle as given above, regardless of the position of the triangle in the plane. For the special case of an angle measuring 0° or 90° we assume the trigonometric values as given in Section 4 of Chapter 4.

3. RIGHT TRIANGLE APPLICATIONS

In order to solve a right triangle problem, only the definitions are required; no formulas need be derived.

EXAMPLE 1 (Case 1). Solve the right triangle ABC if one angle is $38°42'12''$ and the side opposite measures 12.382.

Solution. For convenience we assume the known angle at vertex A and the right angle at vertex B. Since $\alpha + \gamma = 90°$ we find that $\gamma = 51°17'48''$. From the right angle definitions we know that

$$\tan \alpha = \frac{\text{side opp}}{\text{side adj}} = \frac{12.382}{c} \quad \text{and} \quad \sin \alpha = \frac{\text{side opp}}{\text{hyp}} = \frac{12.382}{b}.$$

Making use of logarithms,

$$\log c = \log 12.382 - \log \tan 38°42'12'',$$
$$= 1.18903$$
$$\text{hence } c = 15.454;$$
$$\log b = \log 12.382 - \log \sin 38°42'12''$$
$$= 1.29671;$$
$$\text{hence } b = 19.802.$$

The solution may be grouped conveniently in the following way:

Given	Computed
$\alpha = 38°42'12''$,	$\gamma = 51°17'48''$,
$\beta = 90°$,	$b = 19.802$,
$a = 12.382$,	$c = 15.454$.

EXAMPLE 2 (Case 2). Solve the right triangle ABC if $\beta = 90°$, $a = 7.810$, and $c = 4.329$.

Solution. By the right triangle definition, $\tan \alpha = 7.810/4.329$. Hence $\log \tan \alpha = \log 7.810 - \log 4.329$
$$= 0.25626.$$
Therefore $\alpha = 61°0'2''$, and $\gamma = 90° - \alpha = 28°59'58''$.

The hypotenuse b may be found by the Pythagorean theorem, but this involves much arithmetic that is not well adapted to computation by logarithms. A more satisfactory scheme makes use of the sine function:

$$\sin \alpha = a/b;$$

hence $\log b = \log 7.810 - \log \sin 61°0'2''$

$$= 0.95083;$$

and $b = 8.9296.$

Notice that interpolation is used in each computation, agreeing with the rules suggested in Appendix 2. Round-off, if necessary, occurs at the final step, and in this case the answers are recorded to four significant digits:

Given	Computed
$\beta = 90°,$	$\alpha = 61°0',$
$a = 7.810,$	$\gamma = 29°0',$
$c = 4.329,$	$b = 8.930.$

———————| **Problem Set 9.1** |————————————

Solve the triangle ABC given that $\beta = 90°$.

1. $\alpha = 33°, b = 11.$
2. $\gamma = 42°, c = 8.1.$
3. $\gamma = 78°10', a = 1.32.$
4. $\alpha = 11°13'18'', a = 104.32.$
5. $a = 130, c = 264.$
6. $b = 407.07, c = 249.40.$

7. A ladder 20 feet long leans against a wall. If the foot of the ladder is 6 feet from the wall, find the angle made by the ladder with the wall.

8. A surveyor lays off a right-angle corner of a rectangular building foundation. He then sights on the diagonally opposite corner and finds that his line of sight has moved through an angle of 27°42'. If a short side of the foundation measures 119.3 feet, find the length of a long side.

REMARK. *If the points A and B are in a vertical plane but not on the same level, then the line AB makes an angle θ with the horizontal. If θ is measured above the horizontal it is called an* **angle of elevation**. *If θ is measured below the horizontal it is called an* **angle of depression**. *(See Fig. 9.3).*

9. From a garage to the road a straight driveway is 184 feet in length. If the angle of elevation from the road to the garage is 3°40', find how high the garage is above the road level.

10. An escalator is built so as to rise 1 foot for each 1.7 feet of horizontal travel. Find its angle of elevation.

11. A flagpole 88 feet high stands on a level parade field. A soldier whose eye level is 5.5 feet finds an

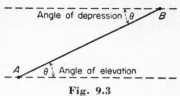

Fig. 9.3

angle of elevation to the top of the flagpole of 23°30′. How far is he from the base of the pole?

12. A surveyor measures a horizontal distance from the foot of a vertical cliff as 798.3 feet. He then measures the angle of elevation to the top of the cliff as 36°18′. How high is the cliff?

13. A boy flying a kite has paid out 415 feet of cord. The kite is directly above a spot 225 feet distant from the boy. Assuming that the cord is taut (and neglecting the height of the boy), how high is the kite and what is its angle of elevation?

14. The great pyramid at Gizeh (in Egypt) has a square base 9,068.8 feet on a side. The angle of elevation of a side is 51°52′.

    (a) Find the height of the pyramid.

    (b) Find the length of one slanting edge of the pyramid.

    (c) If the sun is 27°45′ above the horizon, find the length of shadow cast by the pyramid (assuming level ground).

4. THE OBLIQUE TRIANGLE

Let ABC represent an arbitrary oblique triangle. Suppose we place this triangle on a rectangular co-ordinate system in such a way that one vertex is at the origin while the opposite side is parallel to and above the x-axis (see Fig. 9.4). No matter which vertex is placed at

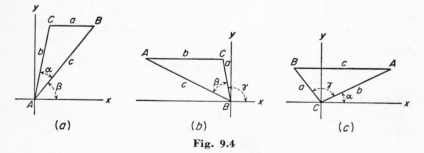

Fig. 9.4

the origin, it is evident that we may list three properties analogous to those following, which are related to part (a) of Fig. 9.4.

(1)   If $\phi = \alpha + \beta$, then $\phi = 180° - \gamma$,

(2) $b \sin \phi = c \sin \beta$,

(3) $c \cos \beta - b \cos \phi = a$.

The proofs of the two theorems in this section make use of these properties.

THEOREM 1. ───────────────────────────

$$\frac{\sin \alpha}{a} = \frac{\sin \beta}{b} = \frac{\sin \gamma}{c}.$$

Proof. From Property (2) we have $(\sin \beta)/b = (\sin \phi)/c$. By Property (1), $\sin \phi = \sin (180° - \gamma) = \sin \gamma$; hence $(\sin \beta)/b = (\sin \gamma)/c$.

The method of proof is independent of which vertex is placed at the origin. By considering Fig. 9.4 (c) and its corresponding properties, we may prove that

$$\frac{\sin \alpha}{a} = \frac{\sin \beta}{b}$$

THEOREM 2. ───────────────────────────

$$\cos \alpha = \frac{b^2 + c^2 - a^2}{2bc}.$$

Proof. By Property (3) we have

$$a^2 = c^2 \cos^2 \beta + b^2 \cos^2 \phi - 2bc \cos \phi \cos \beta.$$

By Property (2), transposing and squaring, we have

$$0 = c^2 \sin^2 \beta + b^2 \sin^2 \phi - 2bc \sin \phi \sin \beta.$$

Adding these two equations we find

$$a^2 = c^2 + b^2 - 2bc (\cos \phi \cos \beta + \sin \phi \sin \beta),$$
$$= c^2 + b^2 - 2bc \cos (\phi - \beta).$$

By definition $\phi - \beta = \alpha$;

hence $\cos \alpha = \dfrac{b^2 + c^2 - a^2}{2bc}.$

Again by making appropriate changes in the angle and sides we may state immediately two other results:

$$\cos \beta = \frac{a^2 + c^2 - b^2}{2ac} \quad \text{and} \quad \cos \gamma = \frac{a^2 + b^2 - c^2}{2ab}.$$

Theorem 1 is called the **law of sines.** From a computational point of view, it is one of the most effective triangle relationships; it is simple, direct, and can be used readily in logarithmic calculations. The law of sines may be used in the solution of triangles related to Case 5 (given two angles and any side). It may also be applied in completing the solution of a triangle in which a different law was used initially.

Theorem 2, in each of its three possible forms, is called the **law of cosines.** It may be used in solving triangles related to Case 3 (given three sides) or to Case 4 (given two sides and the included angle). In the latter case, the law may be stated in a more suitable way. If sides b and c and angle α are known, we may find side a from the formula,

$$a^2 = b^2 + c^2 - 2bc \cos \alpha.$$

In this form the law of cosines is easily seen to be a generalization of the Pythagorean theorem. If $\alpha = 90°$, $\cos \alpha = 0$ and we obtain the equation

$$a^2 = b^2 + c^2,$$

in which side a is the hypotenuse of a right triangle.

5. THE SOLUTION OF OBLIQUE TRIANGLES

EXAMPLE 1 (Case 3). Solve the triangle ABC if $a = 384$, $b = 593$ and $c = 276$.

Solution. (See Fig. 9.5). We use the law of cosines to solve first for the angle α.

$$\cos \alpha = \frac{b^2 + c^2 - a^2}{2bc}.$$

The numerator must be evaluated separately before logarithms can be used satisfactorily in this problem.

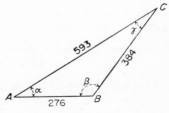

Fig. 9.5

Until the final step in the solution we shall maintain five significant digits wherever possible.

$$b^2 + c^2 - a^2 = 280{,}370,$$
$$2bc = 327{,}340,$$
$$\log \cos \alpha = \log 280370 - \log 327340,$$
$$= 9.93273 - 10.$$

Hence $\qquad \alpha = 31°4'26''.$

Now we may compute the remaining two angles by the law of sines and check that work by the formula $\alpha + \beta + \gamma = 180°$.

$$\frac{\sin \beta}{b} = \frac{\sin \alpha}{a}.$$
$$\log \sin \beta = \log 593 + \log \sin 31°4'26'' - \log 384,$$
$$= 9.90149 - 10.$$

Hence $\qquad \beta = 52°51'0''$ (from the tables).

But we know by a reduction formula that $\sin (180° - \theta) = \sin \theta$; therefore a second possibility for this angle is $180° - 52°51'0'' = 127°9'0''$. The initial sketch tells us that β is greater than $90°$ while α and γ are both less than $90°$, thus the angles must be chosen accordingly. Again using the law of sines we find γ.

$$\log \sin \gamma = \log 276 + \log \sin 31°4'26'' - \log 384,$$
$$= 9.56935 - 10.$$

Hence $\qquad \gamma = 21°46'34''.$

Note that the sum of these three angles is $180°$. Since the original data is given only to three significant digits, the angles should be rounded off to the nearest $10'$. The solution is

Given	Computed
$a = 384,$	$\alpha = 31°0',$
$b = 596,$	$\beta = 127°10',$
$c = 276,$	$\gamma = 21°50'.$

EXAMPLE 2 (Case 4). Solve the triangle ABC if $a = 41, b = 28$, and $\gamma = 58°$.

Solution. To find c we use the law of cosines in the form

$$c^2 = a^2 + b^2 - 2ab \cos \gamma.$$

Again logarithms do not apply readily.

$$c^2 = 1681 + 784 - 1217 = 1248,$$
$$c = 35.$$

Now by the law of sines we find the solution to be

Given	Computed
$\gamma = 58°$,	$\alpha = 79°$,
$a = 41$,	$\beta = 43°$,
$b = 28$,	$c = 35$.

EXAMPLE 3 (Case 5). Solve the triangle ABC if $\alpha = 101°18'0''$, $\beta = 42°31'18''$, and $c = 0.41832$.

Solution.

$$\gamma = 180° - (\alpha + \beta) = 36°10'42''.$$

By the law of sines $\dfrac{\sin \alpha}{a} = \dfrac{\sin \gamma}{c}$.

$\log a = \log \sin \alpha + \log c - \log \sin \gamma.$

Now $\sin 101°18' = \sin (180° - 101°18') = \sin 78°42'$,

hence $\log \sin \alpha = \log \sin 78°42' = 9.99150 - 10.$

Thus $\log a = 9.84193 - 10$,

$a = 0.69492.$

Again we use the law of sines to find b: $\sin \beta/b = \sin \gamma/c$.

$\log b = \log \sin 42°31'18'' + \log 0.41832 - \log \sin 36°10'42''$

$= 9.68030 - 10$,

$b = 0.47896.$

Recorded to five significant digits, the solution is

Given	Computed
$\alpha = 101°18'0''$,	$\gamma = 36°10'42''$,
$\beta = 42°31'18''$,	$a = 0.69492.$
$c = 0.41832$,	$b = 0.47896.$

─────────┤ **Problem Set 9.2** ├─────────

1. Solve the oblique triangle ABC if
  (a) $a = 9.1$, $b = 16$, $c = 5.3$,
  (b) $a = 72$, $b = 28$, $c = 59$.

2. Solve the oblique triangle ABC if
  (a) $\beta = 110°$, $a = 85$, $c = 44$,
  (b) $\gamma = 138°10'$, $a = 100$, $b = 111$.

3. Solve the oblique triangle ABC if
  (a) $\alpha = 131°15'$, $\gamma = 22°0'$, $b = 1.98$,
  (b) $\beta = 72°13'18''$, $\gamma = 50°51'48''$, $a = 150.37$.

4. In any triangle ABC prove that

(a) $\cos(\alpha/2) = \frac{1}{2}\sqrt{(a + b + c)(b + c - a)/bc}$,

(b) $\sin(\alpha/2) = \frac{1}{2}\sqrt{(a + b - c)(a - b + c)/bc}$.

5. In any triangle ABC prove that

$$\frac{\sin \alpha \cdot \sin \beta}{ab} = \frac{1 - \cos^2 \gamma}{a^2 + b^2 - 2ab \cdot \cos \gamma}.$$

6. Two straight highways intersect at an angle of 78°30′. If an automobile is 350 yards from the intersection on one road and a second automobile is 530 yards from the intersection on the other road, how far apart are they (two possible answers)?

7. A triangular lot measures 150 feet, 280 feet, and 300 feet along its sides. Find the vertex angles.

8. A ship is 10 miles directly south of a port. If the ship sails northeast for three miles, how far is it then from the port?

9. From a lakeside dock, a man rows 1.5 miles southeast, then 2.5 miles directly east. How far is he from the dock?

10. Two swimmers are 250 yards apart. Both are swimming towards the same point which is 423 feet from one of them and 360 feet from the other. Find the angle at which their paths intersect.

11. Two houses A and B are 535 feet apart. From a third house C the angle ∡ ACB is 58°19′, and from house A the angle ∡ BAC is 41°37′. What is the distance from house C to each of the others?

12. A cliff overlooks a river of unknown width. From a point on the bank across the river the angle of elevation to the top of the cliff is 71°15′. From a second point, directly in line with the first point but 695 feet farther from the cliff, the angle of elevation is 39°40′. Assuming both points are 10 feet above the river level, how high is the cliff, and how wide is the river?

13. Two buildings of the same height are on opposite sides of a street having eight-foot sidewalks. From a window in building A an observer looks directly across the street at building B and finds that the angle of elevation to the top of B is 48°10′ while the angle of depression to the base of B is 63°15′. If building B is 212 feet high, how wide is the street (not including sidewalks) and how high is the observer?

14. From a common point on level ground between two telephone poles, guy wires are stretched to the top of each pole. The wires measure 140 feet in one case and 220 feet in the other. If the angle of intersection between the two guy wires is 75°, how long must a telephone wire be to reach from the top of one pole to the top of the other?

6. THE AMBIGUOUS CASE

In Section 1 we mentioned a sixth case which sometimes leads to an ambiguous situation. If ABC is any triangle then the following known parts determine either no triangle, a unique triangle, or two distinct triangles.

Case 6. Two sides and a nonincluded angle. If a solution exists, then the law of sines always suffices to determine the missing parts.

To illustrate this case we shall assume that angle α is given and that sides a and c are known. If $\alpha = 90°$ this case is identical with Case 2, therefore we assume $\alpha \neq 90°$. The sketch may be drawn as in Fig. 9.6. Lay off side c and with a protractor draw angle α. With vertex B as center draw an arc of radius a. This geometric construction leads to one of several possible results.

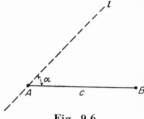

Fig. 9.6

1. If the arc fails to intersect the line l, then there is no solution.

2. If the arc is tangent to the line l, then
   (a) If $\alpha < 90°$ there is a unique right triangle solution.
   (b) If $\alpha > 90°$ there is no solution.

3. If the arc intersects the line l in two points, then
   (a) If vertex A is between the points of intersection there is a unique solution.
   (b) If the points of intersection lie on the same side of A, then
       (i) If $\alpha < 90°$ there are two solutions.
       (ii) If $\alpha > 90°$ there is no solution.
   (c) If one point of intersection coincides with vertex A, then
       (i) If $\alpha < 90°$ there is a unique solution.
       (ii) If $\alpha > 90°$ there is no solution.

It is not necessary to memorize an elaborate set of rules that will indicate into which of these categories a given problem fits. A quick sketch and a single computation usually suffice for this purpose. It is helpful to remember that a law of sines computation leading to a null equation indicates no solution.

EXAMPLE 1. Solve the triangle ABC if $\alpha = 47°10'$, $a = 21.13$, and $c = 28.27$.

Solution. (See Fig. 9.7.) By the law of sines

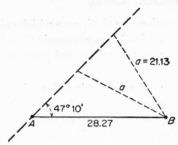

Fig. 9.7

$$\frac{\sin 47°10'}{21.13} = \frac{\sin \gamma}{28.27},$$

$$\log \sin \gamma = \log 28.27 + \log \sin 47°10' - \log 21.13,$$
$$= 9.99173 - 10.$$

Hence $\gamma = 78°51'20''$,   or $\gamma = 101°8'40''$.

This double possibility arises since both θ and $180° - \theta$ have the same sine value. Thus this problem fits into Category 3(b)(i). Since the sum of the angles must be 180°, we have either $\beta = 53°58'40''$, or $\beta = 31°41'20''$. Again applying the law of sines, we have either

$$b = 23.304, \quad \text{or} \quad b = 15.136$$

Rounding off each answer to conform with the given accuracy, we obtain the two possible solutions:

Given	Computed (1)	Computed (2)
$\alpha = 47°10'$,	$\beta = 53°59'$,	$\beta = 31°41'$,
$a = 21.13$,	$\gamma = 78°51'$,	$\gamma = 101°9'$,
$c = 28.27$,	$b = 23.30$,	$b = 15.14$.

EXAMPLE 2. Is there a triangle ABC for which $\alpha = 105°15'$, $a = 152.3$, and $b = 210.4$?

Solution. It is evident from a sketch that no triangle including angle α can be formed unless side a is greater than side b. Hence there is no solution.

EXAMPLE 3. If possible, solve for the unknown parts given $\alpha = 105°15'$, $a = 252.3$, and $b = 210.4$.

Solution. Since $a > b$ there is a solution, and by swinging an arc of radius a from vertex C as center it is seen without a computation that this problem fits Category 3(a). By the law of sines,

$$\frac{\sin 105°15'}{252.3} = \frac{\sin \beta}{210.4}.$$

Thus $\log \sin \beta = \log 210.4 + \log \sin 105°15' - \log 252.3$.
(Note that $\log \sin 105°15' = \log \sin 74°45'$).

$$\log \sin \beta = 9.90556 - 10.$$

Hence $\beta = 53°34'6''$,   or $\beta = 126°25'54''$.

In this problem the second possibility for β must be excluded since $\alpha + \beta$ cannot be greater than 180°. The unique solution (after rounding off) is

Given	Computed
$\alpha = 105°15'$,	$\beta = 53°34'$,
$a = 252.3$,	$\gamma = 21°11'$,
$b = 210.4$,	$c = 94.49$.

——————| **Problem Set 9.3** |————————————

1. From a rough sketch estimate which category the following information fits. Make whatever computation is necessary to check your estimate.

(a) $\alpha = 40°$, $a = 15$, $c = 12$,
(b) $\alpha = 80°$, $a = 17$, $b = 22$,
(c) $\alpha = 115°$, $a = 4.5$, $b = 8.2$,
(d) $\alpha = 140°$, $a = 10$, $c = 10$.

2. Given angle α, side a and side c (see Fig. 9.6). Under what condition will an arc of radius a and center B

(a) be tangent to l?
(b) fail to intersect l?
(c) intersect l in two points?

3. Into which category does the information in Example 2 in the text fit?

4. Solve the following, if possible.

(a) $\alpha = 19°42'$, $a = 38.29$, $b = 30.10$,
(b) $\alpha = 99°56'$, $a = 4.321$, $c = 4.008$.

5. Solve the following, if possible.

$\alpha = 14°32'18''$, $a = 7.3980$, $c = 10.314$.

6. Solve the following, if possible.
(a) $\beta = 57°40'$, $b = 91.31$, $c = 123.2$,
(b) $\gamma = 121°10'$, $a = 8.327$, $c = 11.43$.

7. Solve the following, if possible.
$\beta = 134°15'24''$, $a = 181.32$, $b = 122.42$.

8. The straight-line distance between two towns A and B on a map is 8.7 inches. A third town C is 4.6 inches from B and forms an angle at A ($\angle BAC$) of $23°30'$. What is the straight-line distance from A to C?

9. A horizontal tunnel is to be built through a mountain ridge. Surveyors have marked the proposed entrance A and exit B of the tunnel. From A, the angle of elevation to the peak C of the ridge is $28°31'$ and the distance from A to C is 2,340 feet. If the distance from C to B is 1,718 feet, find the length of the tunnel.

10. Two cables are fastened from level ground to the top of a vertical pole. The angle of elevation of one cable is $41°24'$ and its length is 184 feet. If the other cable is 144 feet in length, find the distance from its lower end to the pole (use law of sines).

———————| **Miscellaneous Problems** |———————

1. Solve the triangle ABC, given that $\beta = 90°$.
(a) $\alpha = 80°50'$, $c = 418$,
(b) $\gamma = 49°38'30''$, $b = 8.3791$.

2. Solve the right triangle ABC, given that side b is the hypotenuse.
(a) $b = 16.3$, $c = 12.8$.
(b) $a = 8.3992$, $b = 11.243$.

3. Refer to Fig. 9.8.

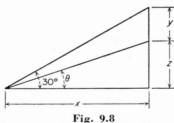

Fig. 9.8

(a) Find y if $x = 6.9282$ and $\tan \theta = 0.38386$.
(b) Find x if $y + z = 8.4830$.

4. Refer to Fig. 9.8.
(a) Find z if $y = 1.38$ and $\theta = 21°30'$.
(b) Find x if $y = 1.3808$ and $\tan \theta = 0.38386$.

5. Solve the oblique triangle ABC.
   (a) $a = 183$, $b = 224$, $c = 491$.
   (b) $\alpha = 40°$, $b = 12$, $c = 7.3$.
6. Solve the oblique triangle ABC.
   (a) $\alpha = 68°$, $\beta = 52°$, $a = 74$.
   (b) $\alpha = 18°33'48''$, $\beta = 140°11'45''$, $b = 8.3246$.
7. Refer to Fig. 9.9.

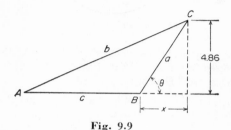

Fig. 9.9

   (a) Solve the triangle ABC if $\alpha = 23°30'$, $\theta = 63°20'$.
   (b) Solve the triangle ABC if $x = 6.18$, $c = 2.97$.
   (c) Solve the triangle ABC if $\alpha = 12°50'$, $a = 5.92$.

8. Solve the triangle, if possible.
   $\alpha = 33°51'42''$, $a = 19.721$, $b = 27.831$.

9. Solve the triangle, if possible.
   $\gamma = 25°0'30''$, $b = 10.087$, $c = 15.329$.

10. A tree 105 feet high stands in a level yard. The corner of a porch is 78 feet from the tree. If the floor of the porch is 4 feet above the yard, find the angle of elevation from the porch floor at the corner to the top of the tree.

11. The observation deck of a building is 840 feet above the ground. An observer sees his house in the distance and estimates its angle of depression at 10°. Assuming level ground, how far is his house from the building?

12. From a fixed point on the floor an extension ladder is leaned against a wall, first unextended then extended. Unextended, it strikes the wall at a point 14 feet above the floor and makes an angle of elevation of 67°. If the extension portion of the ladder is 12 feet in length, find the height above the floor at which the extended ladder strikes the wall. Find also the distance from the foot of the ladder to the wall.

REMARK 1. Given a circle of radius r. Suppose a chord PQ subtends an angle θ, as in Fig. 9.10. The crosshatched area between the chord and the circle is called a **segment** of the circle.

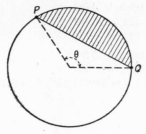

Fig. 9.10

13. Show that the area of the segment shown in Fig. 9.10 is $(r^2/2)(\theta - \sin\theta)$, where θ is measured in radians. [*Hint.* Bisect θ to form two right triangles. Subtract their areas from that of the sector.]

14. In a circle of radius r find the area of the segment corresponding to (a) $\theta = \pi/4$, (b) $\theta = 60°$, (c) $\theta = \pi/2$, (d) $\theta = 150°$.

15. Solve this problem making use of the area of a segment. In a circle of radius 10 units, find the area of an inscribed: (a) equilateral triangle, (b) square, (c) regular pentagon, (d) regular hexagon.

16. A segment corresponding to 30° is cut from a silver coin. Find the amount of metal lost if the diameter of the coin is 1.418 inches and the thickness is 0.1185 inch (assume constant thickness).

17. A bridge truss has the outline of a regular trapezoid (see Fig. 9.11). Find the length of each unknown member.

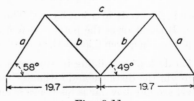

Fig. 9.11

18. A water tower 85 feet high stands on the same level with a high tree. The angle of elevation to the top of the tree is 15°30′ from the top of the tower and is 41°10′ from the base of the tower. Find the height of the tree and its distance from the tower.

REMARK 2. The following is a theorem that can be proved by the methods of plane geometry. *Suppose BC is any chord of a circle* (see Fig. 9.12). *If A and A′ are any two points on the circle not separated by B and C, then* $\measuredangle$ *BAC* = $\measuredangle$ *BA′C.*

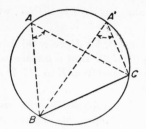

Fig. 9.12

19. Given a triangle ABC. Draw the circumscribed circle and let D be its diameter. Prove that

$$\frac{\sin \alpha}{a} = \frac{\sin \beta}{b} = \frac{\sin \gamma}{c} = \frac{1}{D}.$$

20. Find the diameter of the circumscribed circle of triangle ABC if
    (a) $\alpha = 68°, \beta = 52°, a = 74$,
    (b) $\alpha = 131°15', \gamma = 22°0', b = 1.98$,
    (c) $\beta = 110°, a = 85, c = 44$.

21. Prove that the area of any triangle ABC is $\sqrt{s(s-a)(s-b)(s-c)}$, where $s = (a + b + c)/2$. [*Hint.* Show first that area is $\frac{1}{2} cb \sin \alpha$; then substitute $\sin \alpha = 2 \sin (\alpha/2) \cos (\alpha/2)$. Use the law of cosines to express $\sin (\alpha/2)$ and $\cos (\alpha/2)$ in terms of s and the sides of the triangle.]

22. Let r denote the radius of the circle inscribed in triangle ABC (see Fig. 9.13). Show that $r = \sqrt{(s-a)(s-b)(s-c)/s}$. [*Hint.* Find the

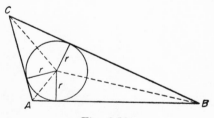

Fig. 9.13

area of ABC in terms of a, b, c, and r. Then equate to the expression given in Problem 21.]

23. Find the radius of the inscribed circle of each triangle in Problem 5.

24. Suppose that two points E and J revolve in the same plane about another point S. The radius of revolution of E is 1.0000 and of J is 5.2028.

If at a certain time the angle ∡ *JES* is 104°55′, what is the distance from *E* to *J*?

25. Referring to Problem 24, let *M* be a third point revolving about *S*, and suppose its radius is 0.38710. If at a certain instant the angle ∡ *MES* is 12°38′12″, what is the distance from *E* to *M*? Is it possible that the angle ∡ *MES* can be as large as 30°?

REMARK 3. The final two problems describe parts of the solar system fairly closely. The letter *E* represents Earth, *S* Sun, *J* Jupiter, and *M* Mercury; the mean distance from the earth to the sun (9.29 × 10⁷ miles) is taken to be one unit.

10

TOPICS
RELATED TO
PERIODICITY

In this chapter we shall study several properties of the trigonometric functions that are important in the solution of problems
related to periodicity.

1. GENERALIZED SINE AND COSINE FUNCTIONS

1.1 PHASE SHIFT

Let α represent a non-negative real number. Of course, α may
be considered an angle measured in radians. The graph of $y =$
$\sin (x - \alpha)$ is similar in every respect except one to the graph of $y =$
$\sin x$. That one difference shows up clearly in Fig. 10.1. Instead of intersecting the x-axis at the values $\{0 \pm n\pi\}$, this function intersects

x	$x-\alpha$	y
α	0	0
$\alpha + \pi/2$	$\pi/2$	1
$\alpha + \pi$	π	0
$\alpha + 3\pi/2$	$3\pi/2$	-1
$\alpha + 2\pi$	2π	0

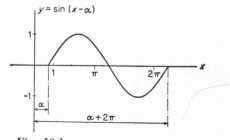

Fig. 10.1
141

the x-axis at the values $\{\alpha \pm n\pi\}$. We may describe the graph as a sine curve shifted to the right α units along the axis. The number α is called the **phase shift** or the **phase displacement**. Notice that the period of this function is 2π and that the graph may be extended arbitrarily in either direction by a simple repetition of values.

1.2 AMPLITUDE

Let m represent a non-negative real number. The graph of $y = m \sin x$ is similar in every respect except one to the graph of $y = \sin x$. That one difference shows up clearly in Fig. 10.2. Each ordinate

x	$\sin x$	$y = m \sin x$
0	0	0
$\pi/2$	1	m
π	0	0
$3\pi/2$	-1	$-m$
2π	0	0

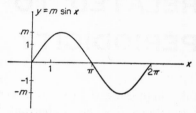

Fig. 10.2

of this function is changed by a factor m from the corresponding ordinate of $y = \sin x$. If $m > 1$, then the ordinates are correspondingly larger, if $m < 1$, they are smaller. The maximum positive ordinate is called the **amplitude** of the function. Since $\sin x$ has a maximum value of 1, the amplitude has the value m.

1.3 PERIOD

This paragraph is related particularly to Theorem 2 in Section 4 of Chapter 5. Let p represent a positive real number. The graph of $y = \sin px$ is similar in every respect except one to the graph of

x	px $(2x)$	$y = \sin 2x$
0	0	0
$\pi/4$	$\pi/2$	1
$\pi/2$	π	0
$3\pi/4$	$3\pi/2$	-1
π	2π	0

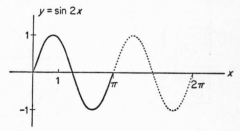

Fig. 10.3

$y = \sin x$. Since the function $\sin x$ has period 2π, we may apply the theorem mentioned to find that $\sin px$ has period $2\pi/p$. How this period affects the graph is illustrated by taking $p = 2$ (see Fig. 10.3). Notice that the function $\sin 2x$ runs through its entire cycle of values for x on the interval $0 \leqq x \leqq \pi$. That is, the interval of length $2\pi/2 = \pi$ represents one full period. Furthermore, note that π is the primitive period of the function $\sin 2x$.

As another illustration of the case just discussed, let $p = \pi$ and consider the function $y = \sin \pi x$. This function has period $2\pi/\pi = 2$. Beginning at a value of x for which $\sin \pi x = 0$, mark off an interval 2 units to the right, then divide that interval into quarters. The function has the value zero at each end point and at the "one-half point" of the interval; it has its maximum value at the "one-quarter point" of the interval; it has its minimum value at the "three-quarter-point" of the interval. Plot these five functional values, then sketch in the remainder of the curve (see Fig. 10.4).

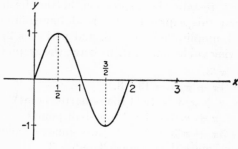

Fig. 10.4

1.4 GENERALIZED SINE

We are now in a position to analyze the important **generalized sine function** $y = m \sin (px - c)$, where $m \geqq 0$, $p > 0$, $c \geqq 0$. This function combines in an obvious way the three properties: phase shift, amplitude, and period. (The function $y = \sin x$ also combines these three properties, but in a way hardly noticeable, since phase shift $= 0$, amplitude $= 1$, and period $= 2\pi$.) Although we will not do so here, it is worth noting that by a further analysis it is possible to remove the restrictions placed on m, p, and c.

To find the phase shift of the generalized sine function we determine the value of x for which the indicated angle is zero; that is, solve $(px - c) = 0$. This value is c/p, as shown immediately by restating the given expression in the equivalent form $y = m \sin p(x - c/p)$. The amplitude is m, the period is $2\pi/p$, and the phase shift is $\alpha = c/p$. The graph may be easily sketched by making the following guide marks.

1. On the x-axis mark $x = \alpha$ (this indicates the phase shift).

2. On the x-axis mark an interval of length $2\pi/p$ to the right of α (this indicates one full period).

3. Mark those values of x which divide the period interval into quarters.

4. On the y-axis mark the values m and $-m$ (this indicates the amplitude).

5. Sketch lightly the horizontal lines $y = m$ and $y = -m$.

EXAMPLE 1. Discuss the function $y = 3 \sin (x/2 - \pi/6)$ and draw the graph.

Solution. First restate the expression in the form $y = 3 \sin \frac{1}{2} (x - \pi/3)$. From this expression we read immediately that phase shift is $\alpha = \pi/3$, amplitude is $m = 3$, and period is $2\pi/\frac{1}{2} = 4\pi$. Make the following guide marks, then sketch the graph (see Fig. 10.5).

1. Mark $x = \pi/3$.
2. Mark $x = 4\pi + \pi/3 = 13\pi/3$.
3. Mark $x = \pi + \pi/3 = 4\pi/3$ (one-quarter point)
   $x = 2\pi + \pi/3 = 7\pi/3$ (one-half point)
   $x = 3\pi + \pi/3 = 10\pi/3$ (three-quarter point).
4. On the y-axis mark the numbers 3 and -3.
5. Sketch the lines $y = 3$ and $y = -3$.

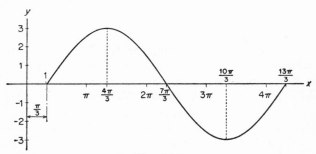

Fig. 10.5

1.5 GENERALIZED COSINE

The **generalized cosine function** $y = m \cos (px - c)$ may be analyzed in a corresponding way. Phase shift, amplitude, and period are defined exactly as before. In drawing the graph of this function we must remember that the basic shape follows the cosine pattern, not the sine pattern.

EXAMPLE 2. Discuss the function $y = \frac{3}{2} \cos (\pi x/2 - \pi)$ and draw the graph.

Solution. First restate the expression in the form $y = \frac{3}{2} \cos [(\pi/2)(x - 2)]$. The phase shift is $\alpha = 2$, amplitude is $m = \frac{3}{2}$, and period is $2\pi/(\pi/2) = 4$.

Make the following guide marks, then sketch the graph (see Fig. 10.6).

1. Mark $x = 2$.

2. Mark $x = 4 + 2 = 6$.

3. Mark $x = 1 + 2 = 3$ (one-quarter point)
   $x = 2 + 2 = 4$ (one-half point)
   $x = 3 + 2 = 5$ (three-quarter point).

4. On the y-axis mark the numbers $3/2$ and $-3/2$.

5. Sketch the lines $y = \frac{3}{2}$ and $y = -\frac{3}{2}$.

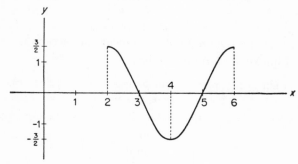

Fig. 10.6

――――――| **Problem Set 10.1** |――――――

1. Sketch the graph on the interval 0 to 2π.
   (a) $y = \sin (\theta - \pi/4)$,   (b) $y = \sin (x - 2\pi/3)$,
   (c) $y = \sin (x - \pi)$.

2. What is the phase shift in each part of Problem 1?

3. Sketch the graph on the interval $-\pi$ to π.
  (a) $y = 4 \sin x$, (b) $y = \frac{1}{3} \cos x$,
  (c) $3y = 5 \sin \theta$, (d) $y = -2 \sin \theta$.

4. What is the amplitude in each part of Problem 3?

5. Sketch the graph for one period.
  (a) $y = \sin 5x$, (b) $y = \cos 3x/2$, (c) $y = \sin 2\pi\theta$.

6. What is the period in each part of Problem 5?

In each of the following, discuss the function and sketch for one period.

7. $y = \frac{3}{2} \sin (2x - \pi)$.

8. $y = 2 \sin (\frac{1}{2}x - \pi/4)$.

9. $y = \pi \sin \pi x$.

10. $2y = \cos \pi(\theta - 1)$. Look at

2. RELATED FORMS

Expressions of the form

(1) $$a \sin \theta - b \cos \theta,$$

where $a \geq 0$ and $b \geq 0$ occur frequently in applications. Expression (1) is related to the generalized sine function, and, as we shall show, it may be analyzed and sketched by the methods introduced in the preceding section. Another occasionally useful, but more laborious, method for drawing the graph of (1) appears in Section 3.

By a multiple-angle formula we have

(2) $$m \sin (px - c) = m(\sin px \cos c - \cos px \sin c),$$
$$= (m \cos c) \sin px - (m \sin c) \cos px.$$

Given Expression (1), we may relate it to (2) by the equations

$$a = m \cos c,$$
$$b = m \sin c,$$
$$\theta = px.$$

Our task is to determine m and c in terms of a and b.

To find m: $$a^2 = m^2 \cos^2 c,$$
$$b^2 = m^2 \sin^2 c.$$

Adding, $$a^2 + b^2 = m^2,$$
$$m = \sqrt{a^2 + b^2}$$

We choose the positive radical since $m \geq 0$.

To find c:
$$\sin c = b/m,$$
$$\cos c = a/m,$$
$$\tan c = b/a.$$

We choose arbitrarily the principal value $c = $ Arc tan b/a. We may now write

(3) $$a \sin \theta - b \cos \theta = m \sin (px - c),$$

where $m = \sqrt{a^2 + b^2}$, $px = \theta$, $c = $ Arc tan b/a.

EXAMPLE. Analyze the expression $y = 3 \sin 2x - 4 \cos 2x$.

Solution. (See Fig. 10.7.)

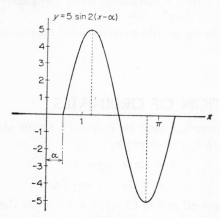

Fig. 10.7

$$m = \sqrt{3^2 + 4^2} = 5,$$
$$c = \text{Arc tan } \tfrac{4}{3} = 0.93 \text{ (approximately)},$$
$$y = 5 \sin (2x - 0.93) = 5 \sin 2(x - 0.46).$$

Phase shift = 0.46 (approximately),

Amplitude = 5,

Period = $2\pi/2 = \pi$.

In a similar way, the expression

(4) $$a \cos \theta + b \sin \theta,$$

where $a \geqq 0$ and $b \geqq 0$, is related to the generalized cosine function.

(5) $$m \cos (px - c) = a \cos \theta + b \sin \theta,$$

where $m = \sqrt{a^2 + b^2}$, $px = \theta$, $c = $ Arc tan b/a.

———————| **Problem Set 10.2** |———————————

Analyze the expression and sketch the graph.

1. $y/2 = \sin x \cos \pi/3 - \cos x \sin \pi/3$.

2. $y = 3 \sin \theta - 4 \cos \theta$.

3. $y = 2\sqrt{3} \sin x - 2 \cos x$.

4. $3\,y = 4 \sin x \cos 1 - 4 \cos x \sin 1$.

5. $y = 3 \cos 2x + 3 \sin 2x$.

6. $y = \cos \pi x + \sqrt{3} \sin \pi x$.

7. What are the further conditions on a and b in Expression (1) if phase shift is $\pi/4$ and period is 2π?

8. What are the further conditions on a and b in Expression (1) if amplitude is π and period is π?

3. COMPOSITION OF ORDINATES

Sometimes a function may be expressed as an algebraic sum of several simple terms. For example,

$$(1) \qquad\qquad y = \sin x - \cos x.$$

$$(2) \qquad\qquad y = 2 \sin x + \cos 2x.$$

By Theorem 3 in Section 4 of Chapter 5, we know that each of these functions is periodic with period 2π. Of course, that theorem does not specify the primitive period of either of Functions (1) or (2). Function (1) can be treated by the methods of the preceding section, but the other cannot since the angles x and $2x$ are not the same. A possible way to draw the graphs of these functions is the following.

1. Sketch lightly each separate term of the expression on the same co-ordinate system.

2. Using some convenient device (ruler, compass, dividers) actually combine corresponding ordinates in the way indicated.

EXAMPLE 1. Draw the graph of $y = \sin x - \cos x$.

Solution. (See Fig. 10.8.)

1. First sketch lightly each separate term.

2. Sketch lightly a number of vertical lines intersecting the curves at convenient points.

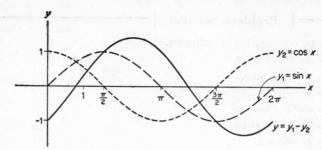

Fig. 10.8

3. On each vertical line mark that point which is the difference of the two ordinates indicated by that line. Be sure to take into account the sign of the ordinate, that is, whether it is above or below the x-axis.

4. Mark enough points to outline the general shape of the graph, then connect these points with a smooth curve.

Since the primitive period of this example is 2π, we have drawn the graph for one complete cycle of values. That it is a generalized sine curve is shown by the equality

$$\sin x - \cos x = \sqrt{2} \sin (x - \pi/4).$$

EXAMPLE 2. Draw the graph of $y = 2 \sin x + \cos 2x$.

Solution. (See Fig. 10.9.) Again sketch each term separately. The

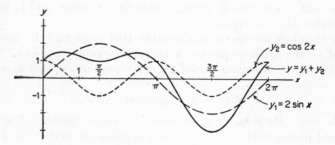

Fig. 10.9

period of $2 \sin x$ is 2π, while that of $\cos 2x$ is π. We must be sure to draw the graph over an interval that is a multiple of each of these periods. Any interval of length less than that may produce an incomplete graph.

——————————| **Problem Set 10.3** |——————————

Sketch by composition of ordinates.

1. $y = \sin \theta + 2 \cos \theta$.

2. $y = \sin \theta + \tan \theta$.

3. $y = \theta - \sin \theta$.

4. $y = \sin^2 \theta + \cos^2 \theta$.

5. $y = 2 \tan \theta - \cot \theta$.

6. $y = 2\theta + \cos \theta$.

7. $y = \sin \theta + \cos \theta + \tan \theta$.

8. Which of the preceding seven expressions are not periodic?

4. SPECIAL TOPIC: SINE AND COSINE SUMS

Consider the following sequence of expressions, in which a_i and b_i represent arbitrary real numbers.

$$y_0 = \text{a constant},$$
$$y_1 = y_0 + a_1 \cos x + b_1 \sin x,$$
$$y_2 = y_1 + a_2 \cos 2x + b_2 \sin 2x,$$
$$y_3 = y_2 + a_3 \cos 3x + b_3 \sin 3x,$$

and in general for $n > 0$,

$$y_n = y_{n-1} + a_n \cos nx + b_n \sin nx.$$

Notice that y_1 contains 3 terms, y_2 contains 5 terms, and in general y_n contains $2n + 1$ terms.

It is shown in advanced mathematics that most periodic functions related to the sciences possess a very remarkable property. *If $f(x)$ is such a function having period 2π, then constants a_i and b_i may be chosen so that*

$$f(x) = y_n \quad (approximately),$$

and the larger the value of n, the closer the approximation. For many practical purposes the approximation is adequate even with a small value of n. This property means that: *under very general conditions, a function f may be approximated on an interval of length 2π by a finite sum of terms involving sines and cosines.*

One of the most important branches of applied mathematics, called *Fourier analysis*, exploits this property. The name commemorates the fact that basic work in this branch was done by the French mathematician and physicist, Jean Baptiste Joseph Fourier (1768–1830). The applications of Fourier analysis extend through nearly the whole range of modern physics, especially in the study of waves or vibrations: for example, the radio waves transmitted by broadcasting stations, the waves set up by dropping a stone into a pool of still water, the sound waves produced by striking a key on a piano. But to indicate still more emphatically the wide range of this branch, we note that Fourier himself developed the subject in connection with his researches into the way heat is conducted.

Each of the examples discussed in Section 4 of Chapter 5 is periodic, but not of period 2π. In each case, however, the period may be changed to 2π by an appropriate change of scale on the horizontal axis. We examine this point in connection with Example 4 of that section.

$$f(x) = \begin{cases} x - z, & z - 1 \leqq x < z, \\ 0, & z \leqq x < z + 1. \end{cases}$$

where z ranges over the set of even whole numbers. Since the period of f is 2, by Theorem 2 of that section

$$g(x) = \begin{cases} (x/\pi) - z, & (z - 1)\pi \leqq x < z\pi, \\ 0, & z\pi \leqq x < (z + 1)\pi, \end{cases}$$

is of period $2/(1/\pi) = 2\pi$ (see Fig. 10.10). Although it does not appear

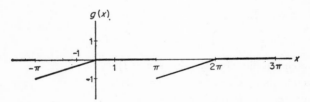

Fig. 10.10

very likely at first glance, it is now possible to approximate the function $g(x)$ by a sine and cosine sum, where n is selected and the constants are computed. Of course, the real difficulty here is the problem of evaluating the constants which requires rather complicated techniques.

We shall leave the present discussion in this incomplete state, since much further study is required for an understanding of the fundamental importance of sine and cosine representations.

———————| **Suggested Exercises** |———————

1. How many terms does the sine and cosine sum y_{17} have?

2. Write out in detail the sine and cosine sum y_6.

3. Write out the sine and cosine sum y_5 if $a_i = i$ and $b_i = i^2$. $\left[Hint.\ a_2 = 2\right.$ and $\left. b_2 = 4.\right]$

4. Show that the sine and cosine sum $y_3 = \sin^3 x$ if $y_0 = a_1 = a_2 = b_2 = a_3 = 0$, and $b_1 = \frac{3}{4}$ and $b_3 = -\frac{1}{4}$.

5. Write $\cos^3 x$ as a sine and cosine sum.

6. By changing the scale on the horizontal axis, convert the following function to one having primitive period 2π:
$$f(x) = x - z,\ z - 1 \leqq x < z + 1$$
where z ranges over the set of even whole numbers.

———————| **Miscellaneous Problems** |———————

1. Draw the graph of (a) $y = \sin (x - \pi/6)$, (b) $y = \sin (x - 1)$.

2. Draw the graph of (a) $y = \sin (x + \pi/6)$, (b) $y = \sin (x + 1)$.

3. Show that $-m \sin x = m \sin (x + \pi)$.

Discuss the function and sketch for two periods.

4. $y = 5 \sin (2x - \pi/5)$;

5. $2y = 7 \cos \left(\dfrac{x - \pi}{3}\right)$;

6. $y = 2 \tan (2x - \pi)$;

7. $y = \frac{1}{2} \cot \left(\dfrac{\pi x - 1}{2}\right)$.

8. Sketch the function $y = \sin (-x - 1)$.

9. Sketch the function $y = \cos (\pi x + 2\pi)$.

10. Solve the equation $\sqrt{3} \sin \theta - \cos \theta = 1$.

11. Solve the equation $3 \cos 2x + 4 \sin 2x = 0$.

12. Solve the equation $\cos \pi x + \sqrt{3} \sin \pi x = -1$.

13. Solve the equation $\sin x \cos (\pi/10) - \cos x \sin (\pi/10)] = 1$.

14. Sketch by composition of ordinates, $y = \cos^2 x - \sin^2 x$.

15. Sketch by composition of ordinates, $y = \sin 2\theta - \cos 3\theta$.

16. Sketch by composition of ordinates, $y = 2 \sin \theta - \cos 2\theta + \theta$.

REMARK. Consider a standard circle C of radius m. Let $P(x, y)$ be a variable point on the circle and let P revolve counterclockwise on C with constant angular velocity denoted by ω radians per second. For any position of P on C, the point $H(0, y)$ is called the **projection** of P on the y-axis. As P revolves with constant angular velocity, the point H oscillates between the points $(0, m)$ and $(0, -m)$ in what is called **simple harmonic motion**

17. If $\omega = 2$ radians per second, what angle is generated by P in π seconds, in $1/2$ second? What is the arc length covered by P in each case?

18. (a) Find the time required by H to cover the interval from $(0, 0)$ to $(0, m/2)$.

(b) Find the time required by H to cover the interval from $(0, m/2)$ to $(0, m)$.

(c) Can we conclude that the speed of H along the y-axis is constant?

19. If P begins its motion at the point $(m, 0)$, show that the equation $y = f(t) = m \sin \omega t$ describes the simple harmonic motion of H.

20. Show that the simple harmonic motion of H is described in general by $y = f(t) = m \sin (\omega t - \alpha)$. What is the geometric significance of the number α?

THE COMPLEX NUMBER SYSTEM

In Section 2 of Chapter 2, the real number system was discussed briefly and it was stated that this system can be evolved from the fundamental counting numbers through a succession of "extensions."

TABLE 11.1

System of numbers	Typical numbers (not in preceding system)	Operations always possible	Operations sometimes impossible
1. Natural	0, 1, 2, 3, 4	Addition Multiplication	Subtraction Division Root extraction
2. Whole	$-1, -2, -3, -4$	Addition Multiplication Subtraction	Division Root extraction
3. Rational	$\frac{1}{2}, \frac{3}{4}, -\frac{5}{8}, -\frac{9}{6}$	Addition Multiplication Subtraction Division (not by 0)	Root extraction
4. Real	$\sqrt{2}, -\sqrt{3}, \pi,$ $1 + \sqrt{7}, 2 - \pi$	Addition Multiplication Subtraction Division (not by 0) Square root extraction for non-negative numbers.	Root extraction

Each extension is dictated by the desire to make a certain elementary arithmetic operation universally applicable. For example, to make the operation of subtraction applicable to the entire set of numbers, it is necessary to extend the system of natural numbers by introducing the negative integers; thus creating the system of whole numbers. We may tabulate these various systems as shown in Table 11.1.

Since root extraction is still not generally possible in the real number system, at least one more extension is indicated. It is shown in more advanced mathematics that no more than one further extension is needed in order to satisfy all usual requirements of algebra. In this extended system, called the **complex number system,** we expect to be able to find all roots; in particular, square roots of negative numbers. Throughout this chapter we shall assume that the symbol i has the property $i^2 = -1$.

1. THE COMPLEX PLANE

We establish in the plane a rectangular co-ordinate system. Let the symbol z represent a point in the plane having co-ordinates (x, y).

If $y = 0$ then z lies on the x-axis, and in this case we may identify the point z with the real number x. In this way the entire set of real numbers corresponds to the set of points on a single line in the plane. We shall assume that each point in the plane represents an example of a new and more general type of number, of which the real numbers are a special case.

Now suppose that the point z does not lie on the x-axis. In this case we cannot think of z as corresponding to a real number. We may, however, consider z to be made up of two components, one of which is horizontal, while the other is vertical. The length of each component is measured by a real number, denoted by $| x |$ for the

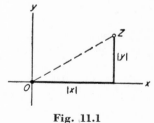

Fig. 11.1

horizontal component and by $| y |$ for the vertical component.

We must now solve a problem in notation: how to express z in terms of the two components. Although the two components are measured in the same unit of length, their directions differ by a right angle. We cannot, therefore, hope to obtain z by the simple addition

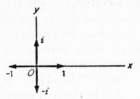

Fig. 11.2

of $|y|$ to $|x|$. We must first agree upon units which not only will measure distance but also will serve to distinguish direction. The customary unit symbols are shown in Fig. 11.2, and if we think of the plane as a map oriented so that the positive x-axis lies to the east, then

1 denotes the unit interval directed east,
i denotes the unit interval directed north,
-1 denotes the unit interval directed west,
$-i$ denotes the unit interval directed south.

We may determine z geometrically by first measuring $(1)|x|$ or $(-1)|x|$ units from the origin, and then from the end point of that interval measuring $(i)|y|$ or $(-i)|y|$ units. We denote this geometric idea by writing $z = (\pm 1)|x| + (\pm i)|y|$. Of course, only one of the unit symbols is used with each component. For example, $z = (1)3 + (-i)2$ means that the horizontal component of z is measured 3 units to the right while the vertical component is measured 2 units down.

In order to simplify the algebraic notation, it is customary to carry the signs of the unit symbols along with the numbers x and y, and also to omit the unit symbol 1. The example above is usually written $z = 3 - i2$. Following this practice, the symbol $x + iy$, where x and y represent any real numbers whatever, denotes a unique point in the plane.

The symbol $x + iy$ represents a **complex number** *in* **rectangular form.** We shall use the symbol to denote both a point in the plane and its related complex number. *The horizontal component is called the* **real part** *of the complex number; the vertical component is called the* **imaginary part** *of the complex number. The entire plane, in which each point corresponds to a complex number, is called the* **complex plane.** *The x-axis is called the* **real axis,** *since any point on this line has zero for its imaginary part. The y-axis is called the* **imaginary axis** *since any point on this line has zero for its real part.*

2. TRIGONOMETRIC FORM

Let z represent an arbitrary complex number, that is, $z = x + iy$. Let r represent the distance from the origin to z, and let θ be an angle generated by z (see Fig. 11.3).
Then

(A) $\qquad \begin{cases} x = r \cos \theta, \\ y = r \sin \theta. \end{cases}$

Solving these equations for r and θ in terms of x and y, we find

(B) $\qquad \begin{cases} r^2 = x^2 + y^2, \\ \theta = \text{arc tan } (y/x). \end{cases}$

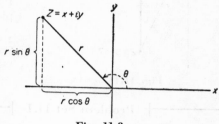

Fig. 11.3

Equations (B) do not lead to unique values for r and θ, and to avoid ambiguity we shall assume that (a) r is non-negative, (b) θ lies in the interval $-\pi < \theta \leq \pi$, which is called the **principal value interval** for the angle.[1] If an angle outside this interval appears in a computation, it shall be replaced with its principal value.

Equations (A) lead directly to an alternative expression for z, $r (\cos \theta + i \sin \theta)$, called the **trigonometric form** of the complex number.

*The distance from the origin to z is called the **modulus** of the complex number, and the angle θ is called the **argument** of the complex number.* The modulus is denoted by any one of the symbols

$$r = |z| = |x + iy| = \sqrt{x^2 + y^2}.$$

EXAMPLE. Discuss the complex number $z = 3 - i7$.

Solution. (See Fig. 11.4.) This complex number is in rectangular form. The real part is 3 and the imaginary part is -7. The modulus is $|z| = \sqrt{3^2 + (-7)^2} = \sqrt{58}$.

---

[1] The quadrant of θ is determined by the signs of x and y.

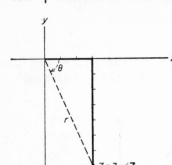

The argument is an angle θ such that tan $\theta = -7/3 = -2.3333$ (approx.). We must choose θ in Quadrant IV and on the principal value interval, hence $\theta = -1.1659$ radians (approx.). The trigonometric form of the complex number is (approx.)

$$z = \sqrt{58}\left[\cos{(-1.17)} + i\sin{(-1.17)}\right].$$

Fig. 11.4

———————| **Problem Set 11.1** |————————

1. With what real numbers are the following complex numbers identified?
(a) $\sqrt{2} + i0$,   (b) $\sqrt{2} - i0$,
(c) $2(\cos 0 + i \sin 0)$,   (d) $2(\cos \pi + i \sin \pi)$,
(e) $\cos 0 + i \sin 0$,   (f) $\cos \pi + i \sin \pi$.

2. Express the following as complex numbers in trigonometric form.
(a) $r = 3, \theta = 5\pi/4$,
(b) $r = 2, \theta = 21\pi/6$,
(c) $r = 1, \theta = -\pi$.

3. Express each point in Problem 2 as a complex number in rectangular form.

4. In each of the following find the modulus and the argument.
(a) $z = 1 - i\sqrt{3}$,   (b) $z = -3 - i3$,
(c) $z = -4 + i3$,   (d) $z = 3 + i4$,
(e) $z = 5$,   (f) $z = -i\sqrt{5}$.

5. What is the complex number in rectangular form if
(a) $|z| = 1$, argument $z = \pi/4$,
(b) $|z| = 4$, argument $z = \pi$?

3. OPERATIONS ON COMPLEX NUMBERS

*Two complex numbers are **equal** provided the real parts are equal and the imaginary parts are equal.* If $w = u + iv$ and $z = x + iy$ then $w = z$ means that both $u = x$ and $v = y$. If w and z are expressed in trigonometric form then the two moduli are equal and the two amplitudes (expressed as principal values) are equal.

EXAMPLE 1. Show that $\sqrt{3} - i = 2\,[\cos(-\pi/6) + i\sin(-\pi/6)]$.
Solution. We convert the trigonometric form to rectangular form.
$$2\,[(\sqrt{3}/2) + i\,(-1/2)] = \sqrt{3} - i.$$
EXAMPLE 2. Find two real numbers a and b so that
$$(a + b) + i\,(a - b) = 5 - i.$$

Solution. By the definition of equality we know that the real parts are equal and the imaginary parts are equal, hence $a + b = 5$ and $a - b = -1$. Solving these two equations simultaneously, we have $a = 2$ and $b = 3$.

Given two complex numbers $w = u + iv$ and $z = x + iy$. Then $w + z = (u + x) + i\,(v + y)$ and $w - z = (u - x) + i\,(v - y)$.

EXAMPLE 3. Suppose $w = -2 + i$ and $z = 5 + i4$. Find, geometrically, $w + z$ and $w - z$.

Solution. To find $w + z$, first sketch w on a rectangular co-ordinate system. Now construct a new co-ordinate system with w as the origin (keeping the real axes parallel), and on it sketch z. As in Fig. 11.5, the relative position of z referred to the original co-ordinate system represents the sum $w + z$. Thus $w + z = 3 + i5$.

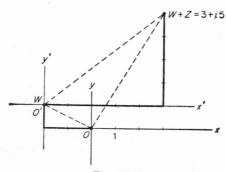

Fig. 11.5

To find $w - z$, change each sign in z and add in the way described above (see Fig. 11.6).

Two complex numbers differing only in the sign before the imaginary unit are called **complex conjugates.** *Each one is the* **conjugate** *of the other.* The usual notation for the conjugate of z is $\bar{z}$. Thus if $z = x + iy$, then $\bar{z} = x - iy$. From the definition of modulus, it follows that $|z| = |\bar{z}|$.

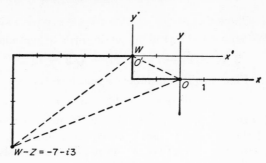

Fig. 11.6

To find the product of two complex numbers we perform the indicated operation treating i as an ordinary unknown and replacing i^2 with -1. *In rectangular form, the product of $w = u + iv$ and $z = x + iy$ is given by*

$$w \cdot z = (u + iv) \cdot (x + iy) = (u \cdot x - v \cdot y) + i(u \cdot y + v \cdot x).$$

The geometric significance of multiplication becomes apparent by use of the trigonometric form. Put $w = a \cos \phi + ai \sin \phi$ and $z = r \cos \theta + ri \sin \theta$. Then $wz = ar[\cos (\phi + \theta) + i \sin (\phi + \theta)]$. From this expression we see that if two complex numbers are in trigonometric form then the modulus of the product is the product of the two moduli, and the argument of the product is the sum of the two arguments.

EXAMPLE 4. Multiply $w = 2 (\cos \pi/6 + i \sin \pi/6)$ and
$z = 3 (\cos 2\pi/3 + i \sin 2\pi/3)$.

Solution. (See Fig. 11.7).

$$wz = 2 \cdot 3 [\cos (\pi/6 + 2\pi/3) + i \sin (\pi/6 + 2\pi/3)]$$
$$= 6 (\cos 5\pi/6 + i \sin 5\pi/6).$$

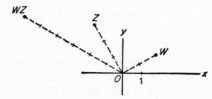

Fig. 11.7

The product of complex conjugates is a real number; in fact, it is the square of the modulus of either of them. This can be shown using either rectangular or trigonometric form. Thus $z \cdot \overline{z} = x^2 + y^2 = r^2$.

To find the quotient, w/z, of two complex numbers, multiply both numerator and denominator by $\overline{z}$. Simplifying we obtain

$$\frac{w}{z} = \frac{(ux + vy) + i(vx - uy)}{x^2 + y^2} .$$

Again the geometric significance of the operation becomes clearer through the use of trigonometric form. Put $w = a \, (\cos \phi + i \sin \phi)$ and $z = r \, (\cos \theta + i \sin \theta)$. The conjugate of z is $\overline{z} = r \, [\cos(-\theta) + i \sin(-\theta)]$, and we know that $z \cdot \overline{z} = r^2$; hence

$$\frac{w}{z} = \frac{a}{r} \, [\cos(\phi - \theta) + i \sin(\phi - \theta)].$$

EXAMPLE 5. Find the quotient, w/z, of the numbers given in the preceding example.

Solution.

$$\frac{w}{z} = \frac{2}{3} \, [\cos(\pi/6 - 2\pi/3) + i \sin(\pi/6 - 2\pi/3)]$$

$$= \frac{2}{3} \, [\cos(-\pi/2) + i \sin(-\pi/2)].$$

The expression for the quotient of two complex numbers is meaningless if $x^2 + y^2 = 0$. When x and y are real numbers, we know that $x^2 + y^2 \geqq 0$ and that the equality holds only when both x and y are zero. Division of complex numbers, therefore, is undefined only when the denominator has zero for both its real and imaginary parts.

——————| **Problem Set 11.2** |——————

1. Show that the following pairs of complex numbers are equal.
   (a) $1 - i$ and $\sqrt{2} \, [\cos(-\pi/4) + i \sin(-\pi/4)]$,
   (b) $-2\sqrt{3} + i2$ and $4 \, (\cos 5\pi/6 + i \sin 5\pi/6)$,
   (c) $-3 - i \cdot 3\sqrt{3}$ and $6 \, [\cos(-2\pi/3) + i \sin(-2\pi/3)]$.

2. Solve for the real numbers a and b if
   (a) $a - ib = 3 + i\sqrt{2}$,
   (b) $a + ib = 5 \, [\cos(-\pi/3) + i \sin(-\pi/3)]$,
   (c) $a + 2b - i \, (a + b) = 1 - i.$

3. (a) Show that the sum of complex conjugates is a complex number with zero imaginary part.

(b) Show that the difference of complex conjugates is a complex number with zero real part.

4. If $z = x + i \cdot 0$, show that $\bar{z} = z$.

5. If $z = 0 + i \cdot y$, show that $\bar{z} = -z$.

6. Plot both the complex number and its conjugate.

(a) $z = i$,   (c) $z = -4$,

(b) $z = -i \cdot 3$,   (d) $z = 2$.

7. If $z = x + iy$, show that argument of $z = -$argument of $\bar{z}$.

8. Plot both the complex number and its conjugate.

(a) $z = 2 (\cos \pi/4 + i \sin \pi/4)$,

(b) $z = \cos (-2\pi/3) + i \sin (-2\pi/3)$,

(c) $z = 3 \left[\cos (-\pi/2) + i \sin (-\pi/2) \right]$,

(d) $z = \sqrt{5} (\cos \pi + i \sin \pi)$.

9. Find in rectangular form the conjugate of the complex number, $|2 + i| + i|2 - i|$.

10. In each of the following find $w + z$ and plot each number and the sum.

(a) $w = 1 + i\sqrt{2}$ and $z = \sqrt{2} + i$,

(b) $w = -3 + i$ and $z = -2 - i4$,

(c) $w = 5$ and $z = -1 + i$,

(d) $w = -2 - i2$ and $z = -i$.

11. Find and plot $w - z$ for each pair of numbers in Problem 10.

12. Show geometrically that the point $w + z$ is the fourth vertex of a parallelogram determined by the three points w, z, and the origin in the complex plane. For this reason, addition of complex numbers is said to satisfy the "parallelogram law."

13. Find the product of each pair of numbers in Problem 10.

14. What is the product of the complex number and its conjugate?

(a) $\sqrt{2} + i$,   (b) $-\sqrt{3} - i\sqrt{2}$,   (c) $i5$.

15. Find the product in trigonometric form.

(a) $3 (\cos \pi/2 + i \sin \pi/2)$ and $\sqrt{2} (\cos \pi/4 + i \sin \pi/4)$;

(b) $5 (\cos 0 + i \sin 0)$ and $5 (\cos \pi + i \sin \pi)$.

16. Show that i^n, where n is a natural number, must be one of the numbers $1, -1, i,$ or $-i$.

17. Simplify each of the following.

(a) i^{18},   (b) i^{27},   (c) i^{31},

(d) $i^{10} \cdot i^7$,   (e) $i^4 \cdot i^8 \cdot i^{12}$,   (f) $i^3 \cdot i^9 \cdot i^{81}$.

18. Find the quotient, w/z, for each pair of numbers in Problem 10.

19. Find the quotients.

(a) $5\,(\cos\,\pi/4 + i\,\sin\,\pi/4)/[\cos\,(-\pi/6) + i\,\sin\,(-\pi/6)]$;

(b) $4\,(\cos\,2\pi/3 + i\,\sin\,2\pi/3)/\sqrt{2}\,[\cos\,(-5\pi/6) + i\,\sin\,(-5\pi/6)]$.

REMARK. For any natural number n, $z^{-n} = 1/z^n$.

20. Simplify each of the following.

(a) i^{-7},   (b) i^{-12},   (c) i^{-35},

(d) i^{-49},   (e) $i^{81} \cdot i^{-6}/i^{-11}$,   (f) $i^{13} \cdot i^{-4} \cdot i^{0}/i^{-30} \cdot i^{21}$.

4. POWERS AND ROOTS

THEOREM

> If $z = r\,(\cos\,\theta + i\,\sin\,\theta)$ and if n is a natural number, then $z^n = r^n\,[\cos\,(n\theta) + i\,\sin\,(n\theta)]$.

Proof. We use mathematical induction. When n is either 0 or 1 the statement is easily verified. We assume $z^k = r^k\,(\cos\,k\theta + i\,\sin\,k\theta)$. When $n = k + 1$ we have

$$z^{k+1} = z^k \cdot z^1 = [r^k\,(\cos\,k\theta + i\,\sin\,k\theta)] \cdot [r\,(\cos\,\theta + i\,\sin\,\theta)],$$
$$= r^k \cdot r\,[\cos\,(k\theta + \theta) + i\,\sin\,(k\theta + \theta)],$$
$$= r^{k+1}\,[\cos\,(k + 1)\theta + i\,\sin\,(k + 1)\theta];$$

which completes the induction.

EXAMPLE 1. If $z = \sqrt{3} - i$, find z^7.

Solution. First express z in trigonometric form (see Fig. 11.8).

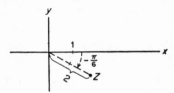

Fig. 11.8

$$r = \sqrt{(\sqrt{3})^2 + (-1)^2} = 2,$$

$\tan\,\theta = -1/\sqrt{3}$; hence argument $z = -\pi/6$.

By the theorem, $z^7 = 2^7\,[\cos\,7(-\pi/6) + i\,\sin\,7(-\pi/6)]$,
$$= 128\,(\cos\,5\pi/6 + i\,\sin\,5\pi/6).$$

The angle is changed so as to lie on the principal value interval. In rectangular form the result is

$$z^7 = -64\sqrt{3} + i64.$$

*Let w represent an arbitrary complex number not equal to $0 + i0$, and let n be a natural number greater than 1. By an **nth root** of w we mean a complex number z such that $z^n = w$.*

To find the roots of this equation we first express w and z in trigonometric form, $w = a (\cos \phi + i \sin \phi)$ and $z = r (\cos \theta + i \sin \theta)$. Then

$$[r (\cos \theta + i \sin \theta)]^n = a (\cos \phi + i \sin \phi),$$

and by the theorem

$$r^n (\cos n\theta + i \sin n\theta) = a (\cos \phi + i \sin \phi).$$

By the definition of equality we have $r^n = a$ and $n\theta = \phi$ (where each angle is a principal value). The modulus of any nth root is $r = \sqrt[n]{a}$, assumed to be a positive real number which may be approximated by use of logarithms if necessary. The argument of an nth root is one of the values θ for which $n\theta$ has ϕ as its principal value. Thus we have

$$n\theta = \phi \pm 2k\pi, \quad \text{where } k = 0, 1, 2, \cdots,$$

$$\theta = \frac{\phi \pm 2k\pi}{n}.$$

From this equation we may obtain exactly n distinct principal values of the argument θ by assigning appropriate values to k. This fact will be recognized most clearly through an example.

EXAMPLE 2. Find the five fifth roots of

$$w = 5 (\cos \pi/4 + i \sin \pi/4).$$

Solution. Let $z = r (\cos \theta + i \sin \theta)$ be such that $z^5 = w$. Then we have $r^5 (\cos 5\theta + i \sin 5\theta) = 5 (\cos \pi/4 + i \sin \pi/4)$ hence $r = \sqrt[5]{5}$ and

$$\theta = \frac{\pi/4 \pm 2k\pi}{5} = (\pi/20)(1 \pm 8k).$$

We examine carefully the possible values of θ

when $k = 0$, $\theta = \pi/20$,
when $k = 1$, $\theta = 9\pi/20$ and $\theta = -7\pi/20$,
when $k = 2$, $\theta = 17\pi/20$ and $\theta = -15\pi/20$.

So far, each of these angles is a principal value, but when $k = 3$, then $\theta = 25\pi/20$, and $\theta = -23\pi/20$. These angles reduce to the principal values $\theta = -15\pi/20$ and $\theta = 17\pi/20$, which have already been obtained. Other values of k also yield principal values already obtained. This repetition is best explained geometrically. Each change in k induces a change in angle of $8\pi/20$ radians. Since there are five such intervals in 2π, we find five distinct arguments and therefore five distinct complex roots of w (see Fig. 11.9):

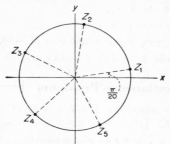

Fig. 11.9

$$z_1 = \sqrt[5]{5} \ (\cos \pi/20 + i \sin \pi/20),$$
$$z_2 = \sqrt[5]{5} \ (\cos 9\pi/20 + i \sin 9\pi/20),$$
$$z_3 = \sqrt[5]{5} \ (\cos 17\pi/20 + i \sin 17\pi/20),$$
$$z_4 = \sqrt[5]{5} \ [\cos (- 15\pi/20) + i \sin (- 15\pi/20)],$$
$$z_5 = \sqrt[5]{5} \ [\cos (- 7\pi/20) + i \sin (- 7\pi/20)].$$

The five fifth roots of w are seen to be equally spaced about a circle of radius $r = \sqrt[5]{5}$ beginning with the angle associated with $k = 0$. The modulus may be approximated by logarithms in the following way. If $r = \sqrt[5]{5}$ then

$$r^5 = 5;$$
$$\log r^5 = \log 5,$$
$$5 \log r = \log 5 = 0.69897,$$
$$\log r = 0.13979,$$
$$r = 1.3797.$$

——————| **Problem Set 11.3** |——————

1. If $z = r (\cos \theta + i \sin \theta)$ and if n is a natural number, prove
$$z^{-n} = r^{-n} \left[\cos (-n\theta) + i \sin (-n\theta) \right].$$

2. If $z = \sqrt{3} - i$, find (a) z^{12}, (b) z^{-12}.

3. Derive the familiar formulas for $\sin 2\theta$ and $\cos 2\theta$, using the Theorem of Section 4. [*Hint.* Put $r = 1$ and $n = 2$.]

4. As in Problem 3, find $\sin 3\theta$ and $\cos 3\theta$.

Draw a sketch with each of the following.

5. Find the four fourth roots of $1 - i$. [*Hint.* Express $1 - i$ as $\sqrt{2}\left[\cos\left(-\pi/4\right) + i\sin\left(-\pi/4\right)\right]$.]

6. Find the five fifth roots of unity. [*Hint.* Express 1 as $(\cos 0 + i\sin 0)$.]

7. Find the sixth roots of $-i$.

8. Find the square roots of $1 + i\sqrt{3}$.

9. Show that $\sqrt{2} - i\sqrt{2}$ is a fourth root of -16.

10. Show that $\cos 13\pi/18 + i\sin 13\pi/18$ is a ninth root of i.

────────────| **Miscellaneous Problems** |────────────

1. Show that the equation $1 + 7/x = 12/(1 + x)$ has the number $2 - \sqrt{-3}$ as one root. [*Hint.* $(i\sqrt{3})^2 = i^2 \cdot 3 = -3$.]

2. Show that $1 - \sqrt{i}$ is a root of the equation $x^2 - 2x + 1 = i$.

3. If $z = 3 + i$, show that $(x - z)(x - \bar{z}) = 0$ is a quadratic equation with real number coefficients.

4. If $z = a + ib$, show that $(x - z)(x - \bar{z}) = 0$ is a quadratic equation with real number coefficients.

5. Show that if a quadratic equation with real number coefficients has a complex root z with nonzero imaginary part, then the conjugate of z is also a root of the equation.

6. Express the following complex numbers in trigonometric form and sketch.

(a) $z = \sqrt{5} - i\sqrt{5}$, (b) $z = -\sqrt{3} + i$,

(c) $z = -5$, (d) $z = i\sqrt{5}$.

7. Sketch the conjugate of the complex number.

(a) $|\sqrt{2} - i| + i \cdot |i3|$, $\sqrt{3} - i\,3$

(b) $\dfrac{4 - i3}{|1 + i|}$, $2\sqrt{2} + i\,\dfrac{3\sqrt{2}}{2}$

(c) $|3 - i| \cdot (1/2 - i5/4)$. $\dfrac{\sqrt{10}}{2} + i\,5\,\dfrac{\sqrt{10}}{4}$

8. Express each of the complex numbers in Problem 7 in trigonometric form (use approximate angle values).

9. Find $w + z$ and plot each number and the sum.

(a) $w = 2 + i4, z = 2 - i4$,

(b) $w = -i3, z = i3$,

(c) $w = (\cos \pi/6 + i\sin \pi/6), z = \sqrt{2}\left[\cos(-3\pi/4) + i\sin(-3\pi/4)\right]$.

10. Show that $(t + w) - z = t + (w - z)$ if

(a) $t = 1 + i, w = -3 + i2, z = 5 - i4$,

(b) $t = -1 - i2, w = 3, z = i5$,

(c) $t = 3 - i5, w = \bar{t}, z = 1/t$.

11. If $z = x + iy$ and $w = u + iv$, show that

   (a) $\overline{(w + z)} = \overline{w} + \overline{z}$,

   (b) $\overline{(w - z)} = \overline{w} - \overline{z}$,

   (c) $w + z = \overline{(\overline{w} + \overline{z})}$.

12. Solve for the real numbers a and b if

   (a) $2a + b(1 - i) = i$,

   (b) $a^2 - b^2 + i(a - b) = -9 - i$,

   (c) $\sqrt{a + ib} = \sqrt{1 - i} \cdot (1 + i)$.

13. If $z = x + iy$, $w = u + iv$, and $t = p + iq$, show that

   (a) $z(w + t) = zw + zt$,

   (b) $(z + w)/t = z/t + w/t$.

14. Suppose $z = 1 - i$, $w = 2 + i3$, and $t = -3 + i$. Find

   (a) $(z + w) \cdot t$,   (b) $(z/w) \cdot t$,   (c) $(w - t)/(z + t)$.

15. If $z = r(\cos\theta + i\sin\theta)$ and $w = a(\cos\phi + i\sin\phi)$, show that argument of z = argument of $(z \cdot w \cdot \overline{w})$.

16. Simplify:

   (a) $(i^{12} - i^{10})/(1 - i)$; (b) $(i^{20} + 1)/(1 + i^5)$.

17. (a) Find the quotient of $x + iy$ by its conjugate.

   (*b*) Find the quotient of $r(\cos\theta + i\sin\theta)$ by its conjugate.

18. Find (a) $(1 - i)^5$; (b) $(-3 + i3\sqrt{2})^4$.

19. Find and sketch the eight eighth roots of -1.

20. Find and sketch all roots of $z^{10} + i + 1 = 0$.

REMARK 1. As described in Section 2, a complex number z ($\neq 0 + i0$) determines in the plane both a magnitude (i.e., the modulus) and a direction (i.e., the argument). *In general, a symbol that determines, in a given coordinate system, both a magnitude and a direction is called a **vector**.* We denote a vector by a boldface letter, **z**, and we represent it geometrically by an arrow pointing in the given direction and having length equal to the given magnitude.

REMARK 2. Two vectors are **equal** provided they determine the same magnitude and direction. A vector with the same magnitude as **z** but with opposite direction is denoted by $-\mathbf{z}$. The **sum** of two vectors, $\mathbf{z} + \mathbf{w}$, obeys the parallelogram law: sketch the two vectors from a common initial point O and complete the parallelogram having O as one vertex and **z** and **w** as two sides; then the direction of $\mathbf{z} + \mathbf{w}$ is indicated by the diagonal through O and the magnitude is given by the length of that diagonal.

21. If **z** and **w** are arbitrary vectors, sketch $\mathbf{z} - \mathbf{w}$, where we write $\mathbf{z} - \mathbf{w} = \mathbf{z} + (-\mathbf{w})$.

22. Find the magnitude and direction determined by the following three complex numbers, and sketch each as a vector having initial point at the origin.

(a) $\sqrt{3} + i$,   (b) $(3 - i2) + (2 - i)$,
(c) $(-1 + i4) - (\sqrt{3} - 1 + i5)$.

23. Show geometrically that for three arbitrary vectors

$(z + w) + t = z + (w + t)$.

24. Construct geometrically the sum of the three given complex numbers, sketched as vectors with initial point at the origin.

(a) $z = 2 + i4$, $w = -3 + i$, $t = -1 - i7$,
(b) $z = -1 + i3$, $w = -5 - i$, $t = 4 - i6$.

25. If z and w are given vectors, and if x is an arbitrary real number, show that the terminal point of $t = z + x(w - z)$ is on the straight line joining the terminal points of w and z.

APPENDIX 1

SCIENTIFIC NOTATION

The measurements and calculations occurring in the physical sciences frequently result in numbers that are unwieldy if written in the usual decimal notation. For example, the following approximate values are encountered: 93,000,000 miles (distance from the earth to the sun); 186,000 miles per second (speed of light); 0.00000000048 electrostatic unit (charge on an electron). Decimal notation, furthermore, gives no indication of the accuracy of these approximations. A system of notation has been devised by which such numbers may be expressed more concisely, and which, at the same time, gives a clue as to just how accurate we may consider such approximations to be. The question of accuracy is discussed in Appendix 2; here we shall simply describe the notation.

The germ of the idea appears in the following table:

$$1000 = 10^3, \qquad 0.1 = 10^{-1},$$
$$100 = 10^2, \qquad 0.01 = 10^{-2},$$
$$10 = 10^1, \qquad 0.001 = 10^{-3}.$$
$$1 = 10^0,$$

Making use of this table, we may express any real positive number as a quantity between 1 and 10 multiplied by some power of 10. A number written in this form is said to be expressed in **scientific notation.**

The effect of multiplying by a power of 10 is simply to shift the decimal point, to the right if the exponent is positive, to the left if the exponent is negative.

The numbers given in the first paragraph are as follows in scientific notation.

$$93,000,000 = 9.3 \times 10^7,$$
$$186,000 = 1.86 \times 10^5,$$
$$0.00000000048 = 4.8 \times 10^{-10}.$$

--------| **Problems** |--------

1. Express the following in scientific notation.
 (a) 1,482.1, (b) one billion and one,
 (c) 0.0000000423, (d) 0.1872.

2. Express the following in decimals.
 (a) 1.732×10^{10}, (b) 9.87×10^{-5},
 (c) 1.00001×10^4, (d) 8.7×10^{-9}.

3. Perform the indicated operations after first changing each number to scientific notation.
 (a) $(0.003)(33,000)$,

 (b) $\dfrac{1,043,000}{0.000001043}$, (c) $\dfrac{(4,000)(0.00000008)}{0.064}$.

REMARK. $\sqrt{360,000} = \sqrt{36 \times 10^4} = (36)^{1/2}(10^4)^{1/2} = 6 \times 10^2 = 600.$

4. Simplify:
 (a) $\sqrt{1600}\ \sqrt{0.0001}$,

 (b) $\sqrt{\dfrac{0.00000049}{19,600}}$, (c) $\sqrt[3]{0.000027}\ \sqrt[3]{64000000}$.

NUMERICAL MEASURE- MENT

In many physical experiments, the act of measuring a quantity such as a length, a temperature, or a weight, results in a number that is only an approximation to what might be called the true value. We say that such a measurement yields a **numerical approximation.**
If we attempt to measure the length of this line segment our

answer will depend largely upon the type of ruler used. If the ruler is graduated in tenths of an inch only, then to say that this segment measures 2.8 inches in length means that we believe 2.8 is closer to the true value than either 2.7 or 2.9. Therefore, we are led to the opinion that the true length x satisfies the inequality $2.75 < x < 2.85$. Thus the error is presumed to be less than 0.05.

Occasionally, numbers containing zeros are ambiguous as to accuracy. Consider, for example, the number 93,000,000, which is an approximation to some number T. As it stands, we guess that the error is less than 500,000; that is, $92,500,000 < T < 93,500,000$. But if the first zero after the 3 is part of the measurement, then the error is, in fact, less than 50,000; that is,

$$92,950,000 < T < 93,050,000.$$

In order to avoid this ambiguity, we write the numerical approximation in scientific notation and assume that the last decimal position occupied by any digit (zero or not) is an indication of our confidence in the given measurement. If we believe that the error above is actually less than 50,000 then we express the number as 9.30×10^7, meaning that the error is less than 0.005×10^7 ($= 50,000$).

EXAMPLES

   (a) 2.783 (error less than 0.0005),
   (b) 2.80   (error less than 0.005),
   (c) 2.8   (error less than 0.05),
   (d) 2.8×10^2 (error less than $0.05 \times 10^2 = 5$),
   (e) 1.37×10^{-2} (error less than $0.005 \times 10^{-2} = 0.00005$).

The actual number of positions occupied by digits in the first part of the scientific notation is called the **number of significant digits** in the approximation. The number of significant digits in the five examples just given, are, respectively, four, three, two, two, and three.

Computations involving numerical approximations nearly always require a detailed analysis in order to determine the possible error contained in the answer. No simple rules can be laid down regarding this matter; in fact, an entire branch of mathematics, called *Numerical Analysis*, is devoted to the study of this problem. Because of the rapidly expanding applications of electronic computing machines, the subject of numerical analysis is undergoing extensive re-examination by mathematicians. Many new results and techniques have been discovered in recent years. We cannot discuss even the elements of this important subject here, and we shall avoid the necessity for it by agreeing upon several simplifying assumptions. *It is important to realize that these assumptions are not valid for some cases*, but they will provide us with a reasonable working compromise between truth and inconvenience. That is, we shall sacrifice a certain amount of accuracy in order to gain a certain freedom from detailed analysis.

1. The natural numbers, fractions, and symbols such as π, $\sqrt{2}$, $2 + \sqrt{3}$, are considered to represent exact measurements. Other real numbers expressed as finite decimals are considered approximations.

2. We adopt the usual round-off convention. If the digits dropped after the nth digit form a number which is more than 5 in the $(n + 1)$st

position, then the nth digit is increased by 1; if less than 5, then the nth digit is unchanged; if exactly 5, then the nth digit is increased by 1 if odd, and is unchanged if even. For example, we round off the following numbers to hundredths, obtaining the results in the second column:

(a) 0.14872   0.15,
(b) 21.01499   21.01,
(c) 3.885001   3.89,
(d) 0.5550   0.56,
(e) 0.565   0.56.

3. If several numerical approximations are used in a computation, we round off the final answer so that it does not imply greater accuracy than the least accurate number involved. For example, the answer to a computation involving the numbers 1.407, 0.0213, 4.01, and 78.3, is rounded off to the nearest tenth (since one of the numbers is presumed accurate only to the nearest tenth).

4. In a computation, all significant digits are retained (as far as practical); only at the final step is rounding-off employed. Wherever possible in computations requiring the use of tables, we interpolate to obtain one additional digit. (See Appendix 3.3 for the technique of interpolation.)

──────────| Problems |──────────

1. Round off the following numbers to three significant digits:
   (a) 0.14348,   (b) 8.21501,
   (c) 38,250,   (d) 1,815,000.

2. Let x represent the length of a line. What can be said about x if the length is recorded approximately as
   (a) 21.4 inches,   (b) 0.001 foot,
   (c) 100 inches,   (d) 1.39 feet?

3. What is the range of possible values for $x + y$ if
   (a) $x = 1.314$ and $y = 0.09$,
   (b) $x = 31,402$ and $y = 8,400$ (that is, 8.4×10^3)?

4. What is the range of possible values for $x \cdot y$ if
   (a) $x = 1.31$ and $y = 0.09$,
   (b) $x = 0.91$ and $y = 0.91$?

APPENDIX 3

LOGARITHMS

Logarithms are useful as an aid in reducing the labor of numerical computation. Historically, it was this property which motivated both the invention of logarithms and the publication of the first logarithmic tables in the early seventeenth century. We shall consider logarithms only in connection with the real number system.

1. DEFINITIONS AND PROPERTIES

Let the symbol a denote a positive number different from 1. If N is a given positive number and if x satisfies the equation $a^x = N$,[1] then x is called the **logarithm of N to the base** a. The usual notation is $\log_a N = x$. A few simple examples are

    (a) $2^5 = 32$, therefore $\log_2 32 = 5$.

    (b) From the same equation we have $\log_{\sqrt{2}} 32 = 10$.

    (c) $10^{-3} = 0.001$, therefore $\log_{10} 0.001 = -3$.

Property 1. Because $a^0 = 1$, $\log_a 1 = 0$.

Property 2. Because $a^1 = a$, $\log_a a = 1$.

Property 3. Because $a^x = N$ has no solution if $N \leqq 0$, $\log_a 0$ is undefined, and also the logarithm to the base a of any negative number is undefined.

---

[1]We assume that this equation has a unique solution, a fact proved in more advanced mathematics.

THEOREM 1.

If M and N are positive numbers, then
$$\log_a (M \cdot N) = \log_a M + \log_a N.$$

Proof. Put $x = \log_a M$ and $y = \log_a N$. By the definition we have $a^x = M$ and $a^y = N$; thus $M \cdot N = a^x a^y = a^{x+y}$. Again applying the definition $x + y = \log_a (M \cdot N)$.

THEOREM 2.

If M and N are positive numbers, then
$$\log_a (M/N) = \log_a M - \log_a N.$$

Proof. As before, put $x = \log_a M$ and $y = \log_a N$. Thus $M/N = a^x/a^y = a^{x-y}$, and $x - y = \log_a (M/N)$.

THEOREM 3.

If M is positive and p is any real number, then
$$\log_a (M^p) = p \log_a M.$$

Proof. Put $x = \log_a M$. By definition $M = a^x$; thus $M^p = (a^x)^p = a^{px}$. Again by the definition $px = \log_a (M^p)$.

The following examples illustrate these theorems.

1. Suppose $M = 32$ and $N = 64$. If $a = 2$, Theorem 1 states $\log_2 (32 \cdot 64) = \log_2 (32) + \log_2 (64)$. This is easily verified since $\log_2 (32 \cdot 64) = \log_2 (2^5 \cdot 2^6) = \log_2 (2^{11}) = 11$ and $\log_2 (32) = 5$ and $\log_2 (64) = 6$.

2. Suppose $M = 81$ and $N = 3$. If $a = 3$, Theorem 2 states $\log_3 (81/3) = \log_3 (81) - \log_3 3 = 4 - 1 = 3$.

3. Suppose $M = 81$ and $p = \frac{1}{2}$. If $a = 3$, Theorem 3 states $\log_3 (\sqrt{81}) = \frac{1}{2} \log_3 (81) = 2$.

For the purposes of computation the base $a = 10$ is most convenient. Throughout the subsequent discussion, we shall use exclusively the base 10, and for simplicity we shall consistently write $\log_{10} x$ as $\log x$. The graph $y = \log x$ is shown in Fig. A.1, and from it we note the following property:

Property 4.

$$\text{If } \begin{cases} 0 < x \leq 1, \\ 1 < x < 10, \\ x \geq 10; \end{cases} \quad \text{then} \quad \begin{cases} \log x \leq 0, \\ 0 < \log x < 1, \\ \log x \geq 1. \end{cases}$$

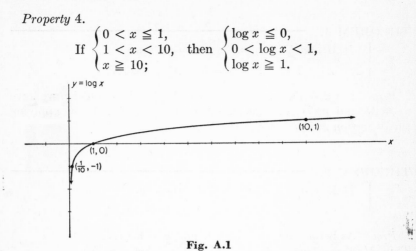

Fig. A.1

2. LOGARITHMS TO THE BASE 10

Five-place tables of logarithms are in common use, and tables are available having many more significant digits. The entry in the table corresponding to a given number depends only upon the order of the digits in the number, and not upon the position of the decimal point. This will become clear in the following examples. The use of scientific notation will be of great assistance here.

EXAMPLE 1. What is the logarithm of the number $N = 93{,}000{,}000$?

Solution. First express N in scientific notation, $N = 9.3 \times 10^7$. Then

$$\begin{aligned} \log (9.3 \times 10^7) &= \log (9.3) + \log (10^7) \text{ [Theorem 1]} \\ &= \log (9.3) + 7 \cdot \log 10 \text{ [Theorem 3]} \\ &= \log (9.3) + 7 \text{ [Property 2].} \end{aligned}$$

From the table of logarithms we find that 96848 is the entry corresponding to the digits 93. But

$$0 < \log (9.3) < 1 \text{ [Property 4]},$$

therefore we are led to conclude that

$$\log (9.3) = 0.96848.$$

Thus it is seen that the logarithm of 93,000,000 is made up of two parts: $\log (93{,}000{,}000) = 0.96848 + 7 = 7.96848$. The integral part

(7) is called the **characteristic** of the logarithm, while the decimal part (0.96848) is called the **mantissa** of the logarithm. The logarithm of any positive number may always be written in two parts determined in a similar way.

EXAMPLE 2. What is the logarithm of the number $N = 9.331$?

Solution. In scientific notation this number is 9.331×10^0, therefore the characteristic is zero. Corresponding to the digits 9331, the entry in the table is 96993; hence log (9.331) = 0.96993.

EXAMPLE 3. What is the logarithm of the number $N = 0.009335$?

Solution. In scientific notation $N = 9.335 \times 10^{-3}$; thus the characteristic is -3. The mantissa is found from the table to be 0.97011 (the starred entry in the table indicates that the first two digits of the mantissa appear at the beginning of the next lower line of entries in the table). Thus the logarithm is a negative number; it is in fact log (0.009335) = 0.97011 $-$ 3 = $-$ (2.02989). From a practical point of view, it is more convenient to keep the logarithm separated into two parts, a positive mantissa and a negative characteristic. As a further convenience, the negative characteristic may be written

$$\log (0.009335) = 7.97011 - 10.$$

As an exercise, verify the following:

$$\log 332.1 = 2.52127,$$
$$\log 186{,}000 = 5.26951,$$
$$\log 8.712 = 0.94012,$$
$$\log 0.0005865 = 6.76827 - 10,$$
$$\log 0.2146 = 9.33163 - 10,$$
$$\log 0.00000000048 = 10.68124 - 20.$$

3. INTERPOLATION

Suppose that a clock has no second hand and that at a certain instant we judge the time to be $20\frac{1}{4}$ minutes past 5. Again, suppose that a thermometer is marked only in degrees and that on a certain day we read the temperature at $87\frac{1}{2}°$. In each instance we have performed an informal interpolation in order to obtain a reading somewhat more accurate than the smallest division on the scale. Interpolation, in general, is simply a technique for estimating the next significant digit beyond those actually indicated by a scale or a table.

In the preceding sections we have found logarithms of numbers having no more than four significant digits. The logarithm table used gives direct readings for all such numbers. In the event a number is known to five significant digits, its logarithm can be estimated from this same table by using a technique known as **linear interpolation,** which is just a formalized version of the guesswork illustrated in the first paragraph.

EXAMPLE 1. Find the logarithm of the number $N = 366.56$.

Solution. From the table we find that log $366.5 = 2.56407$, while log $366.6 = 2.56419$. The number N occupies a position 6/10ths of the way along the interval from 366.5 to 366.6. We shall assume, in general, that the logarithm of N occupies a similar position along the interval from log 366.5 to log 366.6. This assumption would be exact only if the graph of the logarithm function were a straight line (hence the term "linear interpolation"). For most applications in elementary mathematics, this assumption leads to an acceptable approximation.

To find this interpolated value we may use the following scheme:

		N	log N	
$\dfrac{10}{100}\Big\{$	$\dfrac{6}{100}\Big\{$	$\begin{matrix}366.5\\366.56\\366.6\end{matrix}$	$\begin{matrix}2.56407\\x\\2.56419\end{matrix}\Big\}\,a\,\Big\{$	$\dfrac{12}{100,000}$

We wish to choose x so that the interval a is to 12/100,000 as 6 is to 10. But $a = x - 2.56407$; therefore the equation $a/0.00012 = 0.06/0.10 = 6/10$, yields $(x - 2.56407)/0.00012 = 6/10$, from which we obtain $x = 2.56407 + (6/10)(0.00012) = 2.56407 + 0.000072$; $x = 2.56414$ (rounded off to five decimal places). The number x is called an **interpolated value.**

This scheme for writing down the interpolation is used to help clarify the procedure. After a little practice, it should not be necessary to write down the scheme for each interpolation. It is best to perform interpolations mentally, if possible.

To aid interpolation, many tables contain accompanying **proportional parts** columns. In the above example, the tabular difference in logarithms is 12. We find the "pp" columns headed 12 and note the entry opposite 6 in the left-hand column. This gives the number 7 to be added to 2.56407 in the fifth decimal position.

EXAMPLE 2. Find log 0.013722.

Solution. From the tables log 0.01372 = 8.13735 − 10 and log 0.01373 = 8.13767 − 10. From the proportional parts columns headed 32 (the difference in the last two digits of the logarithms) the entry opposite 2 (the fifth significant digit in the number) is 6.4; hence the answer is log 0.013722 = 8.13741 − 10. Instead of using the proportional parts, we might have found the logarithm by adding (2/10) (32) to 8.13735 − 10 in the fifth decimal position.

EXAMPLE 3. Find the number x such that log x = 1.57059.

Solution. The characteristic 1 tells us where to put the decimal point. To find the digits in the number x we must look at the mantissa. The procedure here is exactly the reverse of that described in the first two examples. Schematically, it is

N			$\log N$			
$\dfrac{1}{100} \left\{ \vphantom{a} \right.$	$a \left\{ \vphantom{x} \right.$	$\begin{matrix} 37.20 \\ x \\ 37.21 \end{matrix}$	$\begin{matrix} 1.57054 \\ 1.57059 \\ 1.57066 \end{matrix}$	$\left. \vphantom{x} \right\} \dfrac{5}{100,000}$		$\left. \vphantom{x} \right\} \dfrac{12}{100,000}$

We assume that x satisfies the following equation,

$$\frac{a}{0.01} = \frac{0.00005}{0.00012} = \frac{5}{12} \, ;$$

$$\frac{x - 37.20}{0.01} = \frac{5}{12} \, ;$$

$x = 37.20 + 0.004$ (to the nearest fifth significant digit);

$x = 37.204.$

We might also have used the proportional parts columns headed 12. The closest entry to 5 in the right-hand column is 4.8, opposite which is the number 4. Thus 4 is to be added as the fifth significant digit, giving $x = 37.204.$

4. COMPUTATION WITH LOGARITHMS

Arithmetic problems involving addition and subtraction do not lend themselves readily to logarithmic computation: the laws of logarithms simply do not apply. Problems, however, involving only multiplication, division, powers, and roots can be greatly simplified by use of logarithms.

EXAMPLE. Evaluate $N = \dfrac{\sqrt{1{,}319} \cdot (0.0432)^5}{70.08}$.

Solution. By use of Theorems 1, 2, and 3 we find

$$\log N = \log \left[\sqrt{1{,}319} \cdot (0.0432)^5 \right] - \log 70.08,$$
$$= \tfrac{1}{2} \log 1{,}319 + 5 \log 0.0432 - \log 70.08.$$

From the table we have

$$\log N = \tfrac{1}{2} (3.12024) + 5 \cdot (8.63548 - 10) - 1.84559,$$
$$= 1.56012 + 43.17740 - 50 - 1.84559,$$
$$= 44.73752 - 51.84559.$$

The most convenient way to perform this subtraction is the following,

$$\begin{array}{r} 54.73752 - 10 \\ 51.84559 \\ \hline \end{array}$$
$$\log N = \quad 2.89193 - 10 \ ,$$
$$N = \quad 0.00000007797.$$

In carrying out any lengthy computation, the details are likely to become tedious. In order to avoid unnecessary errors, it is wise to perform the computation in the neatest and most orderly arrangement possible. Develop the habit of neat arithmetic.

Verify the following:

$$N = \frac{(0.00134)^{3/2} (85{,}147)}{(1.3214)^2}, \quad \begin{cases} \log N = 0.37875, \\ \quad N = 2.3919. \end{cases}$$

$$N = \sqrt{\frac{\sqrt[3]{0.0721}}{(5.004)^4}} \quad \begin{cases} \log N = 8.41102 - 10, \\ \quad N = 0.025764. \end{cases}$$

[*Hint.* Express (8. − 10) as (28. − 30).]

———————| **Problems** |————————————————

1. Solve for the unknown in the following equations.
   (a) $\log_3 27 = x$,
   (b) $\log_5 x = -3$,
   (c) $\log_x 64 = 3$,
   (d) $\log_{10} 10{,}000 = x^2$,
   (e) $\log_{\sqrt{2}} \sqrt{2} = x$,
   (f) $\log_{13} x = 0$.

2. The inverse of the function $y = \log x$ is $y = 10^x$.
   (a) Sketch the inverse graph.
   (b) Is the inverse also a function?

3. The range of the function $y = \log x$ is the set of all real numbers.
   (a) What is its domain?
   (b) What is the domain of the inverse?
   (c) What is the range of the inverse?

4. Is it true that $\log 39 = \log 3 + \log 13$?

5. Is it true that $\log 39 = \log 30 + \log 9$?

6. If $a = b + c$ prove in general that $\log a \neq \log b + \log c$.

7. From the tables find x in each of the following.
   (a) $\log 12.01 = x$,
   (b) $\log 0.00013295 = x$,
   (c) $\log x = 5.31298$,
   (d) $\log x = 3.72001 - 10$,
   (e) $\log (\log 5.013) = x$,
   (f) $\log (\log x) = 1.048$.

8. Find N if
   (a) $N = \dfrac{(0.132)\,(0.00321)}{2.31}$,

   (b) $N = \dfrac{8{,}314}{(21.01)\,(408.01)}$,

   (c) $N = \sqrt{\dfrac{(213.14)}{(0.0013922)^3}}$.

APPENDIX 4

TRIGONO-METRIC TABLES

1. TABLES OF FUNCTIONS

In Section 5 of Chapter 4, we mentioned tables of trigonometric functions very briefly. The following discussion concerns the technique of using these tables.

The left-hand column of angles (in degrees) runs from 0° to 45°, and with these angles the column headings at the top are used. The right-hand column of angles (in degrees) runs from 45° to 90° (read up), and with these angles the column headings at the bottom are used. The only difference between the column headings at top and bottom is that the following co-function pairs are interchanged: sine and cosine, tangent and cotangent. The table can be constructed in this way because of the property exhibited in the reduction formulas for the angle 90° − θ. For example

$$\sin 51°20' = \cos (90° - 51°20') = \cos 38°40',$$
$$\tan 67°10' = \cot (90° - 67°10') = \cot 22°50'.$$

In carrying out computations which involve both linear and angular measurement, we shall adopt the following rule, which gives reasonable results for all angles except those near 0° or 90°: *angles must be measured* (1) *within* 6″ *to correspond to 5 significant figures in linear measurement;* (2) *within* 1′ *to correspond to 4 significant figures in linear measurement;* (3) *within* 10′ *to correspond to* 3 *significant figures in linear measurement;* (4) *within* 1° *to correspond to* 2 *significant figures in linear measurement.*

The columns of equivalent radian measure are added to the tables as a convenience (see Table IV).

Verify the following (interpolate in the usual way):

$$\sin\ 11°10' = 0.1937,$$
$$\cos\ 72°35' = 0.2993,$$
$$\tan\ 77°50' = 4.638,$$
$$\cot\ 58°15' = 0.6188.$$

2. TABLES OF LOGARITHMS OF FUNCTIONS

When a trigonometric function appears as a factor in a computation, we usually are interested not in the value of the function but in its logarithm. For example, to find the product

$$x = (\tan 43°40')(\sin 60°10'),$$

we note that $\log x = \log (\tan 43°40') + \log (\sin 60°10')$.

We might, of course, find the value of each function from the table of functions and then find its logarithm from the familiar table of logarithms. Because of the frequent occurrence of this situation, however, there is in common use a third set of tables, which gives the logarithm of a trigonometric function directly from its angle. These tables are used in much the same way as those we have discussed before. Angles run from 0° to 90°, with entries in the table for each minute. For an angle listed at the top of the page, use the left-hand minute column and the upper column headings; for an angle listed at the bottom of the page, use the right-hand minute column (read up) and the lower column headings. For example,

$$\log \tan 43°40' = 9.97978 - 10,$$
$$\log \sin\ 60°10' = 9.93826 - 10.$$

We note that 10 must be subtracted from the characteristic of each entry in the table; that proportional parts columns are related to tenths; and that columns headed "d" (difference) and "cd" (common difference) are inserted for convenience in interpolation.

A note of caution regarding the use of "log trig" *tables.* The interpolation procedure described in Appendix 3 may not be sufficiently accurate when the angle θ is on either of the intervals $0° \leqq \theta < 3°$ or $87° < \theta \leqq 90°$. We shall avoid interpolation within these limits. A satisfactory scheme for interpolation on these intervals can be found in most handbooks of mathematics tables.

Verify the following:

$$\log \sin 12°35' = 9.33818 - 10,$$
$$\log \cos 23°31'18'' = 9.96232 - 10,$$
$$\log \tan 84°20'30'' = 11.00402 - 10 = 1.00402,$$
$$\log \cot 10°48'48'' = 10.71894 - 10 = 0.71897.$$

———————| **Problems** |—————————————————

1. Evaluate:
   (a) sin 13°15',   (b) cos 8°35',
   (c) tan 44°50',   (d) cot 88°45'.

2. Find θ (to nearest 1') if $0 < \theta < 90°$ and
   (a) sin θ = 0.3148,   (b) cos θ = 0.0111,
   (c) tan θ = 1.111,   (d) cot θ = 4.200.

3. Find
   (a) log sin 15°30'12'',   (b) log cos 63°0'12'',
   (c) log tan 86°1'24'',   (d) log cot 33°19'30''.

4. Find θ (to nearest 6'') if $0 < \theta < 90°$ and
   (a) log sin θ = 9.79315 - 10,   (b) log cos θ = 9.65625 - 10,
   (c) log tan θ = 0.48150,   (d) log cot θ = 8.20413 - 10.

Table I

LOGARITHMS OF NUMBERS

1000–1509

N.	L. 0	1	2	3	4	5	6	7	8	9	P. P.
100	00 000	043	087	130	173	217	260	303	346	389	
101	432	475	518	561	604	647	689	732	775	817	
102	860	903	945	988	*030	*072	*115	*157	*199	*242	
103	01 284	326	368	410	452	494	536	578	620	662	

	44	43	42
1	4.4	4.3	4.2
2	8.8	8.6	8.4
3	13.2	12.9	12.6
4	17.6	17.2	16.8
5	22.0	21.5	21.0
6	26.4	25.8	25.2
7	30.8	30.1	29.4
8	35.2	34.4	33.6
9	39.6	38.7	37.8

N.	L. 0	1	2	3	4	5	6	7	8	9
104	703	745	787	828	870	912	953	995	*036	*078
105	02 119	160	202	243	284	325	366	407	449	490
106	531	572	612	653	694	735	776	816	857	898
107	938	979	*019	*060	*100	*141	*181	*222	*262	*302
108	03 342	383	423	463	503	543	583	623	663	703
109	743	782	822	862	902	941	981	*021	*060	*100
110	04 139	179	218	258	297	336	376	415	454	493
111	532	571	610	650	689	727	766	805	844	883
112	922	961	999	*038	*077	*115	*154	*192	*231	*269
113	05 308	346	385	423	461	500	538	576	614	652

	41	40	39
1	4.1	4.0	3.9
2	8.2	8.0	7.8
3	12.3	12.0	11.7
4	16.4	16.0	15.6
5	20.5	20.0	19.5
6	24.6	24.0	23.4
7	28.7	28.0	27.3
8	32.8	32.0	31.2
9	36.9	36.0	35.1

N.	L. 0	1	2	3	4	5	6	7	8	9
114	690	729	767	805	843	881	918	956	994	*032
115	06 070	108	145	183	221	258	296	333	371	408
116	446	483	521	558	595	633	670	707	744	781
117	819	856	893	930	967	*004	*041	*078	*115	*151
118	07 188	225	262	298	335	372	408	445	482	518
119	555	591	628	664	700	737	773	809	846	882
120	918	954	990	*027	*063	*099	*135	*171	*207	*243
121	08 279	314	350	386	422	458	493	529	565	600
122	636	672	707	743	778	814	849	884	920	955
123	991	*026	*061	*096	*132	*167	*202	*237	*272	*307

	38	37	36
1	3.8	3.7	3.6
2	7.6	7.4	7.2
3	11.4	11.1	10.8
4	15.2	14.8	14.4
5	19.0	18.5	18.0
6	22.8	22.2	21.6
7	26.6	25.9	25.2
8	30.4	29.6	28.8
9	34.2	33.3	32.4

N.	L. 0	1	2	3	4	5	6	7	8	9
124	09 342	377	412	447	482	517	552	587	621	656
125	691	726	760	795	830	864	899	934	968	*003
126	10 037	072	106	140	175	209	243	278	312	346
127	380	415	449	483	517	551	585	619	653	687
128	721	755	789	823	857	890	924	958	992	*025
129	11 059	093	126	160	193	227	261	294	327	361
130	394	428	461	494	528	561	594	628	661	694
131	727	760	793	826	860	893	926	959	992	*024
132	12 057	090	123	156	189	222	254	287	320	352
133	385	418	450	483	516	548	581	613	646	678

	35	34	33
1	3.5	3.4	3.3
2	7.0	6.8	6.6
3	10.5	10.2	9.9
4	14.0	13.6	13.2
5	17.5	17.0	16.5
6	21.0	20.4	19.8
7	24.5	23.8	23.1
8	28.0	27.2	26.4
9	31.5	30.6	29.7

N.	L. 0	1	2	3	4	5	6	7	8	9
134	710	743	775	808	840	872	905	937	969	*001
135	13 033	066	098	130	162	194	226	258	290	322
136	354	386	418	450	481	513	545	577	609	640
137	672	704	735	767	799	830	862	893	925	956
138	988	*019	*051	*082	*114	*145	*176	*208	*239	*270
139	14 301	333	364	395	426	457	489	520	551	582
140	613	644	675	706	737	768	799	829	860	891
141	922	953	983	*014	*045	*076	*106	*137	*168	*198
142	15 229	259	290	320	351	381	412	442	473	503
143	534	564	594	625	655	685	715	746	776	806

	32	31	30
1	3.2	3.1	3.0
2	6.4	6.2	6.0
3	9.6	9.3	9.0
4	12.8	12.4	12.0
5	16.0	15.5	15.0
6	19.2	18.6	18.0
7	22.4	21.7	21.0
8	25.6	24.8	24.0
9	28.8	27.9	27.0

N.	L. 0	1	2	3	4	5	6	7	8	9
144	836	866	897	927	957	987	*017	*047	*077	*107
145	16 137	167	197	227	256	286	316	346	376	406
146	435	465	495	524	554	584	613	643	673	702
147	732	761	791	820	850	879	909	938	967	997
148	17 026	056	085	114	143	173	202	231	260	289
149	319	348	377	406	435	464	493	522	551	580
150	609	638	667	696	725	754	782	811	840	869

N.	L. 0	1	2	3	4	5	6	7	8	9	P. P.

TABLE I. LOGARITHMS OF NUMBERS | 187

1500–2009

N.	L. 0	1	2	3	4	5	6	7	8	9
150	17 609	638	667	696	725	754	782	811	840	869
151	.898	926	955	984	*013	*041	*070	*099	*127	*156
152	18 184	213	241	270	298	327	355	384	412	441
153	.469	498	526	554	583	611	639	667	696	724
154	.752	780	808	837	865	893	921	949	977	*005
155	19 033	061	089	117	145	173	201	229	257	285
156	.312	340	368	396	424	451	479	507	535	562
157	.590	618	645	673	700	728	756	783	811	838
158	.866	893	921	948	976	*003	*030	*058	*085	*112
159	20 140	167	194	222	249	276	303	330	358	385
160	.412	439	466	493	520	548	575	602	629	656
161	.683	710	737	763	790	817	844	871	898	925
162	.952	978	*005	*032	*059	*085	*112	*139	*165	*192
163	21 219	245	272	299	325	352	378	405	431	458
164	.484	511	537	564	590	617	643	669	696	722
165	.748	775	801	827	854	880	906	932	958	985
166	22 011	037	063	089	115	141	167	194	220	246
167	.272	298	324	350	376	401	427	453	479	505
168	.531	557	583	608	634	660	686	712	737	763
169	.789	814	840	866	891	917	943	968	994	*019
170	23 045	070	096	121	147	172	198	223	249	274
171	.300	325	350	376	401	426	452	477	502	528
172	.553	578	603	629	654	679	704	729	754	779
173	.805	830	855	880	905	930	955	980	*005	*030
174	24 055	080	105	130	155	180	204	229	254	279
175	.304	329	353	378	403	428	452	477	502	527
176	.551	576	601	625	650	674	699	724	748	773
177	.797	822	846	871	895	920	944	969	993	*018
178	25 042	066	091	115	139	164	188	212	237	261
179	.285	310	334	358	382	406	431	455	479	503
180	.527	551	575	600	624	648	672	696	720	744
181	.768	792	816	840	864	888	912	935	959	983
182	26 007	031	055	079	102	126	150	174	198	221
183	.245	269	293	316	340	364	387	411	435	458
184	.482	505	529	553	576	600	623	647	670	694
185	.717	741	764	788	811	834	858	881	905	928
186	.951	975	998	*021	*045	*068	*091	*114	*138	*161
187	27 184	207	231	254	277	300	323	346	370	393
188	.416	439	462	485	508	531	554	577	600	623
189	.646	669	692	715	738	761	784	807	830	852
190	.875	898	921	944	967	989	*012	*035	*058	*081
191	28 103	126	149	171	194	217	240	262	285	307
192	.330	353	375	398	421	443	466	488	511	533
193	.556	578	601	623	646	668	691	713	735	758
194	.780	803	825	847	870	892	914	937	959	981
195	29 003	026	048	070	092	115	137	159	181	203
196	.226	248	270	292	314	336	358	380	403	425
197	.447	469	491	513	535	557	579	601	623	645
198	.667	688	710	732	754	776	798	820	842	863
199	.885	907	929	951	973	994	*016	*038	*060	*081
200	30 103	125	146	168	190	211	233	255	276	298

P. P.

	29	28
1	2.9	2.8
2	5.8	5.6
3	8.7	8.4
4	11.6	11.2
5	14.5	14.0
6	17.4	16.8
7	20.3	19.6
8	23.2	22.4
9	26.1	25.2

	27	26
1	2.7	2.6
2	5.4	5.2
3	8.1	7.8
4	10.8	10.4
5	13.5	13.0
6	16.2	15.6
7	18.9	18.2
8	21.6	20.8
9	24.3	23.4

	25
1	2.5
2	5.0
3	7.5
4	10.0
5	12.5
6	15.0
7	17.5
8	20.0
9	22.5

	24	23
1	2.4	2.3
2	4.8	4.6
3	7.2	6.9
4	9.6	9.2
5	12.0	11.5
6	14.4	13.8
7	16.8	16.1
8	19.2	18.4
9	21.6	20.7

	22	21
1	2.2	2.1
2	4.4	4.2
3	6.6	6.3
4	8.8	8.4
5	11.0	10.5
6	13.2	12.6
7	15.4	14.7
8	17.6	16.8
9	19.8	18.9

N.	L. 0	1	2	3	4	5	6	7	8	9	P. P.

2000–2509

N.	L. 0	1	2	3	4	5	6	7	8	9
200	30 103	125	146	168	190	211	233	255	276	298
201	320	341	363	384	406	428	449	471	492	514
202	535	557	578	600	621	643	664	685	707	728
203	750	771	792	814	835	856	878	899	920	942
204	963	984	*006	*027	*048	*069	*091	*112	*133	*154
205	31 175	197	218	239	260	281	302	323	345	366
206	387	408	429	450	471	492	513	534	555	576
207	597	618	639	660	681	702	723	744	765	785
208	806	827	848	869	890	911	931	952	973	994
209	32 015	035	056	077	098	118	139	160	181	201
210	222	243	263	284	305	325	346	366	387	408
211	428	449	469	490	510	531	552	572	593	613
212	634	654	675	695	715	736	756	777	797	818
213	838	858	879	899	919	940	960	980	*001	*021
214	33 041	062	082	102	122	143	163	183	203	224
215	244	264	284	304	325	345	365	385	405	425
216	445	465	486	506	526	546	566	586	606	626
217	646	666	686	706	726	746	766	786	806	826
218	846	866	885	905	925	945	965	985	*005	*025
219	34 044	064	084	104	124	143	163	183	203	223
220	242	262	282	301	321	341	361	380	400	420
221	439	459	479	498	518	537	557	577	596	616
222	635	655	674	694	713	733	753	772	792	811
223	830	850	869	889	908	928	947	967	986	*005
224	35 025	044	064	083	102	122	141	160	180	199
225	218	238	257	276	295	315	334	353	372	392
226	411	430	449	468	488	507	526	545	564	583
227	603	622	641	660	679	698	717	736	755	774
228	793	813	832	851	870	889	908	927	946	965
229	984	*003	*021	*040	*059	*078	*097	*116	*135	*154
230	36 173	192	211	229	248	267	286	305	324	342
231	361	380	399	418	436	455	474	493	511	530
232	549	568	586	605	624	642	661	680	698	717
233	736	754	773	791	810	829	847	866	884	903
234	922	940	959	977	996	*014	*033	*051	*070	*088
235	37 107	125	144	162	181	199	218	236	254	273
236	291	310	328	346	365	383	401	420	438	457
237	475	493	511	530	548	566	585	603	621	639
238	658	676	694	712	731	749	767	785	803	822
239	840	858	876	894	912	931	949	967	985	*003
240	38 021	039	057	075	093	112	130	148	166	184
241	202	220	238	256	274	292	310	328	346	364
242	382	399	417	435	453	471	489	507	525	543
243	561	578	596	614	632	650	668	686	703	721
244	739	757	775	792	810	828	846	863	881	899
245	917	934	952	970	987	*005	*023	*041	*058	*076
246	39 094	111	129	146	164	182	199	217	235	252
247	270	287	305	322	340	358	375	393	410	428
248	445	463	480	498	515	533	550	568	585	602
249	620	637	655	672	690	707	724	742	759	777
250	794	811	829	846	863	881	898	915	933	950
N.	L. 0	1	2	3	4	5	6	7	8	9

P. P.

	22	21
1	2.2	2.1
2	4.4	4.2
3	6.6	6.3
4	8.8	8.4
5	11.0	10.5
6	13.2	12.6
7	15.4	14.7
8	17.6	16.8
9	19.8	18.9

	20
1	2.0
2	4.0
3	6.0
4	8.0
5	10.0
6	12.0
7	14.0
8	16.0
9	18.0

	19
1	1.9
2	3.8
3	5.7
4	7.6
5	9.5
6	11.4
7	13.3
8	15.2
9	17.1

	18
1	1.8
2	3.6
3	5.4
4	7.2
5	9.0
6	10.8
7	12.6
8	14.4
9	16.2

	17
1	1.7
2	3.4
3	5.1
4	6.8
5	8.5
6	10.2
7	11.9
8	13.6
9	15.3

TABLE I. LOGARITHMS OF NUMBERS | 189

2500–3009

N.	L. 0	1	2	3	4	5	6	7	8	9
250	39 794	811	829	846	863	881	898	915	933	950
251	967	985	*002	*019	*037	*054	*071	*088	*106	*123
252	40 140	157	175	192	209	226	243	261	278	295
253	312	329	346	364	381	398	415	432	449	466
254	483	.500	518	535	552	569	586	603	620	637
255	654	671	688	705	722	739	756	773	790	807
256	824	841	858	875	892	909	926	943	960	976
257	993	*010	*027	*044	*061	*078	*095	*111	*128	*145
258	41 162	179	196	212	229	246	263	280	296	313
259	330	347	363	380	397	414	430	447	464	481
260	497	514	531	547	564	581	597	614	631	647
261	664	681	697	714	731	747	764	780	797	814
262	830	847	863	880	896	913	929	946	963	979
263	996	*012	*029	*045	*062	*078	*095	*111	*127	*144
264	42 160	177	193	210	226	243	259	275	292	308
265	325	341	357	374	390	406	423	439	455	472
266	488	504	521	537	553	570	586	602	619	635
267	651	667	684	700	716	732	749	765	781	797
268	813	830	846	862	878	894	911	927	943	959
269	975	991	*008	*024	*040	*056	*072	*088	*104	*120
270	43 136	152	169	185	201	217	233	249	265	281
271	297	313	329	345	361	377	393	409	425	441
272	457	473	489	505	521	537	553	569	584	600
273	616	632	648	664	680	696	712	727	743	759
274	775	791	807	823	838	854	870	886	902	917
275	933	949	965	981	996	*012	*028	*044	*059	*075
276	44 091	107	122	138	154	170	185	201	217	232
277	248	264	279	295	311	326	342	358	373	389
278	404	420	436	451	467	483	498	514	529	545
279	560	576	592	607	623	638	654	669	685	700
280	716	731	747	762	778	793	809	824	840	855
281	871	886	902	917	932	948	963	979	994	*010
282	45 025	040	056	071	086	102	117	133	148	163
283	179	194	209	225	240	255	271	286	301	317
284	332	347	362	378	393	408	423	439	454	469
285	484	500	515	530	545	561	576	591	606	621
286	637	652	667	682	697	712	728	743	758	773
287	788	803	818	834	849	864	879	894	909	924
288	939	954	969	984	*000	*015	*030	*045	*060	*075
289	46 090	105	120	135	150	165	180	195	210	225
290	240	255	270	285	300	315	330	345	359	374
291	389	404	419	434	449	464	479	494	509	523
292	538	553	568	583	598	613	627	642	657	672
293	687	702	716	731	746	761	776	790	805	820
294	835	850	864	879	894	909	923	938	953	967
295	982	997	*012	*026	*041	*056	*070	*085	*100	*114
296	47 129	144	159	173	188	202	217	232	246	261
297	276	290	305	319	334	349	363	378	392	407
298	422	436	451	465	480	494	509	524	538	553
299	567	582	596	611	625	640	654	669	683	698
300	712	727	741	756	770	784	799	813	828	842

P. P.

18	17	16	15	14
1 1.8	1 1.7	1 1.6	1 1.5	1 1.4
2 3.6	2 3.4	2 3.2	2 3.0	2 2.8
3 5.4	3 5.1	3 4.8	3 4.5	3 4.2
4 7.2	4 6.8	4 6.4	4 6.0	4 5.6
5 9.0	5 8.5	5 8.0	5 7.5	5 7.0
6 10.8	6 10.2	6 9.6	6 9.0	6 8.4
7 12.6	7 11.9	7 11.2	7 10.5	7 9.8
8 14.4	8 13.6	8 12.8	8 12.0	8 11.2
9 16.2	9 15.3	9 14.4	9 13.5	9 12.6

N.	L. 0	1	2	3	4	5	6	7	8	9	P. P.

3000-3509

N.	L. 0	1	2	3	4	5	6	7	8	9	P. P.	
300	47 712	727	741	756	770	784	799	813	828	842		
301	857	871	885	900	914	929	943	958	972	986		
302	48 001	015	029	044	058	073	087	101	116	130		
303	144	159	173	187	202	216	230	244	259	273		
304	287	302	316	330	344	359	373	387	401	416		
305	430	444	458	473	487	501	515	530	544	558		
306	572	586	601	615	629	643	657	671	686	700		**15**
307	714	728	742	756	770	785	799	813	827	841	1	1.5
308	855	869	883	897	911	926	940	954	968	982	2	3.0
309	996	*010	*024	*038	*052	*066	*080	*094	*108	*122	3	4.5
310	49 136	150	164	178	192	206	220	234	248	262	4	6.0
311	276	290	304	318	332	346	360	374	388	402	5	7.5
312	415	429	443	457	471	485	499	513	527	541	6	9.0
313	554	568	582	596	610	624	638	651	665	679	7	10.5
314	693	707	721	734	748	762	776	790	803	817	8	12.0
315	831	845	859	872	886	900	914	927	941	955	9	13.5
316	969	982	996	*010	*024	*037	*051	*065	*079	*092		
317	50 106	120	133	147	161	174	188	202	215	229		
318	243	256	270	284	297	311	325	338	352	365		**14**
319	379	393	406	420	433	447	461	474	488	501	1	1.4
320	515	529	542	556	569	583	596	610	623	637	2	2.8
321	651	664	678	691	705	718	732	745	759	772	3	4.2
322	786	799	813	826	840	853	866	880	893	907	4	5.6
323	920	934	947	961	974	987	*001	*014	*028	*041	5	7.0
324	51 055	068	081	095	108	121	135	148	162	175	6	8.4
325	188	202	215	228	242	255	268	282	295	308	7	9.8
326	322	335	348	362	375	388	402	415	428	441	8	11.2
327	455	468	481	495	508	521	534	548	561	574	9	12.6
328	587	601	614	627	640	654	667	680	693	706		
329	720	733	746	759	772	786	799	812	825	838		**13**
330	851	865	878	891	904	917	930	943	957	970	1	1.3
331	983	996	*009	*022	*035	*048	*061	*075	*088	*101	2	2.6
332	52 114	127	140	153	166	179	192	205	218	231	3	3.9
333	244	257	270	284	297	310	323	336	349	362	4	5.2
334	375	388	401	414	427	440	453	466	479	492	5	6.5
335	504	517	530	543	556	569	582	595	608	621	6	7.8
336	634	647	660	673	686	699	711	724	737	750	7	9.1
337	763	776	789	802	815	827	840	853	866	879	8	10.4
338	892	905	917	930	943	956	969	982	994	*007	9	11.7
339	53 020	033	046	058	071	084	097	110	122	135		
340	148	161	173	186	199	212	224	237	250	263		**12**
341	275	288	301	314	326	339	352	364	377	390	1	1.2
342	403	415	428	441	453	466	479	491	504	517	2	2.4
343	529	542	555	567	580	593	605	618	631	643	3	3.6
344	656	668	681	694	706	719	732	744	757	769	4	4.8
345	782	794	807	820	832	845	857	870	882	895	5	6.0
346	908	920	933	945	958	970	983	995	*008	*020	6	7.2
347	54 033	045	058	070	083	095	108	120	133	145	7	8.4
348	158	170	183	195	208	220	233	245	258	270	8	9.6
349	283	295	307	320	332	345	357	370	382	394	9	10.8
350	407	419	432	444	456	469	481	494	506	518		
N.	L. 0	1	2	3	4	5	6	7	8	9	P. P.	

Log π = .49715

TABLE I. LOGARITHMS OF NUMBERS | 191

3500–4009

N.	L. 0	1	2	3	4	5	6	7	8	9	P. P.
350	54 407	419	432	444	456	469	481	494	506	518	
351	531	543	555	568	580	593	605	617	630	642	
352	654	667	679	691	704	716	728	741	753	765	
353	777	790	802	814	827	839	851	864	876	888	
354	900	913	925	937	949	962	974	986	998	*011	
355	55 023	035	047	060	072	084	096	108	121	133	
356	145	157	169	182	194	206	218	230	242	255	
357	267	279	291	303	315	328	340	352	364	376	
358	388	400	413	425	437	449	461	473	485	497	
359	509	522	534	546	558	570	582	594	606	618	
360	630	642	654	666	678	691	703	715	727	739	
361	751	763	775	787	799	811	823	835	847	859	
362	871	883	895	907	919	931	943	955	967	979	
363	991	*003	*015	*027	*038	*050	*062	*074	*086	*098	
364	56 110	122	134	146	158	170	182	194	205	217	
365	229	241	253	265	277	289	301	312	324	336	
366	348	360	372	384	396	407	419	431	443	455	
367	467	478	490	502	514	526	538	549	561	573	
368	585	597	608	620	632	644	656	667	679	691	
369	703	714	726	738	750	761	773	785	797	808	
370	820	832	844	855	867	879	891	902	914	926	
371	937	949	961	972	984	996	*008	*019	*031	*043	
372	57 054	066	078	089	101	113	124	136	148	159	
373	171	183	194	206	217	229	241	252	264	276	
374	287	299	310	322	334	345	357	368	380	392	
375	403	415	426	438	449	461	473	484	496	507	
376	519	530	542	553	565	576	588	600	611	623	
377	634	646	657	669	680	692	703	715	726	738	
378	749	761	772	784	795	807	818	830	841	852	
379	864	875	887	898	910	921	933	944	955	967	
380	978	990	*001	*013	*024	*035	*047	*058	*070	*081	
381	58 092	104	115	127	138	149	161	172	184	195	
382	206	218	229	240	252	263	274	286	297	309	
383	320	331	343	354	365	377	388	399	410	422	
384	433	444	456	467	478	490	501	512	524	535	
385	546	557	569	580	591	602	614	625	636	647	
386	659	670	681	692	704	715	726	737	749	760	
387	771	782	794	805	816	827	838	850	861	872	
388	883	894	906	917	928	939	950	961	973	984	
389	995	*006	*017	*028	*040	*051	*062	*073	*084	*095	
390	59 106	118	129	140	151	162	173	184	195	207	
391	218	229	240	251	262	273	284	295	306	318	
392	329	340	351	362	373	384	395	406	417	428	
393	439	450	461	472	483	494	506	517	528	539	
394	550	561	572	583	594	605	616	627	638	649	
395	660	671	682	693	704	715	726	737	748	759	
396	770	780	791	802	813	824	835	846	857	868	
397	879	890	901	912	923	934	945	956	966	977	
398	988	999	*010	*021	*032	*043	*054	*065	*076	*086	
399	60 097	108	119	130	141	152	163	173	184	195	
400	206	217	228	239	249	260	271	282	293	304	
N.	L. 0	1	2	3	4	5	6	7	8	9	P. P.

P. P.

	13
1	1.3
2	2.6
3	3.9
4	5.2
5	6.5
6	7.8
7	9.1
8	10.4
9	11.7

	12
1	1.2
2	2.4
3	3.6
4	4.8
5	6.0
6	7.2
7	8.4
8	9.6
9	10.8

	11
1	1.1
2	2.2
3	3.3
4	4.4
5	5.5
6	6.6
7	7.7
8	8.8
9	9.9

	10
1	1.0
2	2.0
3	3.0
4	4.0
5	5.0
6	6.0
7	7.0
8	8.0
9	9.0

4000–4509

N.	L. 0	1	2	3	4	5	6	7	8	9
400	60 206	217	228	239	249	260	271	282	293	304
401	314	325	336	347	358	369	379	390	401	412
402	423	433	444	455	466	477	487	498	509	520
403	531	541	552	563	574	584	595	606	617	627
404	638	649	660	670	681	692	703	713	724	735
405	746	756	767	778	788	799	810	821	831	842
406	853	863	874	885	895	906	917	927	938	949
407	959	970	981	991	*002	*013	*023	*034	*045	*055
408	61 066	077	087	098	109	119	130	140	151	162
409	172	183	194	204	215	225	236	247	257	268
410	278	289	300	310	321	331	342	352	363	374
411	384	395	405	416	426	437	448	458	469	479
412	490	500	511	521	532	542	553	563	574	584
413	595	606	616	627	637	648	658	669	679	690
414	700	711	721	731	742	752	763	773	784	794
415	805	815	826	836	847	857	868	878	888	899
416	909	920	930	941	951	962	972	982	993	*003
417	62 014	024	034	045	055	066	076	086	097	107
418	118	128	138	149	159	170	180	190	201	211
419	221	232	242	252	263	273	284	294	304	315
420	325	335	346	356	366	377	387	397	408	418
421	428	439	449	459	469	480	490	500	511	521
422	531	542	552	562	572	583	593	603	613	624
423	634	644	655	665	675	685	696	706	716	726
424	737	747	757	767	778	788	798	808	818	829
425	839	849	859	870	880	890	900	910	921	931
426	941	951	961	972	982	992	*002	*012	*022	*033
427	63 043	053	063	073	083	094	104	114	124	134
428	144	155	165	175	185	195	205	215	225	236
429	246	256	266	276	286	296	306	317	327	337
430	347	357	367	377	387	397	407	417	428	438
431	448	458	468	478	488	498	508	518	528	538
432	548	558	568	579	589	599	609	619	629	639
433	649	659	669	679	689	699	709	719	729	739
434	749	759	769	779	789	799	809	819	829	839
435	849	859	869	879	889	899	909	919	929	939
436	949	959	969	979	988	998	*008	*018	*028	*038
437	64 048	058	068	078	088	098	108	118	128	137
438	147	157	167	177	187	197	207	217	227	237
439	246	256	266	276	286	296	306	316	326	335
440	345	355	365	375	385	395	404	414	424	434
441	444	454	464	473	483	493	503	513	523	532
442	542	552	562	572	582	591	601	611	621	631
443	640	650	660	670	680	689	699	709	719	729
444	738	748	758	768	777	787	797	807	816	826
445	836	846	856	865	875	885	895	904	914	924
446	933	943	953	963	972	982	992	*002	*011	*021
447	65 031	040	050	060	070	079	089	099	108	118
448	128	137	147	157	167	176	186	196	205	215
449	225	234	244	254	263	273	283	292	302	312
450	321	331	341	350	360	369	379	389	398	408

N.	L. 0	1	2	3	4	5	6	7	8	9

P. P.

11
1	1.1
2	2.2
3	3.3
4	4.4
5	5.5
6	6.6
7	7.7
8	8.8
9	9.9

10
1	1.0
2	2.0
3	3.0
4	4.0
5	5.0
6	6.0
7	7.0
8	8.0
9	9.0

9
1	0.9
2	1.8
3	2.7
4	3.6
5	4.5
6	5.4
7	6.3
8	7.2
9	8.1

TABLE I. LOGARITHMS OF NUMBERS | 193

4500–5009

N.	L. 0	1	2	3	4	5	6	7	8	9	P. P.
450	65 321	331	341	350	360	369	379	389	398	408	
451	418	427	437	447	456	466	475	485	495	504	
452	514	523	533	543	552	562	571	581	591	600	
453	610	619	629	639	648	658	667	677	686	696	
454	706	715	725	734	744	753	763	772	782	792	
455	801	811	820	830	839	849	858	868	877	887	
456	896	906	916	925	935	944	954	963	973	982	
457	992	*001	*011	*020	*030	*039	*049	*058	*068	*077	
458	66 087	096	106	115	124	134	143	153	162	172	
459	181	191	200	210	219	229	238	247	257	266	
460	276	285	295	304	314	323	332	342	351	361	
461	370	380	389	398	408	417	427	436	445	455	
462	464	474	483	492	502	511	521	530	539	549	
463	558	567	577	586	596	605	614	624	633	642	
464	652	661	671	680	689	699	708	717	727	736	
465	745	755	764	773	783	792	801	811	820	829	
466	839	848	857	867	876	885	894	904	913	922	
467	932	941	950	960	969	978	987	997	*006	*015	
468	67 025	034	043	052	062	071	080	089	099	108	
469	117	127	136	145	154	164	173	182	191	201	
470	210	219	228	237	247	256	265	274	284	293	
471	302	311	321	330	339	348	357	367	376	385	
472	394	403	413	422	431	440	449	459	468	477	
473	486	495	504	514	523	532	541	550	560	569	
474	578	587	596	605	614	624	633	642	651	660	
475	669	679	688	697	706	715	724	733	742	752	
476	761	770	779	788	797	806	815	825	834	843	
477	852	861	870	879	888	897	906	916	925	934	
478	943	952	961	970	979	988	997	*006	*015	*024	
479	68 034	043	052	061	070	079	088	097	106	115	
480	124	133	142	151	160	169	178	187	196	205	
481	215	224	233	242	251	260	269	278	287	296	
482	305	314	323	332	341	350	359	368	377	386	
483	395	404	413	422	431	440	449	458	467	476	
484	485	494	502	511	520	529	538	547	556	565	
485	574	583	592	601	610	619	628	637	646	655	
486	664	673	681	690	699	708	717	726	735	744	
487	753	762	771	780	789	797	806	815	824	833	
488	842	851	860	869	878	886	895	904	913	922	
489	931	940	949	958	966	975	984	993	*002	*011	
490	69 020	028	037	046	055	064	073	082	090	099	
491	108	117	126	135	144	152	161	170	179	188	
492	197	205	214	223	232	241	249	258	267	276	
493	285	294	302	311	320	329	338	346	355	364	
494	373	381	390	399	408	417	425	434	443	452	
495	461	469	478	487	496	504	513	522	531	539	
496	548	557	566	574	583	592	601	609	618	627	
497	636	644	653	662	671	679	688	697	705	714	
498	723	732	740	749	758	767	775	784	793	801	
499	810	819	827	836	845	854	862	871	880	888	
500	897	906	914	923	932	940	949	958	966	975	
N.	L. 0	1	2	3	4	5	6	7	8	9	P. P.

P. P.

10
1	1.0
2	2.0
3	3.0
4	4.0
5	5.0
6	6.0
7	7.0
8	8.0
9	9.0

9
1	0.9
2	1.8
3	2.7
4	3.6
5	4.5
6	5.4
7	6.3
8	7.2
9	8.1

8
1	0.8
2	1.6
3	2.4
4	3.2
5	4.0
6	4.8
7	5.6
8	6.4
9	7.2

5000–5509

N.	L. 0	1	2	3	4	5	6	7	8	9
500	69 897	906	914	923	932	940	949	958	966	975
501	984	992	*001	*010	*018	*027	*036	*044	*053	*062
502	70 070	079	088	096	105	114	122	131	140	148
503	157	165	174	183	191	200	209	217	226	234
504	243	252	260	269	278	286	295	303	312	321
505	329	338	346	355	364	372	381	389	398	406
506	415	424	432	441	449	458	467	475	484	492
507	501	509	518	526	535	544	552	561	569	578
508	586	595	603	612	621	629	638	646	655	663
509	672	680	689	697	706	714	723	731	740	749
510	757	766	774	783	791	800	808	817	825	834
511	842	851	859	868	876	885	893	902	910	919
512	927	935	944	952	961	969	978	986	995	*003
513	71 012	020	029	037	046	054	063	071	079	088
514	096	105	113	122	130	139	147	155	164	172
515	181	189	198	206	214	223	231	240	248	257
516	265	273	282	290	299	307	315	324	332	341
517	349	357	366	374	383	391	399	408	416	425
518	433	441	450	458	466	475	483	492	500	508
519	517	525	533	542	550	559	567	575	584	592
520	600	609	617	625	634	642	650	659	667	675
521	684	692	700	709	717	725	734	742	750	759
522	767	775	784	792	800	809	817	825	834	842
523	850	858	867	875	883	892	900	908	917	925
524	933	941	950	958	966	975	983	991	999	*008
525	72 016	024	032	041	049	057	066	074	082	090
526	099	107	115	123	132	140	148	156	165	173
527	181	189	198	206	214	222	230	239	247	255
528	263	272	280	288	296	304	313	321	329	337
529	346	354	362	370	378	387	395	403	411	419
530	428	436	444	452	460	469	477	485	493	501
531	509	518	526	534	542	550	558	567	575	583
532	591	599	607	616	624	632	640	648	656	665
533	673	681	689	697	705	713	722	730	738	746
534	754	762	770	779	787	795	803	811	819	827
535	835	843	852	860	868	876	884	892	900	908
536	916	925	933	941	949	957	965	973	981	989
537	997	*006	*014	*022	*030	*038	*046	*054	*062	*070
538	73 078	086	094	102	111	119	127	135	143	151
539	159	167	175	183	191	199	207	215	223	231
540	239	247	255	263	272	280	288	296	304	312
541	320	328	336	344	352	360	368	376	384	392
542	400	408	416	424	432	440	448	456	464	472
543	480	488	496	504	512	520	528	536	544	552
544	560	568	576	584	592	600	608	616	624	632
545	640	648	656	664	672	679	687	695	703	711
546	719	727	735	743	751	759	767	775	783	791
547	799	807	815	823	830	838	846	854	862	870
548	878	886	894	902	910	918	926	933	941	949
549	957	965	973	981	989	997	*005	*013	*020	*028
550	74 036	044	052	060	068	076	084	092	099	107

P. P.

9
1 | 0.9
2 | 1.8
3 | 2.7
4 | 3.6
5 | 4.5
6 | 5.4
7 | 6.3
8 | 7.2
9 | 8.1

8
1 | 0.8
2 | 1.6
3 | 2.4
4 | 3.2
5 | 4.0
6 | 4.8
7 | 5.6
8 | 6.4
9 | 7.2

7
1 | 0.7
2 | 1.4
3 | 2.1
4 | 2.8
5 | 3.5
6 | 4.2
7 | 4.9
8 | 5.6
9 | 6.3

TABLE I. LOGARITHMS OF NUMBERS | 195

5500–6009

N.	L. 0	1	2	3	4	5	6	7	8	9
550	74 036	044	052	060	068	076	084	092	099	107
551	115	123	131	139	147	155	162	170	178	186
552	194	202	210	218	225	233	241	249	257	265
553	273	280	288	296	304	312	320	327	335	343
554	351	359	367	374	382	390	398	406	414	421
555	429	437	445	453	461	468	476	484	492	500
556	507	515	523	531	539	547	554	562	570	578
557	586	593	601	609	617	624	632	640	648	656
558	663	671	679	687	695	702	710	718	726	733
559	741	749	757	764	772	780	788	796	803	811
560	819	827	834	842	850	858	865	873	881	889
561	896	904	912	920	927	935	943	950	958	966
562	974	981	989	997	*005	*012	*020	*028	*035	*043
563	75 051	059	066	074	082	089	097	105	113	120
564	128	136	143	151	159	166	174	182	189	197
565	205	213	220	228	236	243	251	259	266	274
566	282	289	297	305	312	320	328	335	343	351
567	358	366	374	381	389	397	404	412	420	427
568	435	442	450	458	465	473	481	488	496	504
569	511	519	526	534	542	549	557	565	572	580
570	587	595	603	610	618	626	633	641	648	656
571	664	671	679	686	694	702	709	717	724	732
572	740	747	755	762	770	778	785	793	800	808
573	815	823	831	838	846	853	861	868	876	884
574	891	899	906	914	921	929	937	944	952	959
575	967	974	982	989	997	*005	*012	*020	*027	035
576	76 042	050	057	065	072	080	087	095	103	110
577	118	125	133	140	148	155	163	170	178	185
578	193	200	208	215	223	230	238	245	253	260
579	268	275	283	290	298	305	313	320	328	335
580	343	350	358	365	373	380	388	395	403	410
581	418	425	433	440	448	455	462	470	477	485
582	492	500	507	515	522	530	537	545	552	559
583	567	574	582	589	597	604	612	619	626	634
584	641	649	656	664	671	678	686	693	701	708
585	716	723	730	738	745	753	760	768	775	782
586	790	797	805	812	819	827	834	842	849	856
587	864	871	879	886	893	901	908	916	923	930
588	938	945	953	960	967	975	982	989	997	*004
589	77 012	019	026	034	041	048	056	063	070	078
590	085	093	100	107	115	122	129	137	144	151
591	159	166	173	181	188	195	203	210	217	225
592	232	240	247	254	262	269	276	283	291	298
593	305	313	320	327	335	342	349	357	364	371
594	379	386	393	401	408	415	422	430	437	444
595	452	459	466	474	481	488	495	503	510	517
596	525	532	539	546	554	561	568	576	583	590
597	597	605	612	619	627	634	641	648	656	663
598	670	677	685	692	699	706	714	721	728	735
599	743	750	757	764	772	779	786	793	801	808
600	815	822	830	837	844	851	859	866	873	880

P. P.

	8
1	0.8
2	1.6
3	2.4
4	3.2
5	4.0
6	4.8
7	5.6
8	6.4
9	7.2

	7
1	0.7
2	1.4
3	2.1
4	2.8
5	3.5
6	4.2
7	4.9
8	5.6
9	6.3

6000–6509

N.	L. 0	1	2	3	4	5	6	7	8	9
600	77 815	822	830	837	844	851	859	866	873	880
601	887	895	902	909	916	924	931	938	945	952
602	960	967	974	981	988	996	*003	*010	*017	*025
603	78 032	039	046	053	061	068	075	082	089	097
604	104	111	118	125	132	140	147	154	161	168
605	176	183	190	197	204	211	219	226	233	240
606	247	254	262	269	276	283	290	297	305	312
607	319	326	333	340	347	355	362	369	376	383
608	390	398	405	412	419	426	433	440	447	455
609	462	469	476	483	490	497	504	512	519	526
610	533	540	547	554	561	569	576	583	590	597
611	604	611	618	625	633	640	647	654	661	668
612	675	682	689	696	704	711	718	725	732	739
613	746	753	760	767	774	781	789	796	803	810
614	817	824	831	838	845	852	859	866	873	880
615	888	895	902	909	916	923	930	937	944	951
616	958	965	972	979	986	993	*000	*007	*014	*021
617	79 029	036	043	050	057	064	071	078	085	092
618	099	106	113	120	127	134	141	148	155	162
619	169	176	183	190	197	204	211	218	225	232
620	239	246	253	260	267	274	281	288	295	302
621	309	316	323	330	337	344	351	358	365	372
622	379	386	393	400	407	414	421	428	435	442
623	449	456	463	470	477	484	491	498	505	511
624	518	525	532	539	546	553	560	567	574	581
625	588	595	602	609	616	623	630	637	644	650
626	657	664	671	678	685	692	699	706	713	720
627	727	734	741	748	754	761	768	775	782	789
628	796	803	810	817	824	831	837	844	851	858
629	865	872	879	886	893	900	906	913	920	927
630	934	941	948	955	962	969	975	982	989	996
631	80 003	010	017	024	030	037	044	051	058	065
632	072	079	085	092	099	106	113	120	127	134
633	140	147	154	161	168	175	182	188	195	202
634	209	216	223	229	236	243	250	257	264	271
635	277	284	291	298	305	312	318	325	332	339
636	346	353	359	366	373	380	387	393	400	407
637	414	421	428	434	441	448	455	462	468	475
638	482	489	496	502	509	516	523	530	536	543
639	550	557	564	570	577	584	591	598	604	611
640	618	625	632	638	645	652	659	665	672	679
641	686	693	699	706	713	720	726	733	740	747
642	754	760	767	774	781	787	794	801	808	814
643	821	828	835	841	848	855	862	868	875	882
644	889	895	902	909	916	922	929	936	943	949
645	956	963	969	976	983	990	996	*003	*010	*017
646	81 023	030	037	043	050	057	064	070	077	084
647	090	097	104	111	117	124	131	137	144	151
648	158	164	171	178	184	191	198	204	211	218
649	224	231	238	245	251	258	265	271	278	285
650	291	298	305	311	318	325	331	338	345	351

N.	L. 0	1	2	3	4	5	6	7	8	9

P. P.

8
1	0.8
2	1.6
3	2.4
4	3.2
5	4.0
6	4.8
7	5.6
8	6.4
9	7.2

7
1	0.7
2	1.4
3	2.1
4	2.8
5	3.5
6	4.2
7	4.9
8	5.6
9	6.3

6
1	0.6
2	1.2
3	1.8
4	2.4
5	3.0
6	3.6
7	4.2
8	4.8
9	5.4

TABLE I. LOGARITHMS OF NUMBERS | 197

6500–7009

N.	L. 0	1	2	3	4	5	6	7	8	9	P. P.
650	81 291	298	305	311	318	325	331	338	345	351	
651	358	365	371	378	385	391	398	405	411	418	
652	425	431	438	445	451	458	465	471	478	485	
653	491	498	505	511	518	525	531	538	544	551	
654	558	564	571	578	584	591	598	604	611	617	
655	624	631	637	644	651	657	664	671	677	684	
656	690	697	704	710	717	723	730	737	743	750	
657	757	763	770	776	783	790	796	803	809	816	
658	823	829	836	842	849	856	862	869	875	882	
659	889	895	902	908	915	921	928	935	941	948	
660	954	961	968	974	981	987	994	*000	*007	*014	
661	82 020	027	033	040	046	053	060	066	073	079	**7**
662	086	092	099	105	112	119	125	132	138	145	1 | 0.7
663	151	158	164	171	178	184	191	197	204	210	2 | 1.4
664	217	223	230	236	243	249	256	263	269	276	3 | 2.1
665	282	289	295	302	308	315	321	328	334	341	4 | 2.8
666	347	354	360	367	373	380	387	393	400	406	5 | 3.5
667	413	419	426	432	439	445	452	458	465	471	6 | 4.2
668	478	484	491	497	504	510	517	523	530	536	7 | 4.9
669	543	549	556	562	569	575	582	588	595	601	8 | 5.6
670	607	614	620	627	633	640	646	653	659	666	9 | 6.3
671	672	679	685	692	698	705	711	718	724	730	
672	737	743	750	756	763	769	776	782	789	795	
673	802	808	814	821	827	834	840	847	853	860	
674	866	872	879	885	892	898	905	911	918	924	
675	930	937	943	950	956	963	969	975	982	988	
676	995	*001	*008	*014	*020	*027	*033	*040	*046	*052	
677	83 059	065	072	078	085	091	097	104	110	117	
678	123	129	136	142	149	155	161	168	174	181	
679	187	193	200	206	213	219	225	232	238	245	
680	251	257	264	270	276	283	289	296	302	308	
681	315	321	327	334	340	347	353	359	366	372	**6**
682	378	385	391	398	404	410	417	423	429	436	1 | 0.6
683	442	448	455	461	467	474	480	487	493	499	2 | 1.2
684	506	512	518	525	531	537	544	550	556	563	3 | 1.8
685	569	575	582	588	594	601	607	613	620	626	4 | 2.4
686	632	639	645	651	658	664	670	677	683	689	5 | 3.0
687	696	702	708	715	721	727	734	740	746	753	6 | 3.6
688	759	765	771	778	784	790	797	803	809	816	7 | 4.2
689	822	828	835	841	847	853	860	866	872	879	8 | 4.8
690	885	891	897	904	910	916	923	929	935	942	9 | 5.4
691	948	954	960	967	973	979	985	992	998	*004	
692	84 011	017	023	029	036	042	048	055	061	067	
693	073	080	086	092	098	105	111	117	123	130	
694	136	142	148	155	161	167	173	180	186	192	
695	198	205	211	217	223	230	236	242	248	255	
696	261	267	273	280	286	292	298	305	311	317	
697	323	330	336	342	348	354	361	367	373	379	
698	386	392	398	404	410	417	423	429	435	442	
699	448	454	460	466	473	479	485	491	497	504	
700	510	516	522	528	535	541	547	553	559	566	
N.	L. 0	1	2	3	4	5	6	7	8	9	P. P.

7000–7509

N.	L. 0	1	2	3	4	5	6	7	8	9	P. P.
700	84 510	516	522	528	535	541	547	553	559	566	
701	572	578	584	590	597	603	609	615	621	628	
702	634	640	646	652	658	665	671	677	683	689	
703	696	702	708	714	720	726	733	739	745	751	
704	757	763	770	776	782	788	794	800	807	813	
705	819	825	831	837	844	850	856	862	868	874	
706	880	887	893	899	905	911	917	924	930	936	
707	942	948	954	960	967	973	979	985	991	997	
708	85 003	009	016	022	028	034	040	046	052	058	
709	065	071	077	083	089	095	101	107	114	120	
710	126	132	138	144	150	156	163	169	175	181	
711	187	193	199	205	211	217	224	230	236	242	
712	248	254	260	266	272	278	285	291	297	303	
713	309	315	321	327	333	339	345	352	358	364	
714	370	376	382	388	394	400	406	412	418	425	
715	431	437	443	449	455	461	467	473	479	485	
716	491	497	503	509	516	522	528	534	540	546	
717	552	558	564	570	576	582	588	594	600	606	
718	612	618	625	631	637	643	649	655	661	667	
719	673	679	685	691	697	703	709	715	721	727	
720	733	739	745	751	757	763	769	775	781	788	
721	794	800	806	812	818	824	830	836	842	848	
722	854	860	866	872	878	884	890	896	902	908	
723	914	920	926	932	938	944	950	956	962	968	
724	974	980	986	992	998	*004	*010	*016	*022	*028	
725	86 034	040	046	052	058	064	070	076	082	088	
726	094	100	106	112	118	124	130	136	141	147	
727	153	159	165	171	177	183	189	195	201	207	
728	213	219	225	231	237	243	249	255	261	267	
729	273	279	285	291	297	303	308	314	320	326	
730	332	338	344	350	356	362	368	374	380	386	
731	392	398	404	410	415	421	427	433	439	445	
732	451	457	463	469	475	481	487	493	499	504	
733	510	516	522	528	534	540	546	552	558	564	
734	570	576	581	587	593	599	605	611	617	623	
735	629	635	641	646	652	658	664	670	676	682	
736	688	694	700	705	711	717	723	729	735	741	
737	747	753	759	764	770	776	782	788	794	800	
738	806	812	817	823	829	835	841	847	853	859	
739	864	870	876	882	888	894	900	906	911	917	
740	923	929	935	941	947	953	958	964	970	976	
741	982	988	994	999	*005	*011	*017	*023	*029	*035	
742	87 040	046	052	058	064	070	075	081	087	093	
743	099	105	111	116	122	128	134	140	146	151	
744	157	163	169	175	181	186	192	198	204	210	
745	216	221	227	233	239	245	251	256	262	268	
746	274	280	286	291	297	303	309	315	320	326	
747	332	338	344	349	355	361	367	373	379	384	
748	390	396	402	408	413	419	425	431	437	442	
749	448	454	460	466	471	477	483	489	495	500	
750	506	512	518	523	529	535	541	547	552	558	
N.	L. 0	1	2	3	4	5	6	7	8	9	P. P.

P. P.

7
1	0.7
2	1.4
3	2.1
4	2.8
5	3.5
6	4.2
7	4.9
8	5.6
9	6.3

6
1	0.6
2	1.2
3	1.8
4	2.4
5	3.0
6	3.6
7	4.2
8	4.8
9	5.4

5
1	0.5
2	1.0
3	1.5
4	2.0
5	2.5
6	3.0
7	3.5
8	4.0
9	4.5

TABLE I. LOGARITHMS OF NUMBERS | 199

7500–8009

N.	L. 0	1	2	3	4	5	6	7	8	9	P. P.
750	87 506	512	518	523	529	535	541	547	552	558	
751	564	570	576	581	587	593	599	604	610	616	
752	622	628	633	639	645	651	656	662	668	674	
753	679	685	691	697	703	708	714	720	726	731	
754	737	743	749	754	760	766	772	777	783	789	
755	795	800	806	812	818	823	829	835	841	846	
756	852	858	864	869	875	881	887	892	898	904	
757	910	915	921	927	933	938	944	950	955	961	
758	967	973	978	984	990	996	*001	*007	*013	*018	
759	88 024	030	036	041	047	053	058	064	070	076	
760	081	087	093	098	104	110	116	121	127	133	
761	138	144	150	156	161	167	173	178	184	190	
762	195	201	207	213	218	224	230	235	241	247	
763	252	258	264	270	275	281	287	292	298	304	
764	309	315	321	326	332	338	343	349	355	360	
765	366	372	377	383	389	395	400	406	412	417	
766	423	429	434	440	446	451	457	463	468	474	
767	480	485	491	497	502	508	513	519	525	530	
768	536	542	547	553	559	564	570	576	581	587	
769	593	598	604	610	615	621	627	632	638	643	
770	649	655	660	666	672	677	683	689	694	700	
771	705	711	717	722	728	734	739	745	750	756	
772	762	767	773	779	784	790	795	801	807	812	
773	818	824	829	835	840	846	852	857	863	868	
774	874	880	885	891	897	902	908	913	919	925	
775	930	936	941	947	953	958	964	969	975	981	
776	986	992	997	*003	*009	*014	*020	*025	*031	*037	
777	89 042	048	053	059	064	070	076	081	087	092	
778	098	104	109	115	120	126	131	137	143	148	
779	154	159	165	170	176	182	187	193	198	204	
780	209	215	221	226	232	237	243	248	254	260	
781	265	271	276	282	287	293	298	304	310	315	
782	321	326	332	337	343	348	354	360	365	371	
783	376	382	387	393	398	404	409	415	421	426	
784	432	437	443	448	454	459	465	470	476	481	
785	487	492	498	504	509	515	520	526	531	537	
786	542	548	553	559	564	570	575	581	586	592	
787	597	603	609	614	620	625	631	636	642	647	
788	653	658	664	669	675	680	686	691	697	702	
789	708	713	719	724	730	735	741	746	752	757	
790	763	768	774	779	785	790	796	801	807	812	
791	818	823	829	834	840	845	851	856	862	867	
792	873	878	883	889	894	900	905	911	916	922	
793	927	933	938	944	949	955	960	966	971	977	
794	982	988	993	998	*004	*009	*015	*020	*026	*031	
795	90 037	042	048	053	059	064	069	075	080	086	
796	091	097	102	108	113	119	124	129	135	140	
797	146	151	157	162	168	173	179	184	189	195	
798	200	206	211	217	222	227	233	238	244	249	
799	255	260	266	271	276	282	287	293	298	304	
800	309	314	320	325	331	336	342	347	352	358	
N.	L. 0	1	2	3	4	5	6	7	8	9	P. P.

P. P.

6
1	0.6
2	1.2
3	1.8
4	2.4
5	3.0
6	3.6
7	4.2
8	4.8
9	5.4

5
1	0.5
2	1.0
3	1.5
4	2.0
5	2.5
6	3.0
7	3.5
8	4.0
9	4.5

8000–8509

N.	L. 0	1	2	3	4	5	6	7	8	9
800	90 309	314	320	325	331	336	342	347	352	358
801	363	369	374	380	385	390	396	401	407	412
802	417	423	428	434	439	445	450	455	461	466
803	472	477	482	488	493	499	504	509	515	520
804	526	531	536	542	547	553	558	563	569	574
805	580	585	590	596	601	607	612	617	623	628
806	634	639	644	650·	655	660	666	671	677	682
807	687	693	698	703	709	714	720	725	730	736
808	741	747	752	757	763	768	773	779	784	789
809	795	800	806	811	816	822	827	832	838	843
810	849	854	859	865	870	875	881	886	891	897
811	902	907	913	918	924	929	934	940	945	950
812	956	961	966	972	977	982	988	993	998	*004
813	91 009	014	020	025	030	036	041	046	052	057
814	062	068	073	078	084	089	094	100	105	110
815	116	121	126	132	137	142	148	153	158	164
816	169	174	180	185	190	196	201	206	212	217
817	222	228	233	238	243	249	254	259·	265	270
818	275	281	286	291	297	302	307	312	318	323
819	328	334	339	344	350	355	360	365	371	376
820	381	387	392	397	403	408	413	418	424	429
821	434	440	445	450	455	461	466	471	477	482
822	487	492	498	503	508	514	519	524	529	535
823	540	545	551	556	561	566	572	577	582	587
824	593	598	603	609	614	619	624	630	635	640
825	645	651	656	661	666	672	677	682	687	693
826	698	703	709	714	719	724	730	735	740	745
827	751	756	761	766	772	777	782	787	793	798
828	803	808	814	819	824	829	834	840	845	850
829	855	861	866	871	876	882	887	892	897	903
830	908	913	918	924	929	934	939	944	950	955
831	960	965	971	976	981	986	991	997	*002	*007
832	92 012	018	023	028	033	038	044	049	054	059
833	065	070	075	080	085	091	096	101	106	111
834	117	122	127	132	137	143	148	153	158	163
835	169	174	179	184	189	195	200	205	210	215
836	221	226	231	236	241	247	252	257	262	267
837	273	278	283	288	293	298	304	309	314	319
838	324	330	335	340	345	350	355	361	366	371
839	376	381	387	392	397	402	407	412	418	423
840	428	433	438	443	449	454	459	464	469	474
841	480	485	490	495	500	505	511	516	521	526
842	531	536	542	547	552	557	562	567	572	578
843	583	588	593	598	603	609	614	619	624	629
844	634	639	645	650	655	660	665	670	675	681
845	686	691	696	701	706	711	716	722	727	732
846	737	742	747	752	758	763	768	773	778	783
847	788	793	799	804	809	814	819	824	829	834
848	840	845	850	855	860	865	870	875	881	886
849	891	896	901	906	911	916	921	927	932	937
850	942	947	952	957	962	967	973	978	983	988

P. P.

6

1	0.6
2	1.2
3	1.8
4	2.4
5	3.0
6	3.6
7	4.2
8	4.8
9	5.4

5

1	0.5
2	1.0
3	1.5
4	2.0
5	2.5
6	3.0
7	3.5
8	4.0
9	4.5

TABLE I. LOGARITHMS OF NUMBERS | 201

8500–9009

N.	L. 0	1	2	3	4	5	6	7	8	9
850	92 942	947	952	957	962	967	973	978	983	988
851	993	998	*003	*008	*013	*018	*024	*029	*034	*039
852	93 044	049	054	059	064	069	075	080	085	090
853	095	100	105	110	115	120	125	131	136	141
854	146	151	156	161	166	171	176	181	186	192
855	197	202	207	212	217	222	227	232	237	242
856	247	252	258	263	268	273	278	283	288	293
857	298	303	308	313	318	323	328	334	339	344
858	349	354	359	364	369	374	379	384	389	394
859	399	404	409	414	420	425	430	435	440	445
860	450	455	460	465	470	475	480	485	490	495
861	500	505	510	515	520	526	531	536	541	546
862	551	556	561	566	571	576	581	586	591	596
863	601	606	611	616	621	626	631	636	641	646
864	651	656	661	666	671	676	682	687	692	697
865	702	707	712	717	722	727	732	737	742	747
866	752	757	762	767	772	777	782	787	792	797
867	802	807	812	817	822	827	832	837	842	847
868	852	857	862	867	872	877	882	887	892	897
869	902	907	912	917	922	927	932	937	942	947
870	952	957	962	967	972	977	982	987	992	997
871	94 002	007	012	017	022	027	032	037	042	047
872	052	057	062	067	072	077	082	086	091	096
873	101	106	111	116	121	126	131	136	141	146
874	151	156	161	166	171	176	181	186	191	196
875	201	206	211	216	221	226	231	236	240	245
876	250	255	260	265	270	275	280	285	290	295
877	300	305	310	315	320	325	330	335	340	345
878	349	354	359	364	369	374	379	384	389	394
879	399	404	409	414	419	424	429	433	438	443
880	448	453	458	463	468	473	478	483	488	493
881	498	503	507	512	517	522	527	532	537	542
882	547	552	557	562	567	571	576	581	586	591
883	596	601	606	611	616	621	626	630	635	640
884	645	650	655	660	665	670	675	680	685	689
885	694	699	704	709	714	719	724	729	734	738
886	743	748	753	758	763	768	773	778	783	787
887	792	797	802	807	812	817	822	827	832	836
888	841	846	851	856	861	866	871	876	880	885
889	890	895	900	905	910	915	919	924	929	934
890	939	944	949	954	959	963	968	973	978	983
891	988	993	998	*002	*007	*012	*017	*022	*027	*032
892	95 036	041	046	051	056	061	066	071	075	080
893	085	090	095	100	105	109	114	119	124	129
894	134	139	143	148	153	158	163	168	173	177
895	182	187	192	197	202	207	211	216	221	226
896	231	236	240	245	250	255	260	265	270	274
897	279	284	289	294	299	303	308	313	318	323
898	328	332	337	342	347	352	357	361	366	371
899	376	381	386	390	395	400	405	410	415	419
900	424	429	434	439	444	448	453	458	463	468

P. P.

6
1	0.6
2	1.2
3	1.8
4	2.4
5	3.0
6	3.6
7	4.2
8	4.8
9	5.4

5
1	0.5
2	1.0
3	1.5
4	2.0
5	2.5
6	3.0
7	3.5
8	4.0
9	4.5

4
1	0.4
2	0.8
3	1.2
4	1.6
5	2.0
6	2.4
7	2.8
8	3.2
9	3.6

N.	L. 0	1	2	3	4	5	6	7	8	9	P. P.

9000–9509

N.	L. 0	1	2	3	4	5	6	7	8	9
900	95 424	429	434	439	444	448	453	458	463	468
901	472	477	482	487	492	497	501	506	511	516
902	521	525	530	535	540	545	550	554	559	564
903	569	574	578	583	588	593	598	602	607	612
904	617	622	626	631	636	641	646	650	655	660
905	665	670	674	679	684	689	694	698	703	708
906	713	718	722	727	732	737	742	746	751	756
907	761	766	770	775	780	785	789	794	799	804
908	809	813	818	823	828	832	837	842	847	852
909	856	861	866	871	875	880	885	890	895	899
910	904	909	914	918	923	928	933	938	942	947
911	952	957	961	966	971	976	980	985	990	995
912	999	*004	*009	*014	*019	*023	*028	*033	*038	*042
913	96 047	052	057	061	066	071	076	080	085	090
914	095	099	104	109	114	118	123	128	133	137
915	142	147	152	156	161	166	171	175	180	185
916	190	194	199	204	209	213	218	223	227	232
917	237	242	246	251	256	261	265	270	275	280
918	284	289	294	298	303	308	313	317	322	327
919	332	336	341	346	350	355	360	365	369	374
920	379	384	388	393	398	402	407	412	417	421
921	426	431	435	440	445	450	454	459	464	468
922	473	478	483	487	492	497	501	506	511	515
923	520	525	530	534	539	544	548	553	558	562
924	567	572	577	581	586	591	595	600	605	609
925	614	619	624	628	633	638	642	647	652	656
926	661	666	670	675	680	685	689	694	699	703
927	708	713	717	722	727	731	736	741	745	750
928	755	759	764	769	774	778	783	788	792	797
929	802	806	811	816	820	825	830	834	839	844
930	848	853	858	862	867	872	876	881	886	890
931	895	900	904	909	914	918	923	928	932	937
932	942	946	951	956	960	965	970	974	979	984
933	988	993	997	*002	*007	*011	*016	*021	*025	*030
934	97 035	039	044	049	053	058	063	067	072	077
935	081	086	090	095	100	104	109	114	118	123
936	128	132	137	142	146	151	155	160	165	169
937	174	179	183	188	192	197	202	206	211	216
938	220	225	230	234	239	243	248	253	257	262
939	267	271	276	280	285	290	294	299	304	308
940	313	317	322	327	331	336	340	345	350	354
941	359	364	368	373	377	382	387	391	396	400
942	405	410	414	419	424	428	433	437	442	447
943	451	456	460	465	470	474	479	483	488	493
944	497	502	506	511	516	520	525	529	534	539
945	543	548	552	557	562	566	571	575	580	585
946	589	594	598	603	607	612	617	621	626	630
947	635	640	644	649	653	658	663	667	672	676
948	681	685	690	695	699	704	708	713	717	722
949	727	731	736	740	745	749	754	759	763	768
950	772	777	782	786	791	795	800	804	809	813

P. P.

5

1	0.5
2	1.0
3	1.5
4	2.0
5	2.5
6	3.0
7	3.5
8	4.0
9	4.5

4

1	0.4
2	0.8
3	1.2
4	1.6
5	2.0
6	2.4
7	2.8
8	3.2
9	3.6

TABLE I. LOGARITHMS OF NUMBERS | 203

9500–10009

N.	L. 0	1	2	3	4	5	6	7	8	9	P. P.
950	97 772	777	782	786	791	795	800	804	809	813	
951	818	823	827	832	836	841	845	850	855	859	
952	864	868	873	877	882	886	891	896	900	905	
953	909	914	918	923	928	932	937	941	946	950	
954	955	959	964	968	973	978	982	987	991	996	
955	98 000	005	009	014	019	023	028	032	037	041	
956	046	050	055	059	064	068	073	078	082	087	
957	091	096	100	105	109	114	118	123	127	132	
958	137	141	146	150	155	159	164	168	173	177	
959	182	186	191	195	200	204	209	214	218	223	
960	227	232	236	241	245	250	254	259	263	268	
961	272	277	281	286	290	295	299	304	308	313	
962	318	322	327	331	336	340	345	349	354	358	
963	363	367	372	376	381	385	390	394	399	403	
964	408	412	417	421	426	430	435	439	444	448	
965	453	457	462	466	471	475	480	484	489	493	
966	498	502	507	511	516	520	525	529	534	538	
967	543	547	552	556	561	565	570	574	579	583	
968	588	592	597	601	605	610	614	619	623	628	
969	632	637	641	646	650	655	659	664	668	673	
970	677	682	686	691	695	700	704	709	713	717	
971	722	726	731	735	740	744	749	753	758	762	
972	767	771	776	780	784	789	793	798	802	807	
973	811	816	820	825	829	834	838	843	847	851	
974	856	860	865	869	874	878	883	887	892	896	
975	900	905	909	914	918	923	927	932	936	941	
976	945	949	954	958	963	967	972	976	981	985	
977	989	994	998	*003	*007	*012	*016	*021	*025	*029	
978	99 034	038	043	047	052	056	061	065	069	074	
979	078	083	087	092	096	100	105	109	114	118	
980	123	127	131	136	140	145	149	154	158	162	
981	167	171	176	180	185	189	193	198	202	207	
982	211	216	220	224	229	233	238	242	247	251	
983	255	260	264	269	273	277	282	286	291	295	
984	300	304	308	313	317	322	326	330	335	339	
985	344	348	352	357	361	366	370	374	379	383	
986	388	392	396	401	405	410	414	419	423	427	
987	432	436	441	445	449	454	458	463	467	471	
988	476	480	484	489	493	498	502	506	511	515	
989	520	524	528	533	537	542	546	550	555	559	
990	564	568	572	577	581	585	590	594	599	603	
991	607	612	616	621	625	629	634	638	642	647	
992	651	656	660	664	669	673	677	682	686	691	
993	695	699	704	708	712	717	721	726	730	734	
994	739	743	747	752	756	760	765	769	774	778	
995	782	787	791	795	800	804	808	813	817	822	
996	826	830	835	839	843	848	852	856	861	865	
997	870	874	878	883	887	891	896	900	904	909	
998	913	917	922	926	930	935	939	944	948	952	
999	957	961	965	970	974	978	983	987	991	996	
1000	00 000	004	009	013	017	022	026	030	035	039	

P. P. column:

5
1 | 0.5
2 | 1.0
3 | 1.5
4 | 2.0
5 | 2.5
6 | 3.0
7 | 3.5
8 | 4.0
9 | 4.5

4
1 | 0.4
2 | 0.8
3 | 1.2
4 | 1.6
5 | 2.0
6 | 2.4
7 | 2.8
8 | 3.2
9 | 3.6

N.	L. 0	1	2	3	4	5	6	7	8	9	P. P.

Table II

NATURAL
TRIGONOMETRIC FUNCTIONS

	Sin	Cos	Tan	Cot	
0° 00′	.0000	1.0000	.0000		**90° 00′**
10	029	000	029	343.8	50
20	058	000	058	171.9	40
30	.0087	1.0000	.0087	114.6	30
40	116	.9999	116	85.94	20
50	145	999	145	68.75	10
1° 00′	.0175	.9998	.0175	57.29	**89° 00′**
10	204	998	204	49.10	50
20	233	997	233	42.96	40
30	.0262	.9997	.0262	38.19	30
40	291	996	291	34.37	20
50	320	995	320	31.24	10
2° 00′	.0349	.9994	.0349	28.64	**88° 00′**
10	378	993	378	26.43	50
20	407	992	407	24.54	40
30	.0436	.9990	.0437	22.90	30
40	465	989	466	21.47	20
50	494	988	495	20.21	10
3° 00′	.0523	.9986	.0524	19.08	**87° 00′**
10	552	985	553	18.07	50
20	581	983	582	17.17	40
30	.0610	.9981	.0612	16.35	30
40	640	980	641	15.60	20
50	669	978	670	14.92	10
4° 00′	.0698	.9976	.0699	14.30	**86° 00′**
10	727	974	729	13.73	50
20	756	971	758	13.20	40
30	.0785	.9969	.0787	12.71	30
40	814	967	816	12.25	20
50	843	964	846	11.83	10
5° 00′	.0872	.9962	.0875	11.43	**85° 00′**
10	901	959	904	11.06	50
20	929	957	934	10.71	40
30	.0958	.9954	.0963	10.39	30
40	987	951	992	10.08	20
50	.1016	948	.1022	9.788	10
6° 00′	.1045	.9945	.1051	9.514	**84° 00′**
10	074	942	080	9.255	50
20	103	939	110	9.010	40
30	.1132	.9936	.1139	8.777	30
40	161	932	169	8.556	20
50	190	929	198	8.345	10
7° 00′	.1219	.9925	.1228	8.144	**83° 00′**
10	248	922	257	7.953	50
20	276	918	287	7.770	40
30	.1305	.9914	.1317	7.596	30
40	334	911	346	7.429	20
50	363	907	376	7.269	10
8° 00′	.1392	.9903	.1405	7.115	**82° 00′**
10	421	899	435	6.968	50
20	449	894	465	6.827	40
30	.1478	.9890	.1495	6.691	30
40	507	886	524	6.561	20
50	536	881	554	6.435	10
9° 00′	.1564	.9877	.1584	6.314	**81° 00′**
	Cos	Sin	Cot	Tan	

TABLE II. NATURAL TRIGONOMETRIC FUNCTIONS | 207

	Sin	Cos	Tan	Cot	
9° 00′	.1564	.9877	.1584	6.314	81° 00′
10	593	872	614	197	50
20	622	868	644	084	40
30	.1650	.9863	.1673	5.976	30
40	679	858	703	871	20
50	708	853	733	769	10
10° 00′	.1736	.9848	.1763	5.671	80° 00′
10	765	843	793	576	50
20	794	838	823	485	40
30	.1822	.9833	.1853	5.396	30
40	851	827	883	309	20
50	880	822	914	226	10
11° 00′	.1908	.9816	.1944	5.145	79° 00′
10	937	811	974	066	50
20	965	805	.2004	4.989	40
30	.1994	.9799	.2035	4.915	30
40	.2022	793	065	843	20
50	051	787	095	773	10
12° 00′	.2079	.9781	.2126	4.705	78° 00′
10	108	775	156	638	50
20	136	769	186	574	40
30	.2164	.9763	.2217	4.511	30
40	193	757	247	449	20
50	221	750	278	390	10
13° 00′	.2250	.9744	.2309	4.331	77° 00′
10	278	737	339	275	50
20	306	730	370	219	40
30	.2334	.9724	.2401	4.165	30
40	363	717	432	113	20
50	391	710	462	061	10
14° 00′	.2419	.9703	.2493	4.011	76° 00′
10	447	696	524	3.962	50
20	476	689	555	914	40
30	.2504	.9681	.2586	3.867	30
40	532	674	617	821	20
50	560	667	648	776	10
15° 00′	.2588	.9659	.2679	3.732	75° 00′
10	616	652	711	689	50
20′	644	644	742	647	40
30	.2672	.9636	.2773	3.606	30
40	700	628	805	566	20
50	728	621	836	526	10
16° 00′	.2756	.9613	.2867	3.487	74° 00′
10	784	605	899	450	50
20	812	596	931	412	40
30	.2840	.9588	.2962	3.376	30
40	868	580	994	340	20
50	896	572	.3026	305	10
17° 00′	.2924	.9563	.3057	3.271	73° 00′
10	952	555	089	237	50
20	979	546	121	204	40
30	.3007	.9537	3153	3.172	30
40	035	528	185	140	20
50	062	520	217	108	10
18° 00′	.3090	.9511	.3249	3.078	72° 00′
	Cos	Sin	Cot	Tan	

	Sin	Cos	Tan	Cot	
18° 00′	.3090	.9511	.3249	3.078	**72° 00′**
10	118	502	281	047	50
20	.145	492	314	018	40
30	.3173	.9483	.3346	2.989	30
40	201	.474	378	960	20
50	228	465	411	932	10
19° 00′	.3256	.9455	.3443	2.904	**71° 00′**
10	283	446	476	877	50
20	311	.436	508	850	40
30	.3338	.9426	.3541	2.824	30
40	365	417	574	798	20
50	393	407	607	773	10
20° 00′	.3420	.9397	.3640	2.747	**70° 00′**
10	448	387	673	723	50
20	475	377	706	699	40
30	.3502	.9367	.3739	2.675	30
40	529	356	772	651	20
50	557	346	805	628	10
21° 00′	.3584	.9336	.3839	2.605	**69° 00′**
10	611	325	872	583	50
20	638	315	906	560	40
30	.3665	.9304	.3939	2.539	30
40	692	293	973	517	20
50	719	283	.4006	496	10
22° 00′	.3746	.9272	.4040	2.475	**68° 00′**
10	773	261	074	455	50
20	800	250	108	434	40
30	.3827	.9239	.4142	2.414	30
40	854	228	176	394	20
50	881	216	210	375	10
23° 00′	.3907	.9205	.4245	2.356	**67° 00′**
10	934	194	279	337	50
20	961	182	314	318	40
30	.3987	.9171	.4348	2.300	30
40	.4014	159	383	282	20
50	041	147	417	264	10
24° 00′	.4067	.9135	.4452	2.246	**66° 00′**
10	094	124	487	229	50
20	120	112	522	211.	40
30	.4147	.9100	.4557	2.194	30
40	173	088	592	177	20
50	200	075	628	161	10
25° 00′	.4226	.9063	.4663	2.145	**65° 00′**
10	253	051	699	128	50
20	279	038	734	112	40
30	.4305	.9026	.4770	2.097	30
40	331	013	806	081	20
50	358	001	841	066	10
26° 00′	.4384	.8988	.4877	2.050	**64° 00′**
10	410	975	913	035	50
20	436	962	950	020	40
30	.4462	.8949	.4986	2.006	30
40	488	936	.5022	1.991	20
50	514	923	059	977	10
27° 00′	.4540	.8910	.5095	1.963	**63° 00′**
	Cos	Sin	Cot	Tan	

TABLE II. NATURAL TRIGONOMETRIC FUNCTIONS | 209

	Sin	Cos	Tan	Cot	
27° 00′	.4540	.8910	.5095	1.963	63° 00′
10	566	897	132	949	50
20	592	884	169	935	40
30	.4617	.8870	.5206	1.921	30
40	643	857	243	907	20
50	669	843	280	894	10
28° 00′	.4695	.8829	.5317	1.881	62° 00′
10	720	816	354	868	50
20	746	802	392	855	40
30	.4772	.8788	.5430	1.842	30
40	797	774	467	829	20
50	823	760	505	816	10
29° 00′	.4848	.8746	.5543	1.804	61° 00′
10	874	732	581	792	50
20	899	718	619	780	40
30	.4924	.8704	.5658	1.767	30
40	950	689	696	756	20
50	975	675	735	744	10
30° 00′	.5000	.8660	.5774	1.732	60° 00′
10	025	646	812	720	50
20	050	631	851	709	40
30	.5075	.8616	.5890	1.698	30
40	100	601	930	686	20
50	125	587	969	675	10
31° 00′	.5150	.8572	.6009	1.664	59° 00′
10	175	557	048	653	50
20	200	542	088	643	40
30	.5225	.8526	.6128	1.632	30
40	250	511	168	621	20
50	275	496	208	611	10
32° 00′	.5299	.8480	.6249	1.600	58° 00′
10	324	465	289	590	50
20	348	450	330	580	40
30	.5373	.8434	.6371	1.570	30
40	398	418	412	560	20
50	422	403	453	550	10
33° 00′	.5446	.8387	.6494	1.540	57° 00′
10	471	371	536	530	50
20	495	355	577	520	40
30	.5519	.8339	.6619	1.511	30
40	544	323	661	501	20
50	568	307	703	1.492	10
34° 00′	.5592	.8290	.6745	1.483	56° 00′
10	616	274	787	473	50
20	640	258	830	464	40
30	.5664	.8241	.6873	1.455	30
40	688	225	916	446	20
50	712	208	959	437	10
35° 00′	.5736	.8192	.7002	1.428	55° 00′
10	760	175	046	419	50
20	783	158	089	411	.40
30	.5807	.8141	.7133	1.402	30
40	831	124	177	393	20
50	854	107	221	385	10
36° 00′	.5878	.8090	.7265	1.376	54° 00′
	Cos	Sin	Cot	Tan	

	Sin	Cos	Tan	Cot	
36° 00′	.5878	.8090	.7265	1.376	54° 00′
10	901	073	310	368	50
20	925	056	355	360	40
30	.5948	.8039	.7400	1.351	30
40	972	021	445	343	20
50	995	004	490	335	10
37° 00′	.6018	.7986	.7536	1.327	53° 00′
10	041	969	581	319	50
20	065	951	627	311	40
30	.6088	.7934	.7673	1.303	30
40	111	916	720	295	20
50	134	898	766	288	10
38° 00′	.6157	.7880	.7813	1.280	52° 00′
10	180	862	860	272	50
20	202	844	907	265	40
30	.6225	.7826	.7954	1.257	30
40	248	808	.8002	250	20
50	271	790	050	242	10
39° 00′	.6293	.7771	.8098	1.235	51° 00′
10	316	753	146	228	50
20	338	735	195	220	40
30	.6361	.7716	.8243	1.213	30
40	383	698	292	206	20
50	406	679	342	199	10
40° 00′	.6428	.7660	.8391	1.192	50° 00′
10	450	642	441	185	50
20	472	623	491	178	40
30	.6494	.7604	.8541	1.171	30
40	517	585	591	164	20
50	539	566	642	157	10
41° 00′	.6561	.7547	.8693	1.150	49° 00′
10	583	528	744	144	50
20	604	509	796	137	40
30	6626	.7490	.8847	1.130	30
40	648	470	899	124	20
50	670	451	952	117	10
42° 00′	6691	.7431	.9004	1.111	48° 00′
10	713	412	057	104	50
20	734	392	110	098	40
30	6756	.7373	.9163	1.091	30
40	777	353	217	085	20
50	799	333	271	079	10
43° 00′	6820	.7314	.9325	1.072	47° 00′
10	841	294	380	066	50
20	862	274	435	060	40
30	6884	.7254	.9490	1.054	30
40	905	234	545	048	20
50	926	214	601	042	10
44° 00′	6947	.7193	.9657	1.036	46° 00′
10	967	173	713	030	50
20	988	153	770	024	40
30	7009	.7133	.9827	1.018	30
40	030	112	884	012	20
50	050	092	942	006	10
45° 00′	7071	.7071	1.000	1.000	45° 00′
	Cos	Sin	Cot	Tan	

Table III

LOGARITHMS
OF THE
TRIGONOMETRIC FUNCTIONS

0°

	L. Sin.	L. Tan.	L. Cot.	L. Cos.	
0	—	—	—	10.00 000	60
1	6.46 373	6.46 373	13.53 627	10.00 000	59
2	6.76 476	6.76 476	13.23 524	10.00 000	58
3	6.94 085	6.94 085	13.05 915	10.00 000	57
4	7.06 579	7.06 579	12.93 421	10.00 000	56
5	7.16 270	7.16 270	12.83 730	10.00 000	55
6	7.24 188	7.24 188	12.75 812	10.00 000	54
7	7.30 882	7.30 882	12.69 118	10.00 000	53
8	7.36 682	7.36 682	12.63 318	10.00 000	52
9	7.41 797	7.41 797	12.58 203	10.00 000	51
10	7.46 373	7.46 373	12.53 627	10.00 000	50
11	7.50 512	7.50 512	12.49 488	10.00 000	49
12	7.54 291	7.54 291	12.45 709	10.00 000	48
13	7.57 767	7.57 767	12.42 233	10.00 000	47
14	7.60 985	7.60 986	12.39 014	10.00 000	46
15	7.63 982	7.63 982	12.36 018	10.00 000	45
16	7.66 784	7.66 785	12.33 215	10.00 000	44
17	7.69 417	7.69 418	12.30 582	9.99 999	43
18	7.71 900	7.71 900	12.28 100	9.99 999	42
19	7.74 248	7.74 248	12.25 752	9.99 999	41
20	7.76 475	7.76 476	12.23 524	9.99 999	40
21	7.78 594	7.78 595	12.21 405	9.99 999	39
22	7.80 615	7.80 615	12.19 385	9.99 999	38
23	7.82 545	7.82 546	12.17 454	9.99 999	37
24	7.84 393	7.84 394	12.15 606	9.99 999	36
25	7.86 166	7.86 167	12.13 833	9.99 999	35
26	7.87 870	7.87 871	12.12 129	9.99 999	34
27	7.89 509	7.89 510	12.10 490	9.99 999	33
28	7.91 088	7.91 089	12.08 911	9.99 999	32
29	7.92 612	7.92 613	12.07 387	9.99 998	31
30	7.94 084	7.94 086	12.05 914	9.99 998	30
31	7.95 508	7.95 510	12.04 490	9.99 998	29
32	7.96 887	7.96 889	12.03 111	9.99 998	28
33	7.98 223	7.98 225	12.01 775	9.99 998	27
34	7.99 520	7.99 522	12.00 478	9.99 998	26
35	8.00 779	8.00 781	11.99 219	9.99 998	25
36	8.02 002	8.02 004	11.97 996	9.99 998	24
37	8.03 192	8.03 194	11.96 806	9.99 997	23
38	8.04 350	8.04 353	11.95 647	9.99 997	22
39	8.05 478	8.05 481	11.94 519	9.99 997	21
40	8.06 578	8.06 581	11.93 419	9.99 997	20
41	8.07 650	8.07 653	11.92 347	9.99 997	19
42	8.08 696	8.08 700	11.91 300	9.99 997	18
43	8.09 718	8.09 722	11.90 278	9.99 997	17
44	8.10 717	8.10 720	11.89 280	9.99 996	16
45	8.11 693	8.11 696	11.88 304	9.99 996	15
46	8.12 647	8.12 651	11.87 349	9.99 996	14
47	8.13 581	8.13 585	11.86 415	9.99 996	13
48	8.14 495	8.14 500	11.85 500	9.99 996	12
49	8.15 391	8.15 395	11.84 605	9.99 996	11
50	8.16 268	8.16 273	11.83 727	9.99 995	10
51	8.17 128	8.17 133	11.82 867	9.99 995	9
52	8.17 971	8.17 976	11.82 024	9.99 995	8
53	8.18 798	8.18 804	11.81 196	9.99 995	7
54	8.19 610	8.19 616	11.80 384	9.99 995	6
55	8.20 407	8.20 413	11.79 587	9.99 994	5
56	8.21 189	8.21 195	11.78 805	9.99 994	4
57	8.21 958	8.21 964	11.78 036	9.99 994	3
58	8.22 713	8.22 720	11.77 280	9.99 994	2
59	8.23 456	8.23 462	11.76 538	9.99 994	1
60	8.24 186	8.24 192	11.75 808	9.99 993	0
	L. Cos.	L. Cot.	L. Tan.	L. Sin.	'

89°

TABLE III. LOGARITHMS OF FUNCTIONS | 213

1°

′	L. Sin.	L. Tan.	L. Cot.	L. Cos.	
0	8.24 186	8.24 192	11.75 808	9.99 993	60
1	8.24 903	8.24 910	11.75 090	9.99 993	59
2	8.25 609	8.25 616	11.74 384	9.99 993	58
3	8.26 304	8.26 312	11.73 688	9.99 993	57
4	8.26 988	8.26 996	11.73 004	9.99 992	56
5	8.27 661	8.27 669	11.72 331	9.99 992	55
6	8.28 324	8.28 332	11.71 668	9.99 992	54
7	8.28 977	8.28 986	11.71 014	9.99 992	53
8	8.29 621	8.29 629	11.70 371	9.99 992	52
9	8.30 255	8.30 263	11.69 737	9.99 991	51
10	8.30 879	8.30 888	11.69 112	9.99 991	50
11	8.31 495	8.31 505	11.68 495	9.99 991	49
12	8.32 103	8.32 112	11.67 888	9.99 990	48
13	8.32 702	8.32 711	11.67 289	9.99 990	47
14	8.33 292	8.33 302	11.66 698	9.99 990	46
15	8.33 875	8.33 886	11.66 114	9.99 990	45
16	8.34 450	8.34 461	11.65 539	9.99 989	44
17	8.35 018	8.35 029	11.64 971	9.99 989	43
18	8.35 578	8.35 590	11.64 410	9.99 989	42
19	8.36 131	8.36 143	11.63 857	9.99 989	41
20	8.36 678	8.36 689	11.63 311	9.99 988	40
21	8.37 217	8.37 229	11.62 771	9.99 988	39
22	8.37 750	8.37 762	11.62 238	9.99 988	38
23	8.38 276	8.38 289	11.61 711	9.99 987	37
24	8.38 796	8.38 809	11.61 191	9.99 987	36
25	8.39 310	8.39 323	11.60 677	9.99 987	35
26	8.39 818	8.39 832	11.60 168	9.99 986	34
27	8.40 320	8.40 334	11.59 666	9.99 986	33
28	8.40 816	8.40 830	11.59 170	9.99 986	32
29	8.41 307	8.41 321	11.58 679	9.99 985	31
30	8.41 792	8.41 807	11.58 193	9.99 985	30
31	8.42 272	8.42 287	11.57 713	9.99 985	29
32	8.42 746	8.42 762	11.57 238	9.99 984	28
33	8.43 216	8.43 232	11.56 768	9.99 984	27
34	8.43 680	8.43 696	11.56 304	9.99 984	26
35	8.44 139	8.44 156	11.55 844	9.99 983	25
36	8.44 594	8.44 611	11.55 389	9.99 983	24
37	8.45 044	8.45 061	11.54 939	9.99 983	23
38	8.45 489	8.45 507	11.54 493	9.99 982	22
39	8.45 930	8.45 948	11.54 052	9.99 982	21
40	8.46 366	8.46 385	11.53 615	9.99 982	20
41	8.46 799	8.46 817	11.53 183	9.99 981	19
42	8.47 226	8.47 245	11.52 755	9.99 981	18
43	8.47 650	8.47 669	11.52 331	9.99 981	17
44	8.48 069	8.48 089	11.51 911	9.99 980	16
45	8.48 485	8.48 505	11.51 495	9.99 980	15
46	8.48 896	8.48 917	11.51 083	9.99 979	14
47	8.49 304	8.49 325	11.50 675	9.99 979	13
48	8.49 708	8.49 729	11.50 271	9.99 979	12
49	8.50 108	8.50 130	11.49 870	9.99 978	11
50	8.50 504	8.50 527	11.49 473	9.99 978	10
51	8.50 897	8.50 920	11.49 080	9.99 977	9
52	8.51 287	8.51 310	11.48 690	9.99 977	8
53	8.51 673	8.51 696	11.48 304	9.99 977	7
54	8.52 055	8.52 079	11.47 921	9.99 976	6
55	8.52 434	8.52 459	11.47 541	9.99 976	5
56	8.52 810	8.52 835	11.47 165	9.99 975	4
57	8.53 183	8.53 208	11.46 792	9.99 975	3
58	8.53 552	8.53 578	11.46 422	9.99 974	2
59	8.53 919	8.53 945	11.46 055	9.99 974	1
60	8.54 282	8.54 308	11.45 692	9.99 974	0
	L. Cos.	L. Cot.	L. Tan.	L. Sin.	′

2°

'	L. Sin.	L. Tan.	L. Cot.	L. Cos.	
0	8.54 282	8.54 308	11.45 692	9.99 974	60
1	8.54 642	8.54 669	11.45 331	9.99 973	59
2	8.54 999	8.55 027	11.44 973	9.99 973	58
3	8.55 354	8.55 382	11.44 618	9.99 972	57
4	8.55 705	8.55 734	11.44 266	9.99 972	56
5	8.56 054	8.56 083	11.43 917	9.99 971	55
6	8.56 400	8.56 429	11.43 571	9.99 971	54
7	8.56 743	8.56 773	11.43 227	9.99 970	53
8	8.57 084	8.57 114	11.42 886	9.99 970	52
9	8.57 421	8.57 452	11.42 548	9.99 969	51
10	8.57 757	8.57 788	11.42 212	9.99 969	50
11	8.58 089	8.58 121	11.41 879	9.99 968	49
12	8.58 419	8.58 451	11.41 549	9.99 968	48
13	8.58 747	8.58 779	11.41 221	9.99 967	47
14	8.59 072	8.59 105	11.40 895	9.99 967	46
15	8.59 395	8.59 428	11.40 572	9.99 967	45
16	8.59 715	8.59 749	11.40 251	9.99 966	44
17	8.60 033	8.60 068	11.39 932	9.99 966	43
18	8.60 349	8.60 384	11.39 616	9.99 965	42
19	8.60 662	8.60 698	11.39 302	9.99 964	41
20	8.60 973	8.61 009	11.38 991	9.99 964	40
21	8.61 282	8.61 319	11.38 681	9.99 963	39
22	8.61 589	8.61 626	11.38 374	9.99 963	38
23	8.61 894	8.61 931	11.38 069	9.99 962	37
24	8.62 196	8.62 234	11.37 766	9.99 962	36
25	8.62 497	8.62 535	11.37 465	9.99 961	35
26	8.62 795	8.62 834	11.37 166	9.99 961	34
27	8.63 091	8.63 131	11.36 869	9.99 960	33
28	8.63 385	8.63 426	11.36 574	9.99 960	32
29	8.63 678	8.63 718	11.36 282	9.99 959	31
30	8.63 968	8.64 009	11.35 991	9.99 959	30
31	8.64 256	8.64 298	11.35 702	9.99 958	29
32	8.64 543	8.64 585	11.35 415	9.99 958	28
33	8.64 827	8.64 870	11.35 130	9.99 957	27
34	8.65 110	8.65 154	11.34 846	9.99 956	26
35	8.65 391	8.65 435	11.34 565	9.99 956	25
36	8.65 670	8.65 715	11.34 285	9.99 955	24
37	8.65 947	8.65 993	11.34 007	9.99 955	23
38	8.66 223	8.66 269	11.33 731	9.99 954	22
39	8.66 497	8.66 543	11.33 457	9.99 954	21
40	8.66 769	8.66 816	11.33 184	9.99 953	20
41	8.67 039	8.67 087	11.32 913	9.99 952	19
42	8.67 308	8.67 356	11.32 644	9.99 952	18
43	8.67 575	8.67 624	11.32 376	9.99 951	17
44	8.67 841	8.67 890	11.32 110	9.99 951	16
45	8.68 104	8.68 154	11.31 846	9.99 950	15
46	8.68 367	8.68 417	11.31 583	9.99 949	14
47	8.68 627	8.68 678	11.31 322	9.99 949	13
48	8.68 886	8.68 938	11.31 062	9.99 948	12
49	8.69 144	8.69 196	11.30 804	9.99 948	11
50	8.69 400	8.69 453	11.30 547	9.99 947	10
51	8.69 654	8.69 708	11.30 292	9.99 946	9
52	8.69 907	8.69 962	11.30 038	9.99 946	8
53	8.70 159	8.70 214	11.29 786	9.99 945	7
54	8.70 409	8.70 465	11.29 535	9.99 944	6
55	8.70 658	8.70 714	11.29 286	9.99 944	5
56	8.70 905	8.70 962	11.29 038	9.99 943	4
57	8.71 151	8.71 208	11.28 792	9.99 942	3
58	8.71 395	8.71 453	11.28 547	9.99 942	2
59	8.71 638	8.71 697	11.28 303	9.99 941	1
60	8.71 880	8.71 940	11.28 060	9.99 940	0
	L. Cos.	L. Cot.	L. Tan.	L. Sin.	'

87°

TABLE III. LOGARITHMS OF FUNCTIONS | 215

3°

′	L. Sin.	d.	L. Tan.	c. d.	L. Cot.	L. Cos.	
0	8.71 880		8.71 940		11.28 060	9.99 940	60
1	8.72 120	240	8.72 181	241	11.27 819	9.99 940	59
2	8.72 359	239	8.72 420	239	11.27 580	9.99 939	58
3	8.72 597	238	8.72 659	239	11.27 341	9.99 938	57
4	8.72 834	237	8.72 896	237	11.27 104	9.99 938	56
5	8.73 069	235	8.73 132	236	11.26 868	9.99 937	55
6	8.73 303	234	8.73 366	234	11.26 634	9.99 936	54
7	8.73 535	232	8.73 600	234	11.26 400	9.99 936	53
8	8.73 767	232	8.73 832	232	11.26 168	9.99 935	52
9	8.73 997	230	8.74 063	231	11.25 937	9.99 934	51
10	8.74 226	229	8.74 292	229	11.25 708	9.99 934	50
11	8.74 454	228	8.74 521	229	11.25 479	9.99 933	49
12	8.74 680	226	8.74 748	227	11.25 252	9.99 932	48
13	8.74 906	226	8.74 974	226	11.25 026	9.99 932	47
14	8.75 130	224	8.75 199	225	11.24 801	9.99 931	46
15	8.75 353	223	8.75 423	224	11.24 577	9.99 930	45
16	8.75 575	222	8.75 645	222	11.24 355	9.99 929	44
17	8.75 795	220	8.75 867	222	11.24 133	9.99 929	43
18	8.76 015	220	8.76 087	220	11.23 913	9.99 928	42
19	8.76 234	219	8.76 306	219	11.23 694	9.99 927	41
20	8.76 451	217	8.76 525	219	11.23 475	9.99 926	40
21	8.76 667	216	8.76 742	217	11.23 258	9.99 926	39
22	8.76 883	216	8.76 958	216	11.23 042	9.99 925	38
23	8.77 097	214	8.77 173	215	11.22 827	9.99 924	37
24	8.77 310	213	8.77 387	214	11.22 613	9.99 923	36
25	8.77 522	212	8.77 600	213	11.22 400	9.99 923	35
26	8.77 733	211	8.77 811	211	11.22 189	9.99 922	34
27	8.77 943	210	8.78 022	211	11.21 978	9.99 921	33
28	8.78 152	209	8.78 232	210	11.21 768	9.99 920	32
29	8.78 360	208	8.78 441	209	11.21 559	9.99 920	31
30	8.78 568	208	8.78 649	208	11.21 351	9.99 919	30
31	8.78 774	206	8.78 855	206	11.21 145	9.99 918	29
32	8.78 979	205	8.79 061	206	11.20 939	9.99 917	28
33	8.79 183	204	8.79 266	205	11.20 734	9.99 917	27
34	8.79 386	203	8.79 470	204	11.20 530	9.99 916	26
35	8.79 588	202	8.79 673	203	11.20 327	9.99 915	25
36	8.79 789	201	8.79 875	202	11.20 125	9.99 914	24
37	8.79 990	201	8.80 076	201	11.19 924	9.99 913	23
38	8.80 189	199	8.80 277	201	11.19 723	9.99 913	22
39	8.80 388	199	8.80 476	199	11.19 524	9.99 912	21
40	8.80 585	197	8.80 674	198	11.19 326	9.99 911	20
41	8.80 782	197	8.80 872	198	11.19 128	9.99 910	19
42	8.80 978	196	8.81 069	196	11.18 932	9.99 909	18
43	8.81 173	195	8.81 264	196	11.18 736	9.99 909	17
44	8.81 367	194	8.81 459	195	11.18 541	9.99 908	16
45	8.81 560	193	8.81 653	194	11.18 347	9.99 907	15
46	8.81 752	192	8.81 846	193	11.18 154	9.99 906	14
47	8.81 944	192	8.82 038	192	11.17 962	9.99 905	13
48	8.82 134	190	8.82 230	192	11.17 770	9.99 904	12
49	8.82 324	190	8.82 420	190	11.17 580	9.99 904	11
50	8.82 513	189	8.82 610	190	11.17 390	9.99 903	10
51	8.82 701	188	8.82 799	189	11.17 201	9.99 902	9
52	8.82 888	187	8.82 987	188	11.17 013	9.99 901	8
53	8.83 075	187	8.83 175	188	11.16 825	9.99 900	7
54	8.83 261	186	8.83 361	186	11.16 639	9.99 899	6
55	8.83 446	185	8.83 547	186	11.16 453	9.99 898	5
56	8.83 630	184	8.83 732	185	11.16 268	9.99 898	4
57	8.83 813	183	8.83 916	184	11.16 084	9.99 897	3
58	8.83 996	183	8.84 100	184	11.15 900	9.99 896	2
59	8.84 177	181	8.84 282	182	11.15 718	9.99 895	1
60	8.84 358	181	8.84 464	182	11.15 536	9.99 894	0
	L. Cos.	d.	L. Cot.	c. d.	L. Tan.	L. Sin.	′

P. P.

	241	239	237	236	234
1	24.1	23.9	23.7	23.6	23.4
2	48.2	47.8	47.4	47.2	46.8
3	72.3	71.7	71.1	70.8	70.2
4	96.4	95.6	94.8	94.4	93.6
5	120.5	119.5	118.5	118.0	117.0
6	144.6	143.4	142.2	141.6	140.4
7	168.7	167.3	165.9	165.2	163.8
8	192.8	191.2	189.6	188.8	187.2
9	216.9	215.1	213.3	212.4	210.6

	232	231	229	227	226
1	23.2	23.1	22.9	22.7	22.6
2	46.4	46.2	45.8	45.4	45.2
3	69.6	69.3	68.7	68.1	67.8
4	92.8	92.4	91.6	90.8	90.4
5	116.0	115.5	114.5	113.5	113.0
6	139.2	138.6	137.4	136.2	135.6
7	162.4	161.7	160.3	158.9	158.2
8	185.6	184.8	183.2	181.6	180.8
9	208.8	207.9	206.1	204.3	203.4

	224	222	220	219	217
1	22.4	22.2	22.0	21.9	21.7
2	44.8	44.4	44.0	43.8	43.4
3	67.2	66.6	66.0	65.7	65.1
4	89.6	88.8	88.0	87.6	86.8
5	112.0	111.0	110.0	109.5	108.5
6	134.4	133.2	132.0	131.4	130.2
7	156.8	155.4	154.0	153.3	151.9
8	179.2	177.6	176.0	175.2	173.6
9	201.6	199.8	198.0	197.1	195.3

	216	214	213	211	209
1	21.6	21.4	21.3	21.1	20.9
2	43.2	42.8	42.6	42.2	41.8
3	64.8	64.2	63.9	63.3	62.7
4	86.4	85.6	85.2	84.4	83.6
5	108.0	107.0	106.5	105.5	104.5
6	129.6	128.4	127.8	126.6	125.4
7	151.2	149.8	149.1	147.7	146.3
8	172.8	171.2	170.4	168.8	167.2
9	194.4	192.6	191.7	189.9	188.1

	208	206	203	201	199
1	20.8	20.6	20.3	20.1	19.9
2	41.6	41.2	40.6	40.2	39.8
3	62.4	61.8	60.9	60.3	59.7
4	83.2	82.4	81.2	80.4	79.6
5	104.0	103.0	101.5	100.5	99.5
6	124.8	123.6	121.8	120.6	119.4
7	145.6	144.2	142.1	140.7	139.3
8	166.4	164.8	162.4	160.8	159.2
9	187.2	185.4	182.7	180.9	179.1

	198	196	194	192	190
1	19.8	19.6	19.4	19.2	19.0
2	39.6	39.2	38.8	38.4	38.0
3	59.4	58.8	58.2	57.6	57.0
4	79.2	78.4	77.6	76.8	76.0
5	99.0	98.0	97.0	96.0	95.0
6	118.8	117.6	116.4	115.2	114.0
7	138.6	137.2	135.8	134.4	133.0
8	158.4	156.8	155.2	153.6	152.0
9	178.2	176.4	174.6	172.8	171.0

	188	186	184	182	181
1	18.8	18.6	18.4	18.2	18.1
2	37.6	37.2	36.8	36.4	36.2
3	56.4	55.8	55.2	54.6	54.3
4	75.2	74.4	73.6	72.8	72.4
5	94.0	93.0	92.0	91.0	90.5
6	112.8	111.6	110.4	109.2	108.6
7	131.6	130.2	128.8	127.4	126.7
8	150.4	148.8	147.2	145.6	144.8
9	169.2	167.4	165.6	163.8	162.9

P. P.

4°

'	L. Sin.	d.	L. Tan.	c. d.	L. Cot.	L. Cos.	
0	8.84 358		8.84 464		11.15 536	9.99 894	60
1	8.84 539	181	8.84 646	182	11.15 354	9.99 893	59
2	8.84 718	179	8.84 826	180	11.15 174	9.99 892	58
3	8.84 897	179	8.85 006	180	11.14 994	9.99 891	57
4	8.85 075	178	8.85 185	179	11.14 815	9.99 891	56
5	8.85 252	177	8.85 363	178	11.14 637	9.99 890	55
6	8.85 429	177	8.85 540	177	11.14 460	9.99 889	54
7	8.85 605	176	8.85 717	177	11.14 283	9.99 888	53
8	8.85 780	175	8.85 893	176	11.14 107	9.99 887	52
9	8.85 955	175	8.86 069	176	11.13 931	9.99 886	51
10	8.86 128	173	8.86 243	174	11.13 757	9.99 885	50
11	8.86 301	173	8.86 417	174	11.13 583	9.99 884	49
12	8.86 474	173	8.86 591	174	11.13 409	9.99 883	48
13	8.86 645	171	8.86 763	172	11.13 237	9.99 882	47
14	8.86 816	171	8.86 935	172	11.13 065	9.99 881	46
15	8.86 987	171	8.87 106	171	11.12 894	9.99 880	45
16	8.87 156	169	8.87 277	171	11.12 723	9.99 879	44
17	8.87 325	169	8.87 447	170	11.12 553	9.99 879	43
18	8.87 494	169	8.87 616	169	11.12 384	9.99 878	42
19	8.87 661	167	8.87 785	169	11.12 215	9.99 877	41
20	8.87 829	168	8.87 953	168	11.12 047	9.99 876	40
21	8.87 995	166	8.88 120	167	11.11 880	9.99 875	39
22	8.88 161	166	8.88 287	167	11.11 713	9.99 874	38
23	8.88 326	165	8.88 453	166	11.11 547	9.99 873	37
24	8.88 490	164	8.88 618	165	11.11 382	9.99 872	36
25	8.88 654	164	8.88 783	165	11.11 217	9.99 871	35
26	8.88 817	163	8.88 948	165	11.11 052	9.99 870	34
27	8.88 980	163	8.89 111	163	11.10 889	9.99 869	33
28	8.89 142	162	8.89 274	163	11.10 726	9.99 868	32
29	8.89 304	162	8.89 437	163	11.10 563	9.99 867	31
30	8.89 464	160	8.89 598	161	11.10 402	9.99 866	30
31	8.89 625	161	8.89 760	162	11.10 240	9.99 865	29
32	8.89 784	159	8.89 920	160	11.10 080	9.99 864	28
33	8.89 943	159	8.90 080	160	11.09 920	9.99 863	27
34	8.90 102	159	8.90 240	160	11.09 760	9.99 862	26
35	8.90 260	158	8.90 399	159	11.09 601	9.99 861	25
36	8.90 417	157	8.90 557	158	11.09 443	9.99 860	24
37	8.90 574	157	8.90 715	158	11.09 285	9.99 859	23
38	8.90 730	156	8.90 872	157	11.09 128	9.99 858	22
39	8.90 885	155	8.91 029	157	11.08 971	9.99 857	21
40	8.91 040	155	8.91 185	156	11.08 815	9.99 856	20
41	8.91 195	155	8.91 340	155	11.08 660	9.99 855	19
42	8.91 349	154	8.91 495	155	11.08 505	9.99 854	18
43	8.91 502	153	8.91 650	155	11.08 350	9.99 853	17
44	8.91 655	153	8.91 803	153	11.08 197	9.99 852	16
45	8.91 807	152	8.91 957	154	11.08 043	9.99 851	15
46	8.91 959	152	8.92 110	153	11.07 890	9.99 850	14
47	8.92 110	151	8.92 262	152	11.07 738	9.99 848	13
48	8.92 261	151	8.92 414	152	11.07 586	9.99 847	12
49	8.92 411	150	8.92 565	151	11.07 435	9.99 846	11
50	8.92 561	150	8.92 716	151	11.07 284	9.99 845	10
51	8.92 710	149	8.92 866	150	11.07 134	9.99 844	9
52	8.92 859	149	8.93 016	150	11.06 984	9.99 843	8
53	8.93 007	148	8.93 165	149	11.06 835	9.99 842	7
54	8.93 154	147	8.93 313	148	11.06 687	9.99 841	6
55	8.93 301	147	8.93 462	149	11.06 538	9.99 840	5
56	8.93 448	147	8.93 609	147	11.06 391	9.99 839	4
57	8.93 594	146	8.93 756	147	11.06 244	9.99 838	3
58	8.93 740	146	8.93 903	146	11.06 097	9.99 837	2
59	8.93 885	145	8.94 049	146	11.05 951	9.99 836	1
60	8.94 030	145	8.94 195	146	11.05 805	9.99 834	0
'	L. Cos.	d.	L. Cot.	c. d.	L. Tan.	L. Sin.	'

P. P.

	182	181	180	179	178
1	18.2	18.1	18.0	17.9	17.8
2	36.4	36.2	36.0	35.8	35.6
3	54.6	54.3	54.0	53.7	53.4
4	72.8	72.4	72.0	71.6	71.2
5	91.0	90.5	90.0	89.5	89.0
6	109.2	108.6	108.0	107.4	106.8
7	127.4	126.7	126.0	125.3	124.6
8	145.6	144.8	144.0	143.2	142.4
9	163.8	162.9	162.0	161.1	160.2

	177	176	175	174	173
1	17.7	17.6	17.5	17.4	17.3
2	35.4	35.2	35.0	34.8	34.6
3	53.1	52.8	52.5	52.2	51.9
4	70.8	70.4	70.0	69.6	69.2
5	88.5	88.0	87.5	87.0	86.5
6	106.2	105.6	105.0	104.4	103.8
7	123.9	123.2	122.5	121.8	121.1
8	141.6	140.8	140.0	139.2	138.4
9	159.3	158.4	157.5	156.6	155.7

	172	171	170	169	168
1	17.2	17.1	17.0	16.9	16.8
2	34.4	34.2	34.0	33.8	33.6
3	51.6	51.3	51.0	50.7	50.4
4	68.8	68.4	68.0	67.6	67.2
5	86.0	85.5	85.0	84.5	84.0
6	103.2	102.6	102.0	101.4	100.8
7	120.4	119.7	119.0	118.3	117.6
8	137.6	136.8	136.0	135.2	134.4
9	154.8	153.9	153.0	152.1	151.2

	167	166	165	164	163
1	16.7	16.6	16.5	16.4	16.3
2	33.4	33.2	33.0	32.8	32.6
3	50.1	49.8	49.5	49.2	48.9
4	66.8	66.4	66.0	65.6	65.2
5	83.5	83.0	82.5	82.0	81.5
6	100.2	99.6	99.0	98.4	97.8
7	116.9	116.2	115.5	114.8	114.1
8	133.6	132.8	132.0	131.2	130.4
9	150.3	149.4	148.5	147.6	146.7

	162	161	160	159	158
1	16.2	16.1	16.0	15.9	15.8
2	32.4	32.2	32.0	31.8	31.6
3	48.6	48.3	48.0	47.7	47.4
4	64.8	64.4	64.0	63.6	63.2
5	81.0	80.5	80.0	79.5	79.0
6	97.2	96.6	96.0	95.4	94.8
7	113.4	112.7	112.0	111.3	110.6
8	129.6	128.8	128.0	127.2	126.4
9	145.8	144.9	144.0	143.1	142.2

	157	156	155	154	153
1	15.7	15.6	15.5	15.4	15.3
2	31.4	31.2	31.0	30.8	30.6
3	47.1	46.8	46.5	46.2	45.9
4	62.8	62.4	62.0	61.6	61.2
5	78.5	78.0	77.5	77.0	76.5
6	94.2	93.6	93.0	92.4	91.8
7	109.9	109.2	108.5	107.8	107.1
8	125.6	124.8	124.0	123.2	122.4
9	141.3	140.4	139.5	138.6	137.7

	152	151	150	149	148
1	15.2	15.1	15.0	14.9	14.8
2	30.4	30.2	30.0	29.8	29.6
3	45.6	45.3	45.0	44.7	44.4
4	60.8	60.4	60.0	59.6	59.2
5	76.0	75.5	75.0	74.5	74.0
6	91.2	90.6	90.0	89.4	88.8
7	106.4	105.7	105.0	104.3	103.6
8	121.6	120.8	120.0	119.2	118.4
9	136.8	135.9	135.0	134.1	133.2

P. P.

TABLE III. LOGARITHMS OF FUNCTIONS | 217

5°

'	L. Sin.	d.	L. Tan.	c. d.	L. Cot.	L. Cos.	'
0	8.94 030	144	8.94 195	145	11.05 805	9.99 834	60
1	8.94 174	143	8.94 340	145	11.05 660	9.99 833	59
2	8.94 317	144	8.94 485	145	11.05 515	9.99 832	58
3	8.94 461	142	8.94 630	143	11.05 370	9.99 831	57
4	8.94 603	143	8.94 773	144	11.05 227	9.99 830	56
5	8.94 746	141	8.94 917	143	11.05 083	9.99 829	55
6	8.94 887	142	8.95 060	142	11.04 940	9.99 828	54
7	8.95 029	141	8.95 202	142	11.04 798	9.99 827	53
8	8.95 170	140	8.95 344	142	11.04 656	9.99 825	52
9	8.95 310	140	8.95 486	141	11.04 514	9.99 824	51
10	8.95 450	139	8.95 627	140	11.04 373	9.99 823	50
11	8.95 589	139	8.95 767	141	11.04 233	9.99 822	49
12	8.95 728	139	8.95 908	139	11.04 092	9.99 821	48
13	8.95 867	138	8.96 047	140	11.03 953	9.99 820	47
14	8.96 005	138	8.96 187	138	11.03 813	9.99 819	46
15	8.96 143	137	8.96 325	139	11.03 675	9.99 817	45
16	8.96 280	137	8.96 464	138	11.03 536	9.99 816	44
17	8.96 417	136	8.96 602	137	11.03 398	9.99 815	43
18	8.96 553	136	8.96 739	138	11.03 261	9.99 814	42
19	8.96 689	136	8.96 877	136	11.03 123	9.99 813	41
20	8.96 825	135	8.97 013	137	11.02 987	9.99 812	40
21	8.96 960	135	8.97 150	135	11.02 850	9.99 810	39
22	8.97 095	134	8.97 285	136	11.02 715	9.99 809	38
23	8.97 229	134	8.97 421	135	11.02 579	9.99 808	37
24	8.97 363	133	8.97 556	135	11.02 444	9.99 807	36
25	8.97 496	133	8.97 691	134	11.02 309	9.99 806	35
26	8.97 629	133	8.97 825	134	11.02 175	9.99 804	34
27	8.97 762	132	8.97 959	134	11.02 041	9.99 803	33
28	8.97 894	132	8.98 092	133	11.01 908	9.99 802	32
29	8.98 026	131	8.98 225	133	11.01 775	9.99 801	31
30	8.98 157	131	8.98 358	132	11.01 642	9.99 800	30
31	8.98 288	131	8.98 490	132	11.01 510	9.99 798	29
32	8.98 419	130	8.98 622	131	11.01 378	9.99 797	28
33	8.98 549	130	8.98 753	131	11.01 247	9.99 796	27
34	8.98 679	129	8.98 884	131	11.01 116	9.99 795	26
35	8.98 808	129	8.99 015	130	11.00 985	9.99 793	25
36	8.98 937	129	8.99 145	130	11.00 855	9.99 792	24
37	8.99 066	128	8.99 275	130	11.00 725	9.99 791	23
38	8.99 194	128	8.99 405	129	11.00 595	9.99 790	22
39	8.99 322	128	8.99 534	129	11.00 466	9.99 788	21
40	8.99 450	127	8.99 662	129	11.00 338	9.99 787	20
41	8.99 577	127	8.99 791	128	11.00 209	9.99 786	19
42	8.99 704	126	8.99 919	127	11.00 081	9.99 785	18
43	8.99 830	126	9.00 046	128	10.99 954	9.99 783	17
44	8.99 956	126	9.00 174	127	10.99 826	9.99 782	16
45	9.00 082	125	9.00 301	126	10.99 699	9.99 781	15
46	9.00 207	125	9.00 427	126	10.99 573	9.99 780	14
47	9.00 332	124	9.00 553	126	10.99 447	9.99 778	13
48	9.00 456	125	9.00 679	126	10.99 321	9.99 777	12
49	9.00 581	123	9.00 805	125	10.99 195	9.99 776	11
50	9.00 704	124	9.00 930	125	10.99 070	9.99 775	10
51	9.00 828	123	9.01 055	124	10.98 945	9.99 773	9
52	9.00 951	123	9.01 179	124	10.98 821	9.99 772	8
53	9.01 074	122	9.01 303	124	10.98 697	9.99 771	7
54	9.01 196	122	9.01 427	123	10.98 573	9.99 769	6
55	9.01 318	122	9.01 550	123	10.98 450	9.99 768	5
56	9.01 440	121	9.01 673	123	10.98 327	9.99 767	4
57	9.01 561	121	9.01 796	122	10.98 204	9.99 765	3
58	9.01 682	121	9.01 918	122	10.98 082	9.99 764	2
59	9.01 803	120	9.02 040	122	10.97 960	9.99 763	1
60	9.01 923		9.02 162		10.97 838	9.99 761	0

| | L. Cos. | d. | L. Cot. | c. d. | L. Tan. | L. Sin. | ' |

P. P.

	147	146	145	144
1	14.7	14.6	14.5	14.4
2	29.4	29.2	29.0	28.8
3	44.1	43.8	43.5	43.2
4	58.8	58.4	58.0	57.6
5	73.5	73.0	72.5	72.0
6	88.2	87.6	87.0	86.4
7	102.9	102.2	101.5	100.8
8	117.6	116.8	116.0	115.2
9	132.3	131.4	130.5	129.6

	143	142	141	140
1	14.3	14.2	14.1	14.0
2	28.6	28.4	28.2	28.0
3	42.9	42.6	42.3	42.0
4	57.2	56.8	56.4	56.0
5	71.5	71.0	70.5	70.0
6	85.8	85.2	84.6	84.0
7	100.1	99.4	98.7	98.0
8	114.4	113.6	112.8	112.0
9	128.7	127.8	126.9	126.0

	139	138	137	136
1	13.9	13.8	13.7	13.6
2	27.8	27.6	27.4	27.2
3	41.7	41.4	41.1	40.8
4	55.6	55.2	54.8	54.4
5	69.5	69.0	68.5	68.0
6	83.4	82.8	82.2	81.6
7	97.3	96.6	95.9	95.2
8	111.2	110.4	109.6	108.8
9	125.1	124.2	123.3	122.4

	135	134	133	132
1	13.5	13.4	13.3	13.2
2	27.0	26.8	26.6	26.4
3	40.5	40.2	39.9	39.6
4	54.0	53.6	53.2	52.8
5	67.5	67.0	66.5	66.0
6	81.0	80.4	79.8	79.2
7	94.5	93.8	93.1	92.4
8	108.0	107.2	106.4	105.6
9	121.5	120.6	119.7	118.8

	131	130	129	128
1	13.1	13.0	12.9	12.8
2	26.2	26.0	25.8	25.6
3	39.3	39.0	38.7	38.4
4	52.4	52.0	51.6	51.2
5	65.5	65.0	64.5	64.0
6	78.6	78.0	77.4	76.8
7	91.7	91.0	90.3	89.6
8	104.8	104.0	103.2	102.4
9	117.9	117.0	116.1	115.2

	127	126	125	124
1	12.7	12.6	12.5	12.4
2	25.4	25.2	25.0	'24.8
3	38.1	37.8	37.5	37.2
4	50.8	50.4	50.0	49.6
5	63.5	63.0	62.5	62.0
6	76.2	75.6	75.0	74.4
7	88.9	88.2	87.5	86.8
8	101.6	100.8	100.0	99.2
9	114.3	113.4	112.5	111.6

	123	122	121	120
1	12.3	12.2	12.1	12.0
2	24.6	24.4	24.2	24.0
3	36.9	36.6	36.3	36.0
4	49.2	48.8	48.4	48.0
5	61.5	61.0	60.5	60.0
6	73.8	73.2	72.6	72.0
7	86.1	85.4	84.7	84.0
8	98.4	97.6	96.8	96.0
9	110.7	109.8	108.9	108.1

6°

'	L. Sin.	d.	L. Tan.	c. d.	L. Cot.	L. Cos.	'
0	9.01 923	120	9.02 162	121	10.97 838	9.99 761	60
1	9.02 043	120	9.02 283	121	10.97 717	9.99 760	59
2	9.02 163	120	9.02 404	121	10.97 596	9.99 759	58
3	9.02 283	119	9.02 525	120	10.97 475	9.99 757	57
4	9.02 402	118	9.02 645	121	10.97 355	9.99 756	56
5	9.02 520	119	9.02 766	119	10.97 234	9.99 755	55
6	9.02 639	118	9.02 885	120	10.97 115	9.99 753	54
7	9.02 757	117	9.03 005	119	10.96 995	9.99 752	53
8	9.02 874	118	9.03 124	118	10.96 876	9.99 751	52
9	9.02 992	117	9.03 242	119	10.96 758	9.99 749	51
10	9.03 109	117	9.03 361	118	10.96 639	9.99 748	50
11	9.03 226	116	9.03 479	118	10.96 521	9.99 747	49
12	9.03 342	116	9.03 597	117	10 96 403	9.99 745	48
13	9.03 458	116	9.03 714	118	10.96 286	9.99 744	47
14	9.03 574	116	9.03 832	116	10.96 168	9.99 742	46
15	9.03 690	115	9.03 948	117	10.96 052	9.99 741	45
16	9.03 805	115	9.04 065	116	10.95 935	9.99 740	44
17	9.03 920	114	9.04 181	116	10.95 819	9.99 738	43
18	9.04 034	115	9.04 297	116	10.95 703	9 99 737	42
19	9.04 149	113	9.04 413	115	10.95 587	9.99 736	41
20	9.04 262	114	9.04 528	115	10.95 472	9.99 734	40
21	9.04 376	114	9.04 643	115	10.95 357	9.99 733	39
22	9.04 490	113	9.04 758	115	10.95 242	9.99 731	38
23	9.04 603	112	9.04 873	114	10.95 127	9.99 730	37
24	9.04 715	113	9.04 987	114	10.95 013	9.99 728	36
25	9.04 828	112	9.05 101	113	10.94 899	9.99 727	35
26	9.04 940	112	9.05 214	114	10.94 786	9.99 726	34
27	9.05 052	112	9.05 328	113	10.94 672	9.99 724	33
28	9.05 164	111	9.05 441	112	10.94 559	9.99 723	32
29	9.05 275	111	9.05 553	113	10.94 447	9.99 721	31
30	9.05 386	111	9.05 666	112	10.94 334	9.99 720	30
31	9.05 497	110	9.05 778	112	10.94 222	9.99 718	29
32	9.05 607	110	9.05 890	112	10.94 110	9.99 717	28
33	9.05 717	110	9.06 002	111	10.93 998	9.99 716	27
34	9.05 827	110	9.06 113	111	10.93 887	9.99 714	26
35	9.05 937	109	9.06 224	111	10.93 776	9.99 713	25
36	9.06 046	109	9.06 335	110	10.93 665	9.99 711	24
37	9.06 155	109	9.06 445	111	10.93 555	9.99 710	23
38	9.06 264	108	9.06 556	110	10.93 444	9.99 708	22
39	9.06 372	109	9.06 666	109	10.93 334	9.99 707	21
40	9.06 481	108	9.06 775	110	10.93 225	9.99 705	20
41	9.06 589	107	9.06 885	109	10.93 115	9.99 704	19
42	9.06 696	108	9.06 994	109	10.93 006	9.99 702	18
43	9.06 804	107	9.07 103	108	10.92 897	9.99 701	17
44	9.06 911	107	9.07 211	109	10.92 789	9.99 699	16
45	9.07 018	106	9.07 320	108	10.92 680	9.99 698	15
46	9.07 124	107	9.07 428	108	10.92 572	9.99 696	14
47	9.07 231	106	9.07 536	107	10.92 464	9.99 695	13
48	9.07 337	105	9.07 643	108	10.92 357	9.99 693	12
49	9.07 442	106	9.07 751	107	10.92 249	9.99 692	11
50	9.07 548	105	9.07 858	106	10.92 142	9.99 690	10
51	9.07 653	105	9.07 964	107	10.92 036	9.99 689	9
52	9.07 758	105	9.08 071	106	10.91 929	9.99 687	8
53	9.07 863	105	9.08 177	106	10.91 823	9.99 686	7
54	9.07 968	104	9.08 283	106	10.91 717	9.99 684	6
55	9.08 072	104	9.08 389	106	10.91 611	9.99 683	5
56	9.08 176	104	9.08 495	105	10.91 505	9.99 681	4
57	9.08 280	103	9.08 600	105	10.91 400	9.99 680	3
58	9.08 383	103	9.08 705	105	10.91 295	9.99 678	2
59	9.08 486	103	9.08 810	104	10.91 190	9.99 677	1
60	9.08 589		9.08 914		10.91 086	9.99 675	0

| | L. Cos. | d. | L. Cot. | c. d. | L. Tan. | L. Sin. | ' |

P. P.

	121	120	119	118
1	12.1	12.0	11.9	11.8
2	24.2	24.0	23.8	23.6
3	36.3	36.0	35.7	35.4
4	48.4	48.0	47.6	47.2
5	60.5	60.0	59.5	59.0
6	72.6	72.0	71.4	70.8
7	84.7	84.0	83.3	82.6
8	96.8	96.0	95.2	94.4
9	108.9	108.0	107.1	106.2

	117	116	115	114
1	11.7	11.6	11.5	11.4
2	23.4	23.2	23.0	22.8
3	35.1	34.8	34.5	34.2
4	46.8	46.4	46.0	45.6
5	58.5	58.0	57.5	57.0
6	70.2	69.6	69.0	68.4
7	81.9	81.2	80.5	79.8
8	93.6	92.8	92.0	91.2
9	105.3	104.4	103.5	102.6

	113	112	111	110
1	11.3	11.2	11.1	11.0
2	22.6	22.4	22.2	22.0
3	33.9	33.6	33.3	33.0
4	45.2	44.8	44.4	44.0
5	56.5	56.0	55.5	55.0
6	67.8	67.2	66.6	66.0
7	79.1	78.4	77.7	77.0
8	90.4	89.6	88.8	88.0
9	101.7	100.8	99.9	99.0

	109	108	107	106
1	10.9	10.8	10.7	10.6
2	21.8	21.6	21.4	21.2
3	32.7	32.4	32.1	31.8
4	43.6	43.2	42.8	42.4
5	54.5	54.0	53.5	53.0
6	65.4	64.8	64.2	63.6
7	76.3	75.6	74.9	74.2
8	87.2	86.4	85.6	84.8
9	98.1	97.2	96.3	95.4

	105	104	103
1	10.5	10.4	10.3
2	21.0	20.8	20.6
3	31.5	31.2	30.9
4	42.0	41.6	41.2
5	52.5	52.0	51.5
6	63.0	62.4	61.8
7	73.5	72.8	72.1
8	84.0	83.2	82.4
9	94.5	93.6	92.7

P. P.

83°

TABLE III. LOGARITHMS OF FUNCTIONS | 219

7°

′	L. Sin.	d.	L. Tan.	c. d.	L. Cot.	L. Cos.	
0	9.08 589	103	9.08 914	105	10.91 086	9.99 675	60
1	9.08 692	103	9.09 019	104	10.90 981	9.99 674	59
2	9.08 795	102	9.09 123	104	10.90 877	9.99 672	58
3	9.08 897	102	9.09 227	103	10.90 773	9.99 670	57
4	9.08 999	102	9.09 330	104	10.90 670	9.99 669	56
5	9.09 101	101	9.09 434	103	10.90 566	9.99 667	55
6	9.09 202	102	9.09 537	103	10.90 463	9.99 666	54
7	9.09 304	101	9.09 640	102	10.90 360	9.99 664	53
8	9.09 405	101	9.09 742	103	10.90 258	9.99 663	52
9	9.09 506	100	9.09 845	102	10.90 155	9.99 661	51
10	9.09 606	101	9.09 947	102	10.90 053	9.99 659	50
11	9.09 707	100	9.10 049	101	10.89 951	9.99 658	49
12	9.09 807	100	9.10 150	102	10.89 850	9.99 656	48
13	9.09 907	99	9.10 252	101	10.89 748	9.99 655	47
14	9.10 006	100	9.10 353	101	10.89 647	9.99 653	46
15	9.10 106	99	9.10 454	101	10.89 546	9.99 651	45
16	9.10 205	99	9.10 555	101	10.89 445	9.99 650	44
17	9.10 304	98	9.10 656	100	10.89 344	9.99 648	43
18	9.10 402	99	9.10 756	100	10.89 244	9.99 647	42
19	9.10 501	98	9.10 856	100	10.89 144	9.99 645	41
20	9.10 599	98	9.10 956	100	10.89 044	9.99 643	40
21	9.10 697	98	9.11 056	99	10.88 944	9.99 642	39
22	9.10 795	98	9.11 155	99	10.88 845	9.99 640	38
23	9.10 893	97	9.11 254	99	10.88 746	9.99 638	37
24	9.10 990	97	9.11 353	99	10.88 647	9.99 637	36
25	9.11 087	97	9.11 452	99	10.88 548	9.99 635	35
26	9.11 184	97	9.11 551	98	10.88 449	9.99 633	34
27	9.11 281	96	9.11 649	98	10.88 351	9.99 632	33
28	9.11 377	97	9.11 747	98	10.88 253	9.99 630	32
29	9.11 474	96	9.11 845	98	10.88 155	9.99 629	31
30	9.11 570	96	9.11 943	97	10.88 057	9.99 627	30
31	9.11 666	95	9.12 040	98	10.87 960	9.99 625	29
32	9.11 761	96	9.12 138	97	10.87 862	9.99 624	28
33	9.11 857	95	9.12 235	97	10.87 765	9.99 622	27
34	9.11 952	95	9.12 332	96	10.87 668	9.99 620	26
35	9.12 047	95	9.12 428	97	10.87 572	9.99 618	25
36	9.12 142	94	9.12 525	96	10.87 475	9.99 617	24
37	9.12 236	95	9.12 621	96	10.87 379	9.99 615	23
38	9.12 331	94	9.12 717	96	10.87 283	9.99 613	22
39	9.12 425	94	9.12 813	96	10.87 187	9.99 612	21
40	9.12 519	93	9.12 909	95	10.87 091	9.99 610	20
41	9.12 612	94	9.13 004	95	10.86 996	9.99 608	19
42	9.12 706	93	9.13 099	95	10.86 901	9.99 607	18
43	9.12 799	93	9.13 194	95	10.86 806	9.99 605	17
44	9.12 892	93	9.13 289	95	10.86 711	9.99 603	16
45	9.12 985	93	9.13 384	94	10.86 616	9.99 601	15
46	9.13 078	93	9.13 478	95	10.86 522	9.99 600	14
47	9.13 171	92	9.13 573	94	10.86 427	9.99 598	13
48	9.13 263	92	9.13 667	94	10.86 333	9.99 596	12
49	9.13 355	92	9.13 761	93	10.86 239	9.99 595	11
50	9.13 447	92	9.13 854	94	10.86 146	9.99 593	10
51	9.13 539	91	9.13 948	93	10.86 052	9.99 591	9
52	9.13 630	92	9.14 041	93	10.85 959	9.99 589	8
53	9.13 722	91	9.14 134	93	10.85 866	9.99 588	7
54	9.13 813	91	9.14 227	93	10.85 773	9.99 586	6
55	9.13 904	90	9.14 320	92	10.85 680	9.99 584	5
56	9.13 994	91	9.14 412	92	10.85 588	9.99 582	4
57	9.14 085	90	9.14 504	93	10.85 496	9.99 581	3
58	9.14 175	91	9.14 597	91	10.85 403	9.99 579	2
59	9.14 266	90	9.14 688	92	10.85 312	9.99 577	1
60	9.14 356		9.14 780		10.85 220	9.99 575	0
	L. Cos.	d.	L. Cot.	c. d.	L. Tan.	L. Sin.	′

P. P.

	105	104	103
1	10.5	10.4	10.3
2	21.0	20.8	20.6
3	31.5	31:2	30.9
4	42.0	41.6	41.2
5	52.5	52.0	51.5
6	63.0	62.4	61.8
7	73.5	72.8	72.1
8	84.0	83.2	82.4
9	94.5	93.6	92.7

	102	101	99
1	10.2	10.1	9.9
2	20.4	20.2	19.8
3	30.6	30.3	29.7
4	40.8	40.4	39.6
5	51.0	50.5	49.5
6	61.2	60.6	59.4
7	71.4	70.7	69.3
8	81.6	80.8	79.2
9	91.8	90.9	89.1

	98	97	96
1	9.8	9.7	9.6
2	19.6	19.4	19.2
3	29.4	29.1	28.8
4	39.2	38.8	38.4
5	49.0	48.5	48.0
6	58.8	58.2	57.6
7	68.6	67.9	67.2
8	78.4	77.6	76.8
9	88.2	87.3	86.4

	95	94	93
1	9.5	9.4	9.3
2	19.0	18.8	18.6
3	28.5	28.2	27.9
4	38.0	37.6	37.2
5	47.5	47.0	46.5
6	57.0	56.4	55.8
7	66.5	65.8	65.1
8	76.0	75.2	74.4
9	85.5	84.6	83.7

	92	91	90
1	9.2	9.1	9.0
2	18.4	18.2	18.0
3	27.6	27.3	27.0
4	36.8	36.4	36.0
5	46.0	45.5	45.0
6	55.2	54.6	54.0
7	64.4	63.7	63.0
8	73.6	72.8	72.0
9	82.8	81.9	81.0

P. P.

82°

8°

'	L. Sin.	d.	L. Tan.	c. d.	L. Cot.	L. Cos.	
0	9.14 356	89	9.14 780	92	10.85 220	9.99 575	60
1	9.14 445	90	9.14 872	91	10.85 128	9.99 574	59
2	9.14 535	89	9.14 963	91	10.85 037	9.99 572	58
3	9.14 624	90	9.15 054	91	10.84 946	9.99 570	57
4	9.14 714	89	9.15 145	91	10.84 855	9.99 568	56
5	9.14 803	88	9.15 236	91	10.84 764	9.99 566	55
6	9.14 891	89	9.15 327	90	10.84 673	9.99 565	54
7	9.14 980	89	9.15 417	91	10.84 583	9.99 563	53
8	9.15 069	88	9.15 508	90	10.84 492	9.99 561	52
9	9.15 157	88	9.15 598	90	10.84 402	9.99 559	51
10	9.15 245	88	9.15 688	89	10.84 312	9.99 557	50
11	9.15 333	88	9.15 777	90	10.84 223	9.99 556	49
12	9.15 421	87	9.15 867	89	10.84 133	9.99 554	48
13	9.15 508	88	9.15 956	90	10.84 044	9.99 552	47
14	9.15 596	87	9.16 046	89	10.83 954	9.99 550	46
15	9.15 683	87	9.16 135	89	10.83 865	9.99 548	45
16	9.15 770	87	9.16 224	88	10.83 776	9.99 546	44
17	9.15 857	87	9.16 312	89	10.83 688	9.99 545	43
18	9.15 944	86	9.16 401	88	10.83 599	9.99 543	42
19	9.16 030	86	9.16 489	88	10.83 511	9.99 541	41
20	9.16 116	87	9.16 577	88	10.83 423	9.99 539	40
21	9.16 203	86	9.16 665	88	10.83 335	9.99 537	39
22	9.16 289	85	9.16 753	88	10.83 247	9.99 535	38
23	9.16 374	86	9.16 841	87	10.83 159	9.99 533	37
24	9.16 460	85	9.16 928	88	10.83 072	9.99 532	36
25	9.16 545	86	9.17 016	87	10.82 984	9.99 530	35
26	9.16 631	85	9.17 103	87	10.82 897	9.99 528	34
27	9.16 716	85	9.17 190	87	10.82 810	9.99 526	33
28	9.16 801	85	9.17 277	86	10.82 723	9.99 524	32
29	9.16 886	84	9.17 363	87	10.82 637	9.99 522	31
30	9.16 970	85	9.17 450	86	10.82 550	9.99 520	30
31	9.17 055	84	9.17 536	86	10.82 464	9.99 518	29
32	9.17 139	84	9.17 622	86	10.82 378	9.99 515	28
33	9.17 223	84	9.17 708	86	10.82 292	9.99 515	27
34	9.17 307	84	9.17 794	86	10.82 206	9.99 513	26
35	9.17 391	83	9.17 880	85	10.82 120	9.99 511	25
36	9.17 474	84	9.17 965	86	10.82 035	9.99 509	24
37	9.17 558	83	9.18 051	85	10.81 949	9.99 507	23
38	9.17 641	83	9.18 136	85	10.81 864	9.99 505	22
39	9.17 724	83	9.18 221	85	10.81 779	9.99 503	21
40	9.17 807	83	9.18 306	85	10.81 694	9.99 501	20
41	9.17 890	83	9.18 391	84	10.81 609	9.99 499	19
42	9.17 973	82	9.18 475	85	10.81 525	9.99 497	18
43	9.18 055	82	9.18 560	84	10.81 440	9.99 495	17
44	9.18 137	83	9.18 644	84	10.81 356	9.99 494	16
45	9.18 220	82	9.18 728	84	10.81 272	9.99 492	15
46	9.18 302	81	9.18 812	84	10.81 188	9.99 490	14
47	9.18 383	82	9.18 896	83	10.81 104	9.99 488	13
48	9.18 465	82	9.18 979	84	10.81 021	9.99 486	12
49	9.18 547	81	9.19 063	83	10.80 937	9.99 484	11
50	9.18 628	81	9.19 146	83	10.80 854	9.99 482	10
51	9.18 709	81	9.19 229	83	10.80 771	9.99 480	9
52	9.18 790	81	9.19 312	83	10.80 688	9.99 478	8
53	9.18 871	81	9.19 395	83	10.80 605	9.99 476	7
54	9.18 952	81	9.19 478	83	10.80 522	9.99 474	6
55	9.19 033	80	9.19 561	82	10.80 439	9.99 472	5
56	9.19 113	80	9.19 643	82	10.80 357	9.99 470	4
57	9.19 193	80	9.19 725	82	10.80 275	9.99 468	3
58	9.19 273	80	9.19 807	82	10.80 193	9.99 466	2
59	9.19 353	80	9.19 889	82	10.80 111	9.99 464	1
60	9.19 433		9.19 971		10.80 029	9.99 462	0
	L. Cos.	d.	L. Cot.	c. d.	L. Tan.	L. Sin.	'

P. P.

	92	91	90
1	9.2	9.1	9.0
2	18.4	18.2	18.0
3	27.6	27.3	27.0
4	36.8	36.4	36.0
5	46.0	45.5	45.0
6	55.2	54.6	54.0
7	64.4	63.7	63.0
8	73.6	72.8	72.0
9	82.8	81.9	81.0

	89	88
1	8.9	8.8
2	17.8	17.6
3	26.7	26.4
4	35.6	35.2
5	44.5	44.0
6	53.4	52.8
7	62.3	61.6
8	71.2	70.4
9	80.1	79.2

	87	86	85
1	8.7	8.6	8.5
2	17.4	17.2	17.0
3	26.1	25.8	25.5
4	34.8	34.4	34.0
5	43.5	43.0	42.5
6	52.2	51.6	51.0
7	60.9	60.2	59.5
8	69.6	68.8	68.0
9	78.3	77.4	76.5

	84	83
1	8.4	8.3
2	16.8	16.6
3	25.2	24.9
4	33.6	33.2
5	42.0	41.5
6	50.4	49.8
7	58.8	58.1
8	67.2	66.4
9	75.6	74.7

	82	81	80
1	8.2	8.1	8.0
2	16.4	16.2	16.0
3	24.6	24.3	24.0
4	32.8	32.4	32.0
5	41.0	40.5	40.0
6	49.2	48.6	48.0
7	57.4	56.7	56.0
8	65.6	64.8	64.0
9	73.8	72.9	72.0

TABLE III. LOGARITHMS OF FUNCTIONS | 221

9°

'	L. Sin.	d.	L. Tan.	c. d.	L. Cot.	L. Cos.	
0	9.19 433	80	9.19 971	82	10.80 029	9.99 462	60
1	9.19 513	79	9.20 053	81	10.79 947	9.99 460	59
2	9.19 592	80	9.20 134	82	10.79 866	9.99 458	58
3	9.19 672	79	9.20 216	81	10.79 784	9.99 456	57
4	9.19 751	79	9.20 297	81	10.79 703	9.99 454	56
5	9.19 830	79	9.20 378	81	10.79 622	9.99 452	55
6	9.19 909	79	9.20 459	81	10.79 541	9.99 450	54
7	9.19 988	79	9.20 540	81	10.79 460	9.99 448	53
8	9.20 067	78	9.20 621	81	10.79 379	9.99 446	52
9	9.20 145	78	9.20 701	80	10.79 299	9.99 444	51
10	9.20 223	79	9.20 782	81	10.79 218	9.99 442	50
11	9.20 302	78	9.20 862	80	10.79 138	9.99 440	49
12	9.20 380	78	9.20 942	80	10.79 058	9.99 438	48
13	9.20 458	77	9.21 022	80	10.78 978	9.99 436	47
14	9.20 535	78	9.21 102	80	10.78 898	9.99 434	46
15	9.20 613	78	9.21 182	80	10.78 818	9.99 432	45
16	9.20 691	77	9.21 261	79	10.78 739	9.99 429	44
17	9.20 768	77	9.21 341	80	10.78 659	9.99 427	43
18	9.20 845	77	9.21 420	79	10.78 580	9.99 425	42
19	9.20 922	77	9.21 499	79	10.78 501	9.99 423	41
20	9.20 999	77	9.21 578	79	10.78 422	9.99 421	40
21	9.21 076	77	9.21 657	79	10.78 343	9.99 419	39
22	9.21 153	76	9.21 736	79	10.78 264	9.99 417	38
23	9.21 229	77	9.21 814	78	10.78 186	9.99 415	37
24	9.21 306	76	9.21 893	79	10.78 107	9.99 413	36
25	9.21 382	76	9.21 971	78	10.78 029	9.99 411	35
26	9.21 458	76	9.22 049	78	10.77 951	9.99 409	34
27	9.21 534	76	9.22 127	78	10.77 873	9.99 407	33
28	9.21 610	75	9.22 205	78	10.77 795	9.99 404	32
29	9.21 685	76	9.22 283	78	10.77 717	9.99 402	31
30	9.21 761	75	9.22 361	77	10.77 639	9.99 400	30
31	9.21 836	76	9.22 438	78	10.77 562	9.99 398	29
32	9.21 912	75	9.22 516	77	10.77 484	9.99 396	28
33	9.21 987	75	9.22 593	77	10.77 407	9.99 394	27
34	9.22 062	75	9.22 670	77	10.77 330	9.99 392	26
35	9.22 137	74	9.22 747	77	10.77 253	9.99 390	25
36	9.22 211	75	9.22 824	77	10.77 176	9.99 388	24
37	9.22 286	75	9.22 901	76	10.77 099	9.99 385	23
38	9.22 361	74	9.22 977	77	10.77 023	9.99 383	22
39	9.22 435	74	9.23 054	76	10.76 946	9.99 381	21
40	9.22 509	74	9.23 130	76	10.76 870	9.99 379	20
41	9.22 583	74	9.23 206	77	10.76 794	9.99 377	19
42	9.22 657	74	9.23 283	76	10.76 717	9.99 375	18
43	9.22 731	74	9.23 359	76	10.76 641	9.99 372	17
44	9.22 805	73	9.23 435	75	10.76 565	9.99 370	16
45	9.22 878	74	9.23 510	76	10.76 490	9.99 368	15
46	9.22 952	73	9.23 586	75	10.76 414	9.99 366	14
47	9.23 025	73	9.23 661	76	10.76 339	9.99 364	13
48	9.23 098	73	9.23 737	75	10.76 263	9.99 362	12
49	9.23 171	73	9.23 812	75	10.76 188	9.99 359	11
50	9.23 244	73	9.23 887	75	10.76 113	9.99 357	10
51	9.23 317	73	9.23 962	75	10.76 038	9.99 355	9
52	9.23 390	72	9.24 037	75	10.75 963	9.99 353	8
53	9.23 462	73	9.24 112	74	10.75 888	9.99 351	7
54	9.23 535	72	9.24 186	75	10.75 814	9.99 348	6
55	9.23 607	72	9.24 261	74	10.75 739	9.99 346	5
56	9.23 679	73	9.24 335	75	10.75 665	9.99 344	4
57	9.23 752	71	9.24 410	74	10.75 590	9.99 342	3
58	9.23 823	72	9.24 484	74	10.75 516	9.99 340	2
59	9.23 895	72	9.24 558	74	10.75 442	9.99 337	1
60	9.23 967		9.24 632		10.75 368	9.99 335	0
	L. Cos.	d.	L. Cot.	c. d.	L. Tan.	L. Sin.	'

P. P.

	82	81	80
1	8.2	8.1	8.0
2	16.4	16.2	16.0
3	24.6	24.3	24.0
4	32.8	32.4	32.0
5	41.0	40.5	40.0
6	49.2	48.6	48.0
7	57.4	56.7	56.0
8	65.6	64.8	64.0
9	73.8	72.9	72.0

	79	78	77
1	7.9	7.8	7.7
2	15.8	15.6	15.4
3	23.7	23.4	23.1
4	31.6	31.2	30.8
5	39.5	39.0	38.5
6	47.4	46.8	46.2
7	55.3	54.6	53.9
8	63.2	62.4	61.6
9	71.1	70.2	69.3

	76	75	74
1	7.6	7.5	7.4
2	15.2	15.0	14.8
3	22.8	22.5	22.2
4	30.4	30.0	29.6
5	38.0	37.5	37.0
6	45.6	45.0	44.4
7	53.2	52.5	51.8
8	60.8	60.0	59.2
9	68.4	67.5	66.6

	73	72	71
1	7.3	7.2	7.1
2	14.6	14.4	14.2
3	21.9	21.6	21.3
4	29.2	28.8	28.4
5	36.5	36.0	35.5
6	43.8	43.2	42.6
7	51.1	50.4	49.7
8	58.4	57.6	56.8
9	65.7	64.8	63.9

	3	2
1	0.3	0.2
2	0.6	0.4
3	0.9	0.6
4	1.2	0.8
5	1.5	1.0
6	1.8	1.2
7	2.1	1.4
8	2.4	1.6
9	2.7	1.8

80°

10°

'	L. Sin.	d.	L. Tan.	c. d.	L. Cot.	L. Cos.	d.	'
0	9.23 967		9.24 632		10.75 368	9.99 335		60
1	9.24 039	72	9.24 706	74	10.75 294	9.99 333	2	59
2	9.24 110	71	9.24 779	73	10.75 221	9.99 331	2	58
3	9.24 181	71	9.24 853	74	10.75 147	9.99 328	3	57
4	9.24 253	72	9.24 926	73	10.75 074	9.99 326	2	56
5	9.24 324	71	9.25 000	74	10.75 000	9.99 324	2	55
6	9.24 395	71	9.25 073	73	10.74 927	9.99 322	2	54
7	9.24 466	71	9.25 146	73	10.74 854	9.99 319	3	53
8	9.24 536	70	9.25 219	73	10.74 781	9.99 317	2	52
9	9.24 607	71	9.25 292	73	10.74 708	9.99 315	2	51
10	9.24 677	70	9.25 365	73	10.74 635	9.99 313	2	50
11	9.24 748	71	9.25 437	72	10.74 563	9.99 310	3	49
12	9.24 818	70	9.25 510	73	10.74 490	9.99 308	2	48
13	9.24 888	70	9.25 582	72	10.74 418	9.99 306	2	47
14	9.24 958	70	9.25 655	73	10.74 345	9.99 304	3	46
15	9.25 028	70	9.25 727	72	10.74 273	9.99 301	2	45
16	9.25 098	70	9.25 799	72	10.74 201	9.99 299	2	44
17	9.25 168	70	9.25 871	72	10.74 129	9.99 297	2	43
18	9.25 237	69	9.25 943	72	10.74 057	9.99 294	3	42
19	9.25 307	70	9.26 015	72	10.73 985	9.99 292	2	41
20	9.25 376	69	9.26 086	71	10.73 914	9.99 290	2	40
21	9.25 445	69	9.26 158	72	10.73 842	9.99 288	3	39
22	9.25 514	69	9.26 229	71	10.73 771	9.99 285	2	38
23	9.25 583	69	9.26 301	72	10.73 699	9.99 283	2	37
24	9.25 652	69	9.26 372	71	10.73 628	9.99 281	3	36
25	9.25 721	69	9.26 443	71	10.73 557	9.99 278	2	35
26	9.25 790	69	9.26 514	71	10.73 486	9.99 276	2	34
27	9.25 858	68	9.26 585	71	10.73 415	9.99 274	3	33
28	9.25 927	69	9.26 655	70	10.73 345	9.99 271	2	32
29	9.25 995	68	9.26 726	71	10.73 274	9.99 269	2	31
30	9.26 063	68	9.26 797	71	10.73 203	9.99 267	3	30
31	9.26 131	68	9.26 867	70	10.73 133	9.99 264	2	29
32	9.26 199	68	9.26 937	70	10.73 063	9.99 262	2	28
33	9.26 267	68	9.27 008	71	10.72 992	9.99 260	3	27
34	9.26 335	68	9.27 078	70	10.72 922	9.99 257	2	26
35	9.26 403	68	9.27 148	70	10.72 852	9.99 255	3	25
36	9.26 470	67	9.27 218	70	10.72 782	9.99 252	2	24
37	9.26 538	68	9.27 288	70	10.72 712	9.99 250	2	23
38	9.26 605	67	9.27 357	69	10.72 643	9.99 248	3	22
39	9.26 672	67	9.27 427	70	10.72 573	9.99 245	2	21
40	9.26 739	67	9.27 496	70	10.72 504	9.99 243	2	20
41	9.26 806	67	9.27 566	69	10.72 434	9.99 241	3	19
42	9.26 873	67	9.27 635	69	10.72 365	9.99 238	2	18
43	9.26 940	67	9.27 704	69	10.72 296	9.99 236	3	17
44	9.27 007	66	9.27 773	69	10.72 227	9.99 233	2	16
45	9.27 073	67	9.27 842	69	10.72 158	9.99 231	2	15
46	9.27 140	66	9.27 911	69	10.72 089	9.99 229	3	14
47	9.27 206	67	9.27 980	69	10.72 020	9.99 226	2	13
48	9.27 273	66	9.28 049	68	10.71 951	9.99 224	3	12
49	9.27 339	66	9.28 117	69	10.71 883	9.99 221	2	11
50	9.27 405	66	9.28 186	68	10.71 814	9.99 219	2	10
51	9.27 471	66	9.28 254	69	10.71 746	9.99 217	3	9
52	9.27 537	65	9.28 323	68	10.71 677	9.99 214	2	8
53	9.27 602	66	9.28 391	68	10.71 609	9.99 212	2	7
54	9.27 668	66	9.28 459	68	10.71 541	9.99 209	3	6
55	9.27 734	65	9.28 527	68	10.71 473	9.99 207	2	5
56	9.27 799	65	9.28 595	67	10.71 405	9.99 204	3	4
57	9.27 864	66	9.28 662	68	10.71 338	9.99 202	2	3
58	9.27 930	65	9.28 730	68	10.71 270	9.99 200	2	2
59	9.27 995	65	9.28 798	67	10.71 202	9.99 197	2	1
60	9.28 060		9.28 865		10.71 135	9.99 195		0
	L. Cos.	d.	L. Cot.	c. d.	L. Tan.	L. Sin.	d.	'

P. P.

	74	73	72
1	7.4	7.3	7.2
2	14.8	14.6	14.4
3	22.2	21.9	21.6
4	29.6	29.2	28.8
5	37.0	36.5	36.0
6	44.4	43.8	43.2
7	51.8	51.1	50.4
8	59.2	58.4	57.6
9	66.6	65.7	64.8

	71	70	69
1	7.1	7.0	6.9
2	14.2	14.0	13.8
3	21.3	21.0	20.7
4	28.4	28.0	27.6
5	35.5	35.0	34.5
6	42.6	42.0	41.4
7	49.7	49.0	48.3
8	56.8	56.0	55.2
9	63.9	63.0	62.1

	68	67	66
1	6.8	6.7	6.6
2	13.6	13.4	13.2
3	20.4	20.1	19.8
4	27.2	26.8	26.4
5	34.0	33.5	33.0
6	40.8	40.2	39.6
7	47.6	46.9	46.2
8	54.4	53.6	52.8
9	61.2	60.3	59.4

	65	3
1	6.5	0.3
2	13.0	0.6
3	19.5	0.9
4	26.0	1.2
5	32.5	1.5
6	39.0	1.8
7	45.5	2.1
8	52.0	2.4
9	58.5	2.7

TABLE III. LOGARITHMS OF FUNCTIONS | 223

11°

′	L. Sin.	d.	L. Tan.	c. d.	L. Cot.	L. Cos.	d.	′
0	9.28 060	65	9.28 865	68	10.71 135	9.99 195	3	60
1	9.28 125	65	9.28 933	67	10.71 067	9.99 192	2	59
2	9.28 190	64	9.29 000	67	10.71 000	9.99 190	3	58
3	9.28 254	65	9.29 067	67	10.70 933	9.99 187	2	57
4	9.28 319	65	9.29 134	67	10.70 866	9.99 185	3	56
5	9.28 384	64	9.29 201	67	10.70 799	9.99 182	2	55
6	9.28 448	64	9.29 268	67	10.70 732	9.99 180	3	54
7	9.28 512	65	9.29 335	67	10.70 665	9.99 177	2	53
8	9.28 577	64	9.29 402	66	10.70 598	9.99 175	3	52
9	9.28 641	64	9.29 468	67	10.70 532	9.99 172	2	51
10	9.28 705	64	9.29 535	66	10.70 465	9.99 170	3	50
11	9.28 769	64	9.29 601	67	10.70 399	9.99 167	2	49
12	9.28 833	63	9.29 668	66	10.70 332	9.99 165	3	48
13	9.28 896	64	9.29 734	66	10.70 266	9.99 162	2	47
14	9.28 960	64	9.29 800	66	10.70 200	9.99 160	3	46
15	9.29 024	63	9.29 866	66	10.70 134	9.99 157	2	45
16	9.29 087	63	9.29 932	66	10.70 068	9.99 155	3	44
17	9.29 150	64	9.29 998	66	10.70 002	9.99 152	2	43
18	9.29 214	63	9.30 064	66	10.69 936	9.99 150	3	42
19	9.29 277	63	9.30 130	65	10.69 870	9.99 147	2	41
20	9.29 340	63	9.30 195	66	10.69 805	9.99 145	3	40
21	9.29 403	63	9.30 261	65	10.69 739	9.99 142	2	39
22	9.29 466	63	9.30 326	65	10.69 674	9.99 140	3	38
23	9.29 529	62	9.30 391	66	10.69 609	9.99 137	2	37
24	9.29 591	63	9.30 457	65	10.69 543	9.99 135	3	36
25	9.29 654	62	9.30 522	65	10.69 478	9.99 132	2	35
26	9.29 716	63	9.30 587	65	10.69 413	9.99 130	3	34
27	9.29 779	62	9.30 652	65	10.69 348	9.99 127	3	33
28	9.29 841	62	9.30 717	65	10.69 283	9.99 124	2	32
29	9.29 903	63	9.30 782	64	10.69 218	9.99 122	3	31
30	9.29 966	62	9.30 846	65	10.69 154	9.99 119	2	30
31	9.30 028	62	9.30 911	64	10.69 089	9.99 117	3	29
32	9.30 090	61	9.30 975	65	10.69 025	9.99 114	2	28
33	9.30 151	62	9.31 040	64	10.68 960	9.99 112	3	27
34	9.30 213	62	9.31 104	64	10.68 896	9.99 109	3	26
35	9.30 275	61	9.31 168	65	10.68 832	9.99 106	2	25
36	9.30 336	62	9.31 233	64	10.68 767	9.99 104	3	24
37	9.30 398	61	9.31 297	64	10.68 703	9.99 101	2	23
38	9.30 459	62	9.31 361	64	10.68 639	9.99 099	3	22
39	9.30 521	61	9.31 425	64	10.68 575	9.99 096	3	21
40	9.30 582	61	9.31 489	63	10.68 511	9.99 093	2	20
41	9.30 643	61	9.31 552	64	10.68 448	9.99 091	3	19
42	9.30 704	61	9.31 616	63	10.68 384	9.99 088	2	18
43	9.30 765	61	9.31 679	64	10.68 321	9.99 086	3	17
44	9.30 826	61	9.31 743	63	10.68 257	9.99 083	3	16
45	9.30 887	60	9.31 806	64	10.68 194	9.99 080	2	15
46	9.30 947	61	9.31 870	63	10.68 130	9.99 078	3	14
47	9.31 008	60	9.31 933	63	10.68 067	9.99 075	3	13
48	9.31 068	61	9.31 996	63	10.68 004	9.99 072	2	12
49	9.31 129	60	9.32 059	63	10.67 941	9.99 070	3	11
50	9.31 189	61	9.32 122	63	10.67 878	9.99 067	3	10
51	9.31 250	60	9.32 185	63	10.67 815	9.99 064	2	9
52	9.31 310	60	9.32 248	63	10.67 752	9.99 062	3	8
53	9.31 370	60	9.32 311	62	10.67 689	9.99 059	3	7
54	9.31 430	60	9.32 373	63	10.67 627	9.99 056	2	6
55	9.31 490	59	9.32 436	62	10.67 564	9.99 054	3	5
56	9.31 549	60	9.32 498	63	10.67 502	9.99 051	3	4
57	9.31 609	60	9.32 561	62	10.67 439	9.99 048	2	3
58	9.31 669	59	9.32 623	62	10.67 377	9.99 046	3	2
59	9.31 728	60	9.32 685	62	10.67 315	9.99 043	3	1
60	9.31 788		9.32 747		10.67 253	9.99 040		0
	L. Cos.	d.	L. Cot.	c. d.	L. Tan.	L. Sin.	d.	′

P. P.

	68	67	66
1	6.8	6.7	6.6
2	13.6	13.4	13.2
3	20.4	20.1	19.8
4	27.2	26.8	26.4
5	34.0	33.5	33.0
6	40.8	40.2	39.6
7	47.6	46.9	46.2
8	54.4	53.6	52.8
9	61.2	60.3	59.4

	65	64	63
1	6.5	6.4	6.3
2	13.0	12.8	12.6
3	19.5	19.2	18.9
4	26.0	25.6	25.2
5	32.5	32.0	31.5
6	39.0	38.4	37.8
7	45.5	44.8	44.1
8	52.0	51.2	50.4
9	58.5	57.6	56.7

	62	61	60
1	6.2	6.1	6.0
2	12.4	12.2	12.0
3	18.6	18.3	18.0
4	24.8	24.4	24.0
5	31.0	30.5	30.0
6	37.2	36.6	36.0
7	43.4	42.7	42.0
8	49.6	48.8	48.0
9	55.8	54.9	54.0

	59	3	2
1	5.9	0.3	0.2
2	11.8	0.6	0.4
3	17.7	0.9	0.6
4	23.6	1.2	0.8
5	29.5	1.5	1.0
6	35.4	1.8	1.2
7	41.3	2.1	1.4
8	47.2	2.4	1.6
9	53.1	2.7	1.8

78°

12°

'	L. Sin.	d.	L. Tan.	c. d.	L. Cot.	L. Cos.	d.	
0	9.31 788	59	9.32 747	63	10.67 253	9.99 040	2	60
1	9.31 847		9.32 810	62	10.67 190	9.99 038	3	59
2	9.31 907	60	9.32 872	61	10.67 128	9.99 035		58
3	9.31 966	59	9.32 933	62	10.67 067	9.99 032	2	57
4	9.32 025	59	9.32 995	62	10.67 005	9.99 030	3	56
5	9.32 084	59	9.33 057	62	10.66 943	9.99 027		55
6	9.32 143	59	9.33 119	62	10.66 881	9.99 024	3	54
7	9.32 202	59	9.33 180	61	10.66 820	9.99 022	2	53
8	9.32 261	59	9.33 242	62	10.66 758	9.99 019	3	52
9	9.32 319	58	9.33 303	61	10.66 697	9.99 016		51
10	9.32 378	59	9.33 365	62	10.66 635	9.99 013	3	50
11	9.32 437	59	9.33 426	61	10.66 574	9.99 011	2	49
12	9.32 495	58	9.33 487	61	10.66 513	9.99 008	3	48
13	9.32 553	58	9.33 548	61	10.66 452	9.99 005	3	47
14	9.32 612	59	9.33 609	61	10.66 391	9.99 002	3	46
15	9.32 670	58	9.33 670	61	10.66 330	9.99 000	2	45
16	9.32 728	58	9.33 731	61	10.66 269	9.98 997	3	44
17	9.32 786	58	9.33 792	61	10.66 208	9.98 994	3	43
18	9.32 844	58	9.33 853	61	10.66 147	9.98 991	3	42
19	9.32 902	58	9.33 913	60	10.66 087	9.98 989	2	41
20	9.32 960	58	9.33 974	61	10.66 026	9.98 986	3	40
21	9.33 018	58	9.34 034	60	10.65 966	9.98 983	3	39
22	9.33 075	57	9.34 095	61	10.65 905	9.98 980	2	38
23	9.33 133	58	9.34 155	60	10.65 845	9.98 978	3	37
24	9.33 190	57	9.34 215	60	10.65 785	9.98 975	3	36
25	9.33 248	58	9.34 276	61	10.65 724	9.98 972	3	35
26	9.33 305	57	9.34 336	60	10.65 664	9.98 969	2	34
27	9.33 362	57	9.34 396	60	10.65 604	9.98 967	3	33
28	9.33 420	58	9.34 456	60	10.65 544	9.98 964	2	32
29	9.33 477	57	9.34 516	60	10.65 484	9.98 961	3	31
30	9.33 534	57	9.34 576	60	10.65 424	9.98 958	3	30
31	9.33 591	57	9.34 635	59	10.65 365	9.98 955	3	29
32	9.33 647	56	9.34 695	60	10.65 305	9.98 953	2	28
33	9.33 704	57	9.34 755	60	10.65 245	9.98 950	3	27
34	9.33 761	57	9.34 814	59	10.65 186	9.98 947	3	26
35	9.33 818	57	9.34 874	60	10.65 126	9.98 944	3	25
36	9.33 874	56	9.34 933	59	10.65 067	9.98 941	3	24
37	9.33 931	57	9.34 992	59	10.65 008	9.98 938	3	23
38	9.33 987	56	9.35 051	59	10.64 949	9.98 936	2	22
39	9.34 043	56	9.35 111	60	10.64 889	9.98 933	3	21
40	9.34 100	57	9.35 170	59	10.64 830	9.98 930	3	20
41	9.34 156	56	9.35 229	59	10.64 771	9.98 927	3	19
42	9.34 212	56	9.35 288	59	10.64 712	9.98 924	3	18
43	9.34 268	56	9.35 347	59	10.64 653	9.98 921	2	17
44	9.34 324	56	9.35 405	58	10.64 595	9.98 919	3	16
45	9.34 380	56	9.35 464	59	10.64 536	9.98 916	3	15
46	9.34 436	56	9.35 523	59	10.64 477	9.98 913	3	14
47	9.34 491	55	9.35 581	58	10.64 419	9.98 910	3	13
48	9.34 547	56	9.35 640	59	10.64 360	9.98 907	3	12
49	9.34 602	55	9.35 698	58	10.64 302	9.98 904	3	11
50	9.34 658	56	9.35 757	59	10.64 243	9.98 901	3	10
51	9.34 713	55	9.35 815	58	10.64 185	9.98 898	2	9
52	9.34 769	56	9.35 873	58	10.64 127	9.98 896	3	8
53	9.34 824	55	9.35 931	58	10.64 069	9.98 893	3	7
54	9.34 879	55	9.35 989	58	10.64 011	9.98 890	3	6
55	9.34 934	55	9.36 047	58	10.63 953	9.98 887	3	5
56	9.34 989	55	9.36 105	58	10.63 895	9.98 884	3	4
57	9.35 044	55	9.36 163	58	10.63 837	9.98 881	3	3
58	9.35 099	55	9.36 221	58	10.63 779	9.98 878	3	2
59	9.35 154	55	9.36 279	57	10.63 721	9.98 875	3	1
60	9.35 209		9.36 336		10.63 664	9.98 872		0
	L. Cos.	d.	L. Cot.	c. d.	L. Tan.	L. Sin.	d.	'

P. P.

	63	62	61
1	6.3	6.2	6.1
2	12.6	12.4	12.2
3	18.9	18.6	18.3
4	25.2	24.8	24.4
5	31.5	31.0	30.5
6	37.8	37.2	36.6
7	44.1	43.4	42.7
8	50.4	49.6	48.8
9	56.7	55.8	54.9

	60	59
1	6.0	5.9
2	12.0	11.8
3	18.0	17.7
4	24.0	23.6
5	30.0	29.5
6	36.0	35.4
7	42.0	41.3
8	48.0	47.2
9	54.0	53.1

	58	57
1	5.8	5.7
2	11.6	11.4
3	17.4	17.1
4	23.2	22.8
5	29.0	28.5
6	34.8	34.2
7	40.6	39.9
8	46.4	45.6
9	52.2	51.3

	56	55	3
1	5.6	5.5	0.3
2	11.2	11.0	0.6
3	16.8	16.5	0.9
4	22.4	22.0	1.2
5	28.0	27.5	1.5
6	33.6	33.0	1.8
7	39.2	38.5	2.1
8	44.8	44.0	2.4
9	50.4	49.5	2.7

P. P.

TABLE III. LOGARITHMS OF FUNCTIONS | 225

13°

'	L. Sin.	d.	L. Tan.	c. d.	L. Cot.	L. Cos.	d.	'
0	9.35 209	54	9.36 336	58	10.63 664	9.98 872	3	60
1	9.35 263	55	9.36 394	58	10.63 606	9.98 869	2	59
2	9.35 318	55	9.36 452	57	10.63 548	9.98 867	3	58
3	9.35 373	55	9.36 509	57	10.63 491	9.98 864	3	57
4	9.35 427	54	9.36 566	58	10.63 434	9.98 861	3	56
5	9.35 481	55	9.36 624	57	10.63 376	9.98 858	3	55
6	9.35 536	54	9.36 681	57	10.63 319	9.98 855	3	54
7	9.35 590	54	9.36 738	57	10.63 262	9.98 852	3	53
8	9.35 644	54	9.36 795	57	10.63 205	9.98 849	3	52
9	9.35 698	54	9.36 852	57	10.63 148	9.98 846	3	51
10	9.35 752	54	9.36 909	57	10.63 091	9.98 843	3	50
11	9.35 806	54	9.36 966	57	10.63 034	9.98 840	3	49
12	9.35 860	54	9.37 023	57	10.62 977	9.98 837	3	48
13	9.35 914	54	9.37 080	57	10.62 920	9.98 834	3	47
14	9.35 968	54	9.37 137	56	10.62 863	9.98 831	3	46
15	9.36 022	53	9.37 193	57	10.62 807	9.98 828	3	45
16	9.36 075	54	9.37 250	56	10.62 750	9.98 825	3	44
17	9.36 129	53	9.37 306	57	10.62 694	9.98 822	3	43
18	9.36 182	54	9.37 363	56	10.62 637	9.98 819	3	42
19	9.36 236	53	9.37 419	57	10.62 581	9.98 816	3	41
20	9.36 289	53	9.37 476	56	10.62 524	9.98 813	3	40
21	9.36 342	53	9.37 532	56	10.62 468	9.98 810	3	39
22	9.36 395	54	9.37 588	56	10.62 412	9.98 807	3	38
23	9.36 449	53	9.37 644	56	10.62 356	9.98 804	3	37
24	9.36 502	53	9.37 700	56	10.62 300	9.98 801	3	36
25	9.36 555	53	9.37 756	56	10.62 244	9.98 798	3	35
26	9.36 608	52	9.37 812	56	10.62 188	9.98 795	3	34
27	9.36 660	53	9.37 868	56	10.62 132	9.98 792	3	33
28	9.36 713	53	9.37 924	56	10.62 076	9.98 789	3	32
29	9.36 766	53	9.37 980	55	10.62 020	9.98 786	3	31
30	9.36 819	52	9.38 035	56	10.61 965	9.98 783	3	30
31	9.36 871	53	9.38 091	56	10.61 909	9.98 780	3	29
32	9.36 924	52	9.38 147	55	10.61 853	9.98 777	3	28
33	9.36 976	52	9.38 202	55	10.61 798	9.98 774	3	27
34	9.37 028	53	9.38 257	56	10.61 743	9.98 771	3	26
35	9.37 081	52	9.38 313	55	10.61 687	9.98 768	3	25
36	9.37 133	52	9.38 368	55	10.61 632	9.98 765	3	24
37	9.37 185	52	9.38 423	56	10.61 577	9.98 762	3	23
38	9.37 237	52	9.38 479	55	10.61 521	9.98 759	3	22
39	9.37 289	52	9.38 534	55	10.61 466	9.98 756	3	21
40	9.37 341	52	9.38 589	55	10.61 411	9.98 753	3	20
41	9.37 393	52	9.38 644	55	10.61 356	9.98 750	4	19
42	9.37 445	52	9.38 699	55	10.61 301	9.98 746	3	18
43	9.37 497	52	9.38 754	54	10.61 246	9.98 743	3	17
44	9.37 549	51	9.38 808	55	10.61 192	9.98 740	3	16
45	9.37 600	52	9.38 863	55	10.61 137	9.98 737	3	15
46	9.37 652	51	9.38 918	54	10.61 082	9.98 734	3	14
47	9.37 703	52	9.38 972	55	10.61 028	9.98 731	3	13
48	9.37 755	51	9.39 027	55	10.60 973	9.98 728	3	12
49	9.37 806	52	9.39 082	54	10.60 918	9.98 725	3	11
50	9.37 858	51	9.39 136	54	10.60 864	9.98 722	3	10
51	9.37 909	51	9.39 190	55	10.60 810	9.98 719	4	9
52	9.37 960	51	9.39 245	54	10.60 755	9.98 715	3	8
53	9.38 011	51	9.39 299	54	10.60 701	9.98 712	3	7
54	9.38 062	51	9.39 353	54	10.60 647	9.98 709	3	6
55	9.38 113	51	9.39 407	54	10.60 593	9.98 706	3	5
56	9.38 164	51	9.39 461	54	10.60 539	9.98 703	3	4
57	9.38 215	51	9.39 515	54	10.60 485	9.98 700	3	3
58	9.38 266	51	9.39 569	54	10.60 431	9.98 697	3	2
59	9.38 317	51	9.39 623	54	10.60 377	9.98 694	4	1
60	9.38 368		9.39 677		10.60 323	9.98 690		0
	L. Cos.	d.	L. Cot.	c. d.	L. Tan.	L. Sin.	d.	'

P. P.

	58	57	56
1	5.8	5.7	5.6
2	11.6	11.4	11.2
3	17.4	17.1	16.8
4	23.3	22.8	22.4
5	29.0	28.5	28.0
6	34.8	34.2	33.6
7	40.6	39.9	39.2
8	46.4	45.6	44.8
9	52.2	51.3	50.4

	55	54	53
1	5.5	5.4	5.3
2	11.0	10.8	10.6
3	16.5	16.2	15.9
4	22.0	21.6	21.2
5	27.5	27.0	26.5
6	33.0	32.4	31.8
7	38.5	37.8	37.1
8	44.0	43.2	42.4
9	49.5	48.6	47.7

	52	51
1	5.2	5.1
2	10.4	10.2
3	15.6	15.3
4	20.8	20.4
5	26.0	25.5
6	31.2	30.6
7	36.4	35.7
8	41.6	40.8
9	46.8	45.9

	4	3	2
1	0.4	0.3	0.2
2	0.8	0.6	0.4
3	1.2	0.9	0.6
4	1.6	1.2	0.8
5	2.0	1.5	1.0
6	2.4	1.8	1.2
7	2.8	2.1	1.4
8	3.2	2.4	1.6
9	3.6	2.7	1.8

14°

′	L. Sin.	d.	L. Tan.	c. d.	L. Cot.	L. Cos.	d.		P. P.
0	9.38 368	50	9.39 677	54	10.60 323	9.98 690	3	60	
1	9.38 418	51	9.39 731	54	10.60 269	9.98 687	3	59	
2	9.38 469	50	9.39 785	53	10.60 215	9.98 684	3	58	
3	9.38 519	51	9.39•838	54	10.60 162	9.98 681	3	57	
4	9.38 570	50	9.39 892	53	10.60 108	9.98 678	3	56	
									54 53
5	9.38 620	50	9.39 945	54	10.60 055	9.98 675	4	55	
6	9.38 670	51	9.39 999	53	10.60 001	9.98 671	3	54	1| 5.4 5.3
7	9.38 721	50	9.40 052	54	10.59 948	9.98 668	3	53	2| 10.8 10.6
8	9.38 771	50	9.40 106	53	10.59 894	9.98 665	3	52	3| 16.2 15.9
9	9.38 821	50	9.40 159	53	10.59 841	9.98 662	3	51	4| 21.6 21.2
									5| 27.0 26.5
									6| 32.4 31.8
10	9.38 871	50	9.40 212	54	10.59 788	9.98 659	3	50	7| 37.8 37.1
11	9.38 921	50	9.40 266	53	10.59 734	9.98 656	4	49	8| 43.2 42.4
12	9.38 971	50	9.40 319	53	10.59 681	9.98 652	3	48	9| 48.6 47.7
13	9.39 021	50	9.40 372	53	10.59 628	9.98 649	3	47	
14	9.39 071	50	9.40 425	53	10.59 575	9.98 646	3	46	
15	9.39 121	49	9.40 478	53	10.59 522	9.98 643	3	45	
16	9.39 170	50	9.40 531	53	10.59 469	9.98 640	4	44	
17	9.39 220	50	9.40 584	52	10.59 416	9.98 636	3	43	
18	9.39 270	49	9.40 636	53	10.59 364	9.98 633	3	42	
19	9.39 319	50	9.40 689	53	10.59 311	9.98 630	3	41	52 51 50
20	9.39 369	49	9.40 742	53	10.59 258	9.98 627	4	40	1| 5.2 5.1 5.0
21	9.39 418	49	9.40 795	52	10.59 205	9.98 623	3	39	2| 10.4 10.2 10.0
22	9.39 467	50	9.40 847	53	10.59 153	9.98 620	3	38	3| 15.6 15.3 15.0
23	9.39 517	49	9.40 900	52	10.59 100	9.98 617	3	37	4| 20.8 20.4 20.0
24	9.39 566	49	9.40 952	53	10.59 048	9.98 614	4	36	5| 26.0 25.5 25.0
									6| 31.2 30.6 30.0
25	9.39 615	49	9.41 005	52	10.58 995	9.98 610	3	35	7| 36.4 35.7 35.0
26	9.39 664	49	9.41 057	52	10.58 943	9.98 607	3	34	8| 41.6 40.8 40.0
27	9.39 713	49	9.41 109	52	10.58 891	9.98 604	3	33	9| 46.8 45.9 45.0
28	9.39·762	49	9.41 161	53	10.58 839	9.98 601	4	32	
29	9.39 811	49	9.41 214	52	10.58 786	9.98 597	3	31	
30	9.39 860	49	9.41 266	52	10.58 734	9.98 594	3	30	
31	9.39 909	49	9.41 318	52	10.58 682	9.98 591	3	29	
32	9.39 958	48	9.41 370	52	10.58 630	9.98 588	4	28	
33	9.40 006	49	9.41 422	52	10.58 578	9.98 584	3	27	
34	9.40 055	48	9.41 474	52	10.58 526	9.98 581	3	26	49 48 47
35	9.40 103	49	9.41 526	52	10.58 474	9.98 578	4	25	1| 4.9 4.8 4.7
36	9.40 152	48	9.41 578	51	10.58 422	9.98 574	3	24	2| 9.8 9.6 9.4
37	9.40 200	49	9.41 629	52	10.58 371	9.98 571	3	23	3| 14.7 14.4 14.1
38	9.40 249	48	9.41 681	52	10.58 319	9.98 568	3	22	4| 19.6 19.2 18.8
39	9.40 297	49	9.41 733	51	10.58 267	9.98 565	4	21	5| 24.5 24.0 23.5
									6| 29.4 28.8 28.2
40	9.40 346	48	9.41 784	52	10.58 216	9.98 561	3	20	7| 34.3 33.6 32.9
41	9.40 394	48	9.41 836	51	10.58 164	9.98 558	3	19	8| 39.2 38.4 37.6
42	9.40 442	48	9.41 887	52	10.58 113	9.98 555	4	18	9| 44.1 43.2 42.3
43	9.40 490	48	9.41 939	51	10.58 061	9.98 551	3	17	
44	9.40 538	48	9.41 990	51	10.58 010	9.98 548	3	16	
45	9.40 586	48	9.42 041	52	10.57 959	9.98 545	4	15	
46	9.40 634	48	9.42 093	51	10.57 907	9.98 541	3	14	
47	9.40 682	48	9.42 144	51	10.57 856	9.98 538	3	13	
48	9.40 730	48	9.42 195	51	10.57 805	9.98 535	4	12	4 3
49	9.40 778	47	9.42 246	51	10.57 754	9.98 531	3	11	1| 0.4 0.3
50	9.40 825	48	9.42 297	51	10.57 703	9.98 528	3	10	2| 0.8 0.6
51	9.40 873	48	9.42 348	51	10.57 652	9.98 525	4	9	3| 1.2 0.9
52	9.40 921	47	9.42 399	51	10.57 601	9.98 521	3	8	4| 1.6 1.2
53	9.40 968	48	9.42 450	51	10.57 550	9.98 518	3	7	5| 2.0 1.5
54	9.41 016	47	9.42 501	51	10.57 499	9.98 515	4	6	6| 2.4 1.8
									7| 2.8 2.1
55	9.41 063	48	9.42 552	51	10.57 448	9.98 511	3	5	8| 3.2 2.4
56	9.41 111	47	9.42 603	50	10.57 397	9.98 508	3	4	9| 3.6 2.7
57	9.41 158	47	9.42 653	51	10.57 347	9.98 505	4	3	
58	9.41 205	47	9.42 704	51	10.57 296	9.98 501	3	2	
59	9.41 252	48	9.42 755	50	10.57 245	9.98 498	4	1	
60	9.41 300		9.42 805		10.57 195	9.98 494		0	
	L. Cos.	d.	L. Cot.	c. d.	L. Tan.	L. Sin.	d.	′	P. P.

75°

TABLE III. LOGARITHMS OF FUNCTIONS | 227

15°

'	L. Sin.	d.	L. Tan.	c. d.	L. Cot.	L. Cos.	d.	
0	9.41 300	47	9.42 805	51	10.57 195	9.98 494	3	60
1	9.41 347	47	9.42 856	50	10.57 144	9.98 491	3	59
2	9.41 394	47	9.42 906	51	10.57 094	9.98 488	4	58
3	9.41 441	47	9.42 957	50	10.57 043	9.98 484	3	57
4	9.41 488	47	9.43 007	50	10.56 993	9.98 481	4	56
5	9.41 535	47	9.43 057	51	10.56 943	9.98 477	3	55
6	9.41 582	46	9.43 108	50	10.56 892	9.98 474	3	54
7	9.41 628	47	9.43 158	50	10.56 842	9.98 471	4	53
8	9.41 675	47	9.43 208	50	10.56 792	9.98 467	3	52
9	9.41 722	46	9.43 258	50	10.56 742	9.98 464	4	51
10	9.41 768	47	9.43 308	50	10.56 692	9.98 460	3	50
11	9.41 815	46	9.43 358	50	10.56 642	9.98 457	4	49
12	9.41 861	47	9.43 408	50	10.56 592	9.98 453	3	48
13	9.41 908	46	9.43 458	50	10.56 542	9.98 450	3	47
14	9.41 954	47	9.43 508	50	10.56 492	9.98 447	4	46
15	9.42 001	46	9.43 558	49	10.56 442	9.98 443	3	45
16	9.42 047	46	9.43 607	50	10.56 393	9.98 440	4	44
17	9.42 093	47	9.43 657	50	10.56 343	9.98 436	3	43
18	9.42 140	46	9.43 707	49	10.56 293	9.98 433	4	42
19	9.42 186	46	9.43 756	50	10.56 244	9.98 429	3	41
20	9.42 232	46	9.43 806	49	10.56 194	9.98 426	4	40
21	9.42 278	46	9.43 855	50	10.56 145	9.98 422	4	39
22	9.42 324	46	9.43 905	49	10.56 095	9.98 419	3	38
23	9.42 370	46	9.43 954	50	10.56 046	9.98 415	3	37
24	9.42 416	45	9.44 004	49	10.55 996	9.98 412	3	36
25	9.42 461	46	9.44 053	49	10.55 947	9.98 409	4	35
26	9.42 507	46	9.44 102	49	10.55 898	9.98 405	3	34
27	9.42 553	46	9.44 151	50	10.55 849	9.98 402	4	33
28	9.42 599	45	9.44 201	49	10.55 799	9.98 398	3	32
29	9.42 644	46	9.44 250	49	10.55 750	9.98 395	4	31
30	9.42 690	45	9.44 299	49	10.55 701	9.98 391	3	30
31	9.42 735	46	9.44 348	49	10.55 652	9.98 388	4	29
32	9.42 781	45	9.44 397	49	10.55 603	9.98 384	3	28
33	9.42 826	46	9.44 446	49	10.55 554	9.98 381	4	27
34	9.42 872	45	9.44 495	49	10.55 505	9.98 377	4	26
35	9.42 917	45	9.44 544	48	10.55 456	9.98 373	3	25
36	9.42 962	46	9.44 592	49	10.55 408	9.98 370	4	24
37	9.43 008	45	9.44 641	49	10.55 359	9.98 366	3	23
38	9.43 053	45	9.44 690	48	10.55 310	9.98 363	4	22
39	9.43 098	45	9.44 738	49	10.55 262	9.98 359	3	21
40	9.43 143	45	9.44 787	49	10.55 213	9.98 356	4	20
41	9.43 188	45	9.44 836	48	10.55 164	9.98 352	3	19
42	9.43 233	45	9.44 884	49	10.55 116	9.98 349	4	18
43	9.43 278	45	9.44 933	48	10.55 067	9.98 345	4	17
44	9.43 323	44	9.44 981	48	10.55 019	9.98 342	3	16
45	9.43 367	45	9.45 029	49	10.54 971	9.98 338	4	15
46	9.43 412	45	9.45 078	48	10.54 922	9.98 334	3	14
47	9.43 457	45	9.45 126	48	10.54 874	9.98 331	4	13
48	9.43 502	44	9.45 174	48	10.54 826	9.98 327	3	12
49	9.43 546	45	9.45 222	49	10.54 778	9.98 324	4	11
50	9.43 591	44	9.45 271	48	10.54 729	9.98 320	3	10
51	9.43 635	45	9.45 319	48	10.54 681	9.98 317	4	9
52	9.43 680	44	9.45 367	48	10.54 633	9.98 313	4	8
53	9.43 724	45	9.45 415	48	10.54 585	9.98 309	3	7
54	9.43 769	44	9.45 463	48	10.54 537	9.98 306	4	6
55	9.43 813	44	9.45 511	48	10.54 489	9.98 302	3	5
56	9.43 857	44	9.45 559	47	10.54 441	9.98 299	4	4
57	9.43 901	45	9.45 606	48	10.54 394	9.98 295	4	3
58	9.43 946	44	9.45 654	48	10.54 346	9.98 291	3	2
59	9.43 990	44	9.45 702	48	10.54 298	9.98 288	4	1
60	9.44 034		9.45 750		10.54 250	9.98 284		0
	L. Cos.	d.	L. Cot.	c. d.	L. Tan.	L. Sin.	d.	'

P. P.

	51	50	49
1	5.1	5.0	4.9
2	10.2	10.0	9.8
3	15.3	15.0	14.7
4	20.4	20.0	19.6
5	25.5	25.0	24.5
6	30.6	30.0	29.4
7	35.7	35.0	34.3
8	40.8	40.0	39.2
9	45.9	45.0	44.1

	48	47	46
1	4.8	4.7	4.6
2	9.6	9.4	9.2
3	14.4	14.1	13.8
4	19.2	18.8	18.4
5	24.0	23.5	23.0
6	28.8	28.2	27.6
7	33.6	32.9	32.3
8	38.4	37.6	36.8
9	43.2	42.3	41.4

	45	44
1	4.5	4.4
2	9.0	8.8
3	13.5	13.2
4	18.0	17.6
5	22.5	22.0
6	27.0	26.4
7	31.5	30.8
8	36.0	35.2
9	40.5	39.6

	4	3
1	0.4	0.3
2	0.8	0.6
3	1.2	0.9
4	1.6	1.2
5	2.0	1.5
6	2.4	1.8
7	2.8	2.1
8	3.2	2.4
9	3.6	2.7

74°

16°

'	L. Sin.	d.	L. Tan.	c. d.	L. Cot.	L. Cos.	d.	'
0	9.44 034	44	9.45 750	47	10.54 250	9.98 284	3	60
1	9.44 078	44	9.45 797	48	10.54 203	9.98 281		59
2	9.44 122	44	9.45 845	47	10.54 155	9.98 277	4	58
3	9.44 166	44	9.45 892	48	10.54 108	9.98 273		57
4	9.44 210	43	9.45 940	47	10.54 060	9.98 270	3	56
5	9.44 253	44	9.45 987	48	10.54 013	9.98 266	4	55
6	9.44 297	44	9.46 035	47	10.53 965	9.98 262		54
7	9.44 341	44	9.46 082	48	10.53 918	9.98 259	3	53
8	9.44 385	43	9.46 130	47	10.53 870	9.98 255		52
9	9.44 428	44	9.46 177	47	10.53 823	9.98 251	4	51
10	9.44 472	44	9.46 224	47	10.53 776	9.98 248		50
11	9.44 516	43	9.46 271	48	10.53 729	9.98 244	4	49
12	9.44 559	43	9.46 319	47	10.53 681	9.98 240	3	48
13	9.44 602	44	9.46 366	47	10.53 634	9.98 237	4	47
14	9.44 646	43	9.46 413	47	10.53 587	9.98 233		46
15	9.44 689	44	9.46 460	47	10.53 540	9.98 229	3	45
16	9.44 733	43	9.46 507	47	10.53 493	9.98 226	4	44
17	9.44 776	43	9.46 554	47	10.53 446	9.98 222	4	43
18	9.44 819	43	9.46 601	47	10.53 399	9.98 218	3	42
19	9.44 862	43	9.46 648	46	10.53 352	9.98 215	4	41
20	9.44 905	43	9.46 694	47	10.53 306	9.98 211		40
21	9.44 948	44	9.46 741	47	10.53 259	9.98 207	3	39
22	9.44 992	43	9.46 788	47	10.53 212	9.98 204	4	38
23	9.45 035	43	9.46 835	46	10.53 165	9.98 200	4	37
24	9.45 077	42	9.46 881	47	10.53 119	9.98 196		36
25	9.45 120	43	9.46 928	47	10.53 072	9.98 192	3	35
26	9.45 163	43	9.46 975	46	10.53 025	9.98 189	4	34
27	9.45 206	43	9.47 021	47	10.52 979	9.98 185	4	33
28	9.45 249	43	9.47 068	46	10.52 932	9.98 181		32
29	9.45 292	42	9.47 114	46	10.52 886	9.98 177	3	31
30	9.45 334	43	9.47 160	47	10.52 840	9.98 174	4	30
31	9.45 377	42	9.47 207	46	10.52 793	9.98 170	4	29
32	9.45 419	43	9.47 253	46	10.52 747	9.98 166		28
33	9.45 462	42	9.47 299	47	10.52 701	9.98 162	3	27
34	9.45 504	43	9.47 346	46	10.52 654	9.98 159	4	26
35	9.45 547	42	9.47 392	46	10.52 608	9.98 155	4	25
36	9.45 589	43	9.47 438	46	10.52 562	9.98 151		24
37	9.45 632	42	9.47 484	46	10.52 516	9.98 147	3	23
38	9.45 674	42	9.47 530	46	10.52 470	9.98 144	4	22
39	9.45 716	42	9.47 576	46	10.52 424	9.98 140	4	21
40	9.45 758	43	9.47 622	46	10.52 378	9.98 136		20
41	9.45 801	42	9.47 668	46	10.52 332	9.98 132	3	19
42	9.45 843	42	9.47 714	46	10.52 286	9.98 129	4	18
43	9.45 885	42	9.47 760	46	10.52 240	9.98 125	4	17
44	9.45 927	42	9.47 806	46	10.52 194	9.98 121	4	16
45	9.45 969	42	9.47 852	45	10.52 148	9.98 117		15
46	9.46 011	42	9.47 897	46	10.52 103	9.98 113	3	14
47	9.46 053	42	9.47 943	46	10.52 057	9.98 110	4	13
48	9.46 095	41	9.47 989	46	10.52 011	9.98 106	4	12
49	9.46 136	42	9.48 035	45	10.51 965	9.98 102	4	11
50	9.46 178	42	9.48 080	46	10.51 920	9.98 098		10
51	9.46 220	42	9.48 126	45	10.51 874	9.98 094	4	9
52	9.46 262	41	9.48 171	46	10.51 829	9.98 090	3	8
53	9.46 303	42	9.48 217	45	10.51 783	9.98 087	4	7
54	9.46 345	41	9.48 262	45	10.51 738	9.98 083	4	6
55	9.46 386	42	9.48 307	46	10.51 693	9.98 079	4	5
56	9.46 428	41	9.48 353	45	10.51 647	9.98 075	4	4
57	9.46 469	42	9.48 398	45	10.51 602	9.98 071	4	3
58	9.46 511	41	9.48 443	46	10.51 557	9.98 067	4	2
59	9.46 552	42	9.48 489	45	10.51 511	9.98 063	3	1
60	9.46 594		9.48 534		10.51 466	9.98 060		0
	L. Cos.	d.	L. Cot.	c. d.	L. Tan.	L. Sin.	d.	'

P. P.

	48	47	46
1	4.8	4.7	4.6
2	9.6	9.4	9.2
3	14.4	14.1	13.8
4	19.2	18.8	18.4
5	24.0	23.5	23.0
6	28.8	28.2	27.6
7	33.6	32.9	32.2
8	38.4	37.6	36.8
9	43.2	42.3	41.4

	45	44	43
1	4.5	4.4	4.3
2	9.0	8.8	8.6
3	13.5	13.2	12.9
4	18.0	17.6	17.2
5	22.5	22.0	21.5
6	27.0	26.4	25.8
7	31.5	30.8	30.1
8	36.0	35.2	34.4
9	40.5	39.6	38.7

	42	41
1	4.2	4.1
2	8.4	8.2
3	12.6	12.3
4	16.8	16.4
5	21.0	20.5
6	25.2	24.6
7	29.4	28.7
8	33.6	32.8
9	37.8	36.9

	4	3
1	0.4	0.3
2	0.8	0.6
3	1.2	0.9
4	1.6	1.2
5	2.0	1.5
6	2.4	1.8
7	2.8	2.1
8	3.2	2.4
9	3.6	2.7

TABLE III. LOGARITHMS OF FUNCTIONS | 229

17°

'	L. Sin.	d.	L. Tan.	c. d.	L. Cot.	L. Cos.	d.		P. P.
0	9.46 594		9.48 534		10.51 466	9.98 060		60	
1	9.46 635	41	9.48 579	45	10.51 421	9.98 056	4	59	
2	9.46 676	41	9.48 624	45	10.51 376	9.98 052	4	58	
3	9.46 717	41	9.48 669	45	10.51 331	9.98 048	4	57	
4	9.46 758	41	9.48 714	45	10.51 286	9.98 044	4	56	
5	9.46 800	42	9.48 759	45	10.51 241	9.98 040	4	55	
6	9.46 841	41	9.48 804	45	10.51 196	9.98 036	4	54	
7	9.46 882	41	9.48 849	45	10.51 151	9.98 032	4	53	
8	9.46 923	41	9.48 894	45	10.51 106	9.98 029	3	52	
9	9.46 964	41	9.48 939	45	10.51 061	9.98 025	4	51	
10	9.47 005	41	9.48 984	45	10.51 016	9.98 021	4	50	45 44 43
11	9.47 045	40	9.49 029	45	10.50 971	9.98 017	4	49	1| 4.5 4.4 4.3
12	9.47 086	41	9.49 073	44	10.50 927	9.98 013	4	48	2| 9.0 8.8 8.6
13	9.47 127	41	9.49 118	45	10.50 882	9.98 009	4	47	3| 13.5 13.2 12.9
14	9.47 168	41	9.49 163	45	10.50 837	9.98 005	4	46	4| 18.0 17.6 17.2
15	9.47 209	41	9.49 207	44	10.50 793	9.98 001	4	45	5| 22.5 22.0 21.5
16	9.47 249	40	9.49 252	45	10.50 748	9.97 997	4	44	6| 27.0 26.4 25.8
17	9.47 290	41	9.49 296	44	10.50 704	9.97 993	4	43	7| 31.5 30.8 30.1
18	9.47 330	40	9.49 341	45	10.50 659	9.97 989	4	42	8| 36.0 35.2 34.4
19	9.47 371	41	9.49 385	44	10.50 615	9.97 986	3	41	9| 40.5 39.6 38.7
20	9.47 411	40	9.49 430	45	10.50 570	9.97 982	4	40	
21	9.47 452	41	9.49 474	44	10.50 526	9.97 978	4	39	
22	9.47 492	40	9.49 519	45	10.50 481	9.97 974	4	38	
23	9.47 533	41	9.49 563	44	10.50 437	9.97 970	4	37	
24	9.47 573	40	9.49 607	45	10.50 393	9.97 966	4	36	
25	9.47 613	40	9.49 652	44	10.50 348	9.97 962	4	35	
26	9.47 654	41	9.49 696	44	10.50 304	9.97 958	4	34	42 41 40
27	9.47 694	40	9.49 740	44	10.50 260	9.97 954	4	33	1| 4.2 4.1 4.0
28	9.47 734	40	9.49 784	44	10.50 216	9.97 950	4	32	2| 8.4 8.2 8.0
29	9.47 774	40	9.49 828	44	10.50 172	9.97 946	4	31	3| 12.6 12.3 12.0
30	9.47 814	40	9.49 872	44	10.50 128	9.97 942	4	30	4| 16.8 16.4 16.0
31	9.47 854	40	9.49 916	44	10.50 084	9.97 938	4	29	5| 21.0 20.5 20.0
32	9.47 894	40	9.49 960	44	10.50 040	9.97 934	4	28	6| 25.2 24.6 24.0
33	9.47 934	40	9.50 004	44	10.49 996	9.97 930	4	27	7| 29.4 28.7 28.0
34	9.47 974	40	9.50 048	44	10.49 952	9.97 926	4	26	8| 33.6 32.8 32.0
35	9.48 014	40	9.50 092	44	10.49 908	9.97 922	4	25	9| 37.8 36.9 36.0
36	9.48 054	40	9.50 136	44	10.49 864	9.97 918	4	24	
37	9.48 094	40	9.50 180	44	10.49 820	9.97 914	4	23	
38	9.48 133	39	9.50 223	43	10.49 777	9.97 910	4	22	
39	9.48 173	40	9.50 267	44	10.49 733	9.97 906	4	21	
40	9.48 213	40	9.50 311	44	10.49 689	9.97 902	4	20	
41	9.48 252	39	9.50 355	44	10.49 645	9.97 898	4	19	
42	9.48 292	40	9.50 398	43	10.49 602	9.97 894	4	18	
43	9.48 332	40	9.50 442	44	10.49 558	9.97 890	4	17	39 5 4 3
44	9.48 371	39	9.50 485	43	10.49 515	9.97 886	4	16	
45	9.48 411	40	9.50 529	44	10.49 471	9.97 882	4	15	1| 3.9 0.5 0.4 0.3
46	9.48 450	39	9.50 572	43	10.49 428	9.97 878	4	14	2| 7.8 1.0 0.8 0.6
47	9.48 490	40	9.50 616	44	10.49 384	9.97 874	4	13	3| 11.7 1.5 1.2 0.9
48	9.48 529	39	9.50 659	43	10.49 341	9.97 870	4	12	4| 15.6 2.0 1.6 1.2
49	9.48 568	39	9.50 703	44	10.49 297	9.97 866	5	11	5| 19.5 2.5 2.0 1.5
50	9.48 607	39	9.50 746	43	10.49 254	9.97 861	4	10	6| 23.4 3.0 2.4 1.8
51	9.48 647	40	9.50 789	43	10.49 211	9.97 857	4	9	7| 27.3 3.5 2.8 2.1
52	9.48 686	39	9.50 833	43	10.49 167	9.97 853	4	8	8| 31.2 4.0 3.2 2.4
53	9.48 725	39	9.50 876	43	10.49 124	9.97 849	4	7	9| 35.1 4.5 3.6 2.7
54	9.48 764	39	9.60 919	43	10.49 081	9.97 845	4	6	
55	9.48 803	39	9.50 962	43	10.49 038	9.97 841	4	5	
56	9.48 842	39	9.51 005	43	10.48 995	9.97 837	4	4	
57	9.48 881	39	9.51 048	44	10.48 952	9.97 833	4	3	
58	9.48 920	39	9.51 092	43	10.48 908	9.97 829	4	2	
59	9.48 959	39	9.51 135	43	10.48 865	9.97 825	4	1	
60	9.48 998		9.51 178		10.48 822	9.97 821		0	

	L. Cos.	d.	L. Cot.	c. d.	L. Tan.	L. Sin.	d.	'	P. P.

18°

′	L. Sin.	d.	L. Tan.	c. d.	L. Cot.	L. Cos.	d.	
0	9.48 998		9.51 178		10.48 822	9.97 821		60
1	9.49 037	39	9.51 221	43	10.48 779	9.97 817	4	59
2	9.49 076	39	9.51 264	43	10.48 736	9.97 812	5	58
3	9.49 115	39	9.51 306	42	10.48 694	9.97 808	4	57
4	9.49 153	38	9.51 349	43	10.48 651	9.97 804	4	56
5	9.49 192	39	9.51 392	43	10.48 608	9.97 800	4	55
6	9.49 231	39	9.51 435	43	10.48 565	9.97 796	4	54
7	9.49 269	38	9.51 478	43	10.48 522	9.97 792	4	53
8	9.49 308	39	9.51 520	42	10.48 480	9.97 788	4	52
9	9.49 347	39	9.51 563	43	10.48 437	9.97 784	4	51
10	9.49 385	38	9.51 606	43	10.48 394	9.97 779	5	50
11	9.49 424	39	9.51 648	42	10.48 352	9.97 775	4	49
12	9.49 462	38	9.51 691	43	10.48 309	9.97 771	4	48
13	9.49 500	38	9.51 734	43	10.48 266	9.97 767	4	47
14	9.49 539	38	9.51 776	42	10.48 224	9.97 763	4	46
15	9.49 577	39	9.51 819	43	10.48 181	9.97 759	4	45
16	9.49 615	38	9.51 861	42	10.48 139	9.97 754	5	44
17	9.49 654	39	9.51 903	42	10.48 097	9.97 750	4	43
18	9.49 692	38	9.51 946	43	10.48 054	9.97 746	4	42
19	9.49 730	38	9.51 988	42	10.48 012	9.97 742	4	41
20	9.49 768	38	9.52 031	43	10.47 969	9.97 738	4	40
21	9.49 806	38	9.52 073	42	10.47 927	9.97 734	4	39
22	9.49 844	38	9.52 115	42	10.47 885	9.97 729	5	38
23	9.49 882	38	9.52 157	42	10.47 843	9.97 725	4	37
24	9.49 920	38	9.52 200	43	10.47 800	9.97 721	4	36
25	9.49 958	38	9.52 242	42	10.47 758	9.97 717	4	35
26	9.49 996	38	9.52 284	42	10.47 716	9.97 713	4	34
27	9.50 034	38	9.52 326	42	10.47 674	9.97 708	5	33
28	9.50 072	38	9.52 368	42	10.47 632	9.97 704	4	32
29	9.50 110	38	9.52 410	42	10.47 590	9.97 700	4	31
30	9.50 148	38	9.52 452	42	10.47 548	9.97 696	5	30
31	9.50 185	37	9.52 494	42	10.47 506	9.97 691	4	29
32	9.50 223	38	9.52 536	42	10.47 464	9.97 687	4	28
33	9.50 261	38	9.52 578	42	10.47 422	9.97 683	4	27
34	9.50 298	37	9.52 620	41	10.47 380	9.97 679	5	26
35	9.50 336	38	9.52 661	42	10.47 339	9.97 674	4	25
36	9.50 374	38	9.52 703	42	10.47 297	9.97 670	4	24
37	9.50 411	37	9.52 745	42	10.47 255	9.97 666	4	23
38	9.50 449	38	9.52 787	42	10.47 213	9.97 662	4	22
39	9.50 486	37	9.52 829	42	10.47 171	9.97 657	4	21
40	9.50 523	37	9.52 870	41	10.47 130	9.97 653	4	20
41	9.50 561	38	9.52 912	42	10.47 088	9.97 649	4	19
42	9.50 598	37	9.52 953	41	10.47 047	9.97 645	5	18
43	9.50 635	37	9.52 995	42	10.47 005	9.97 640	4	17
44	9.50 673	38	9.53 037	41	10.46 963	9.97 636	4	16
45	9.50 710	37	9.53 078	42	10.46 922	9.97 632	4	15
46	9.50 747	37	9.53 120	41	10.46 880	9.97 628	5	14
47	9.50 784	37	9.53 161	41	10.46 839	9.97 623	4	13
48	9.50 821	37	9.53 202	41	10.46 798	9.97 619	4	12
49	9.50 858	38	9.53 244	42	10.46 756	9.97 615	5	11
50	9.50 896	37	9.53 285	41	10.46 715	9.97 610	4	10
51	9.50 933	37	9.53 327	42	10.46 673	9.97 606	4	9
52	9.50 970	37	9.53 368	41	10.46 632	9.97 602	5	8
53	9.51 007	36	9.53 409	41	10.46 591	9.97 597	4	7
54	9.51 043	37	9.53 450	41	10.46 550	9.97 593	5	6
55	9.51 080	37	9.53 492	42	10.46 508	9.97 589	5	5
56	9.51 117	37	9.53 533	41	10.46 467	9.97 584	4	4
57	9.51 154	37	9.53 574	41	10.46 426	9.97 580	4	3
58	9.51 191	36	9.53 615	41	10.46 385	9.97 576	5	2
59	9.51 227	37	9.53 656	41	10.46 344	9.97 571	4	1
60	9.51 264		9.53 697		10.46 303	9.97 567		0
	L. Cos.	d.	L. Cot.	c. d.	L. Tan.	L. Sin.	d.	′

P. P.

	43	42	41
1	4.3	4.2	4.1
2	8.6	8.4	8.2
3	12.9	12.6	12.3
4	17.2	16.8	16.4
5	21.5	21.0	20.5
6	25.8	25.2	24.6
7	30.1	29.4	28.7
8	34.4	33.6	32.8
9	38.7	37.8	36.9

	39	38	37
1	3.9	3.8	3.7
2	7.8	7.6	7.4
3	11.7	11.4	11.1
4	15.6	15.2	14.8
5	19.5	19.0	18.5
6	23.4	22.8	22.2
7	27.3	26.6	25.9
8	31.2	30.4	29.6
9	35.1	34.2	33.3

	36	5	4
1	3.6	0.5	0.4
2	7.2	1.0	0.8
3	10.8	1.5	1.2
4	14.4	2.0	1.6
5	18.0	2.5	2.0
6	21.6	3.0	2.4
7	25.2	3.5	2.8
8	28.8	4.0	3.2
9	32.4	4.5	3.6

TABLE III. LOGARITHMS OF FUNCTIONS | 231

19°

′	L. Sin.	d.	L. Tan.	c. d.	L. Cot.	L. Cos.	d.	′	P. P.
0	9.51 264	37	9.53 697	41	10.46 303	9.97 567	4	60	
1	9.51 301	37	9.53 738	41	10.46 262	9.97 563	5	59	
2	9.51 338	36	9.53 779	41	10.46 221	9.97 558	4	58	
3	9.51 374	37	9.53 820	41	10.46 180	9.97 554	4	57	
4	9.51 411	36	9.53 861	41	10.46 139	9.97 550	5	56	
5	9.51 447	37	9.53 902	41	10.46 098	9.97 545	4	55	
6	9.51 484	36	9.53 943	41	10.46 057	9.97 541	4	54	
7	9.51 520	37	9.53 984	41	10.46 016	9.97 536	5	53	
8	9.51 557	36	9.54 025	40	10.45 975	9.97 532	4	52	
9	9.51 593	36	9.54 065	41	10.45 935	9.97 528	4	51	
10	9.51 629	37	9.54 106	41	10.45 894	9.97 523	5	50	**41 40 39**
11	9.51 666	36	9.54 147	40	10.45 853	9.97 519	4	49	1 4.1 4.0 3.9
12	9.51 702	36	9.54 187	41	10.45 813	9.97 515	4	48	2 8.2 8.0 7.8
13	9.51 738	36	9.54 228	41	10.45 772	9.97 510	5	47	3 12.3 12.0 11.7
14	9.51 774	37	9.54 269	40	10.45 731	9.97 506	4	46	4 16.4 16.0 15.6
15	9.51 811	36	9.54 309	41	10.45 691	9.97 501	4	45	5 20.5 20.0 19.5
16	9.51 847	36	9.54 350	40	10.45 650	9.97 497	5	44	6 24.6 24.0 23.4
17	9.51 883	36	9.54 390	41	10.45 610	9.97 492	4	43	7 28.7 28.0 27.3
18	9.51 919	36	9.54 431	40	10.45 569	9.97 488	4	42	8 32.8 32.0 31.2
19	9.51 955	36	9.54 471	41	10.45 529	9.97 484	5	41	9 36.9 36.0 35.1
20	9.51 991	36	9.54 512	40	10.45 488	9.97 479	4	40	
21	9.52 027	36	9.54 552	41	10.45 448	9.97 475	5	39	
22	9.52 063	36	9.54 593	40	10.45 407	9.97 470	4	38	
23	9.52 099	36	9.54 633	40	10.45 367	9.97 466	5	37	
24	9.52 135	36	9.54 673	41	10.45 327	9.97 461	4	36	
25	9.52 171	36	9.54 714	40	10.45 286	9.97 457	4	35	
26	9.52 207	35	9.54 754	40	10.45 246	9.97 453	5	34	
27	9.52 242	36	9.54 794	41	10.45 206	9.97 448	4	33	**37 36 35**
28	9.52 278	36	9.54 835	40	10.45 165	9.97 444	5	32	1 3.7 3.6 3.5
29	9.52 314	36	9.54 875	40	10.45 125	9.97 439	4	31	2 7.4 7.2 7.0
30	9.52 350	35	9.54 915	40	10.45 085	9.97 435	5	30	3 11.1 10.8 10.5
31	9.52 385	36	9.54 955	40	10.45 045	9.97 430	4	29	4 14.8 14.4 14.0
32	9.52 421	35	9.54 995	40	10.45 005	9.97 426	5	28	5 18.5 18.0 17.5
33	9.52 456	36	9.55 035	40	10.44 965	9.97 421	4	27	6 22.2 21.6 21.0
34	9.52 492	35	9.55 075	40	10.44 925	9.97 417	5	26	7 25.9 25.2 24.5
35	9.52 527	36	9.55 115	40	10.44 885	9.97 412	4	25	8 29.6 28.8 28.0
36	9.52 563	35	9.55 155	40	10.44 845	9.97 408	5	24	9 33.3 32.4 31.5
37	9.52 598	36	9.55 195	40	10.44 805	9.97 403	4	23	
38	9.52 634	35	9.55 235	40	10.44 765	9.97 399	5	22	
39	9.52 669	36	9.55 275	40	10.44 725	9.97 394	4	21	
40	9.52 705	35	9.55 315	40	10.44 685	9.97 390	5	20	
41	9.52 740	35	9.55 355	40	10.44 645	9.97 385	4	19	
42	9.52 775	36	9.55 395	39	10.44 605	9.97 381	5	18	
43	9.52 811	35	9.55 434	40	10.44 566	9.97 376	4	17	
44	9.52 846	35	9.55 474	40	10.44 526	9.97 372	5	16	**34 5**
45	9.52 881	35	9.55 514	40	10.44 486	9.97 367	4	15	1 3.4 0.5 0.4
46	9.52 916	35	9.55 554	39	10.44 446	9.97 363	5	14	2 6.8 1.0 0.8
47	9.52 951	35	9.55 593	40	10.44 407	9.97 358	5	13	3 10.2 1.5 1.2
48	9.52 986	35	9.55 633	40	10.44 367	9.97 353	4	12	4 13.6 2.0 1.6
49	9.53 021	35	9.55 673	39	10.44 327	9.97 349	5	11	5 17.0 2.5 2.0
50	9.53 056	36	9.55 712	40	10.44 288	9.97 344	4	10	6 20.4 3.0 2.4
51	9.53 092	34	9.55 752	39	10.44 248	9.97 340	5	9	7 23.8 3.5 2.8
52	9.53 126	35	9.55 791	40	10.44 209	9.97 335	4	8	8 27.2 4.0 3.2
53	9.53 161	35	9.55 831	39	10.44 169	9.97 331	5	7	9 30.6 4.5 3.6
54	9.53 196	35	9.55 870	40	10.44 130	9.97 326	4	6	
55	9.53 231	35	9.55 910	39	10.44 090	9.97 322	5	5	
56	9.53 266	35	9.55 949	40	10.44 051	9.97 317	5	4	
57	9.53 301	35	9.55 989	39	10.44 011	9.97 312	4	3	
58	9.53 336	34	9.56 028	39	10.43 972	9.97 308	5	2	
59	9.53 370	35	9.56 067	40	10.43 933	9.97 303	4	1	
60	9.53 405		9.56 107		10.43 893	9.97 299		0	
	L. Cos.	d.	L. Cot.	c. d.	L. Tan.	L. Sin.	d.	′	P. P.

20°

'	L. Sin.	d.	L. Tan.	c. d.	L. Cot.	L. Cos.	d.	
0	9.53 405	35	9.56 107	39	10.43 893	9.97 299	5	60
1	9.53 440	35	9.56 146	39	10.43 854	9.97 294	5	59
2	9.53 475	34	9.56 185	39	10.43 815	9.97 289	4	58
3	9.53 509	35	9.56 224	40	10.43 776	9.97 285	5	57
4	9.53 544	34	9.56 264	39	10.43 736	9.97 280	4	56
5	9.53 578	35	9.56 303	39	10.43 697	9.97 276	5	55
6	9.53 613	34	9.56 342	39	10.43 658	9.97 271	5	54
7	9.53 647	35	9.56 381	39	10.43 619	9.97 266	4	53
8	9.53 682	34	9.56 420	39	10.43 580	9.97 262	5	52
9	9.53 716	35	9.56 459	39	10.43 541	9.97 257	5	51
10	9.53 751	34	9.56 498	39	10.43 502	9.97 252	4	50
11	9.53 785	34	9.56 537	39	10.43 463	9.97 248	5	49
12	9.53 819	35	9.56 576	39	10.43 424	9.97 243	5	48
13	9.53 854	34	9.56 615	39	10.43 385	9.97 238	4	47
14	9.53 888	34	9.56 654	39	10.43 346	9.97 234	5	46
15	9.53 922	35	9.56 693	39	10.43 307	9.97 229	5	45
16	9.53 957	34	9.56 732	39	10.43 268	9.97 224	4	44
17	9.53 991	34	9.56 771	39	10.43 229	9.97 220	5	43
18	9.54 025	34	9.56 810	39	10.43 190	9.97 215	5	42
19	9.54 059	34	9.56 849	38	10.43 151	9.97 210	4	41
20	9.54 093	34	9.56 887	39	10.43 113	9.97 206	5	40
21	9.54 127	34	9.56 926	39	10.43 074	9.97 201	5	39
22	9.54 161	34	9.56 965	39	10.43 035	9.97 196	4	38
23	9.54 195	34	9.57 004	38	10.42 996	9.97 192	5	37
24	9.54 229	34	9.57 042	39	10.42 958	9.97 187	5	36
25	9.54 263	34	9.57 081	39	10.42 919	9.97 182	4	35
26	9.54 297	34	9.57 120	38	10.42 880	9.97 178	5	34
27	9.54 331	34	9.57 158	39	10.42 842	9.97 173	5	33
28	9.54 365	34	9.57 197	38	10.42 803	9.97 168	5	32
29	9.54 399	34	9.57 235	39	10.42 765	9.97 163	4	31
30	9.54 433	33	9.57 274	38	10.42 726	9.97 159	5	30
31	9.54 466	34	9.57 312	39	10.42 688	9.97 154	5	29
32	9.54 500	34	9.57 351	38	10.42 649	9.97 149	4	28
33	9.54 534	33	9.57 389	39	10.42 611	9.97 145	5	27
34	9.54 567	34	9.57 428	38	10.42 572	9.97 140	5	26
35	9.54 601	34	9.57 466	38	10.42 534	9.97 135	5	25
36	9.54 635	33	9.57 504	39	10.42 496	9.97 130	4	24
37	9.54 668	34	9.57 543	38	10.42 457	9.97 126	5	23
38	9.54 702	33	9.57 581	38	10.42 419	9.97 121	5	22
39	9.54 735	34	9.57 619	39	10.42 381	9.97 116	5	21
40	9.54 769	33	9.57 658	38	10.42 342	9.97 111	4	20
41	9.54 802	34	9.57 696	38	10.42 304	9.97 107	5	19
42	9.54 836	33	9.57 734	38	10.42 266	9.97 102	5	18
43	9.54 869	34	9.57 772	38	10.42 228	9.97 097	5	17
44	9.54 903	33	9.57 810	39	10.42 190	9.97 092	5	16
45	9.54 936	33	9.57 849	38	10.42 151	9.97 087	4	15
46	9.54 969	34	9.57 887	38	10.42 113	9.97 083	5	14
47	9.55 003	33	9.57 925	38	10.42 075	9.97 078	5	13
48	9.55 036	33	9.57 963	38	10.42 037	9.97 073	5	12
49	9.55 069	33	9.58 001	38	10.41 999	9.97 068	5	11
50	9.55 102	34	9.58 039	38	10.41 961	9.97 063	5	10
51	9.55 136	33	9.58 077	38	10.41 923	9.97 059	5	9
52	9.55 169	33	9.58 115	38	10.41 885	9.97 054	5	8
53	9.55 202	33	9.58 153	38	10.41 847	9.97 049	5	7
54	9.55 235	33	9.58 191	38	10.41 809	9.97 044	5	6
55	9.55 268	33	9.58 229	38	10.41 771	9.97 039	4	5
56	9.55 301	33	9.58 267	37	10.41 733	9.97 035	5	4
57	9.55 334	33	9.58 304	38	10.41 696	9.97 030	5	3
58	9.55 367	33	9.58 342	38	10.41 658	9.97 025	5	2
59	9.55 400	33	9.58 380	38	10.41 620	9.97 020	5	1
60	9.55 433		9.58 418		10.41 582	9.97 015		0
	L. Cos.	c.	L. Cot.	c. d.	L. Tan.	L. Sin.	d.	'

P. P.

	40	39	38
1	4.0	3.9	3.8
2	8.0	7.8	7.6
3	12.0	11.7	11.4
4	16.0	15.6	15.2
5	20.0	19.5	19.0
6	24.0	23.4	22.8
7	28.0	27.3	26.6
8	32.0	31.2	30.4
9	36.0	35.1	34.2

	37	35	34
1	3.7	3.5	3.4
2	7.4	7.0	6.8
3	11.1	10.5	10.2
4	14.8	14.0	13.6
5	18.5	17.5	17.0
6	22.2	21.0	20.4
7	25.9	24.5	23.8
8	29.6	28.0	27.2
9	33.3	31.5	30.6

	33	5	4
1	3.3	0.5	0.4
2	6.6	1.0	0.8
3	9.9	1.5	1.2
4	13.2	2.0	1.6
5	16.5	2.5	2.0
6	19.8	3.0	2.4
7	23.1	3.5	2.8
8	26.4	4.0	3.2
9	29.7	4.5	3.6

TABLE III. LOGARITHMS OF FUNCTIONS | 233

21°

'	L. Sin.	d.	L. Tan.	c. d.	L. Cot.	L. Cos.	d.	
0	9.55 433		9.58 418		10.41 582	9.97 015		60
1	9.55 466	33	9.58 455	37	10.41 545	9.97 010	5	59
2	9.55 499	33	9.58 493	38	10.41 507	9.97 005	5	58
3	9.55 532	33	9.58 531	38	10.41 469	9.97 001	4	57
4	9.55 564	32	9.58 569	38	10.41 431	9.96 996	5	56
5	9.55 597	33	9.58 606	37	10.41 394	9.96 991	5	55
6	9.55 630	33	9.58 644	38	10.41 356	9.96 986	5	54
7	9.55 663	33	9.58 681	37	10.41 319	9.96 981	5	53
8	9.55 695	32	9.58 719	38	10.41 281	9.96 976	5	52
9	9.55 728	33	9.58 757	38	10.41 243	9.96 971	5	51
10	9.55 761	33	9.58 794	37	10.41 206	9.96 966	5	50
11	9.55 793	32	9.58 832	38	10.41 168	9.96 962	4	49
12	9.55 826	33	9.58 869	37	10.41 131	9.96 957	5	48
13	9.55 858	32	9.58 907	38	10.41 093	9.96 952	5	47
14	9.55 891	33	9.58 944	37	10.41 056	9.96 947	5	46
15	9.55 923	32	9.58 981	37	10.41 019	9.96 942	5	45
16	9.55 956	33	9.59 019	38	10.40 981	9.96 937	5	44
17	9.55 988	32	9.59 056	37	10.40 944	9.96 932	5	43
18	9.56 021	33	9.59 094	38	10.40 906	9.96 927	5	42
19	9.56 053	32	9.59 131	37	10.40 869	9.96 922	5	41
20	9.56 085	32	9.59 168	37	10.40 832	9.96 917	5	40
21	9.56 118	33	9.59 205	38	10.40 795	9.96 912	5	39
22	9.56 150	32	9.59 243	37	10.40 757	9.96 907	5	38
23	9.56 182	32	9.59 280	37	10.40 720	9.96 903	4	37
24	9.56 215	33	9.59 317	37	10.40 683	9.96 898	5	36
25	9.56 247	32	9.59 354	37	10.40 646	9.96 893	5	35
26	9.56 279	32	9.59 391	37	10.40 609	9.96 888	5	34
27	9.56 311	32	9.59 429	38	10.40 571	9.96 883	5	33
28	9.56 343	32	9.59 466	37	10.40 534	9.96 878	5	32
29	9.56 375	32	9.59 503	37	10.40 497	9.96 873	5	31
30	9.56 408	33	9.59 540	37	10.40 460	9.96 868	5	30
31	9.56 440	32	9.59 577	37	10.40 423	9.96 863	5	29
32	9.56 472	32	9.59 614	37	10.40 386	9.96 858	5	28
33	9.56 504	32	9.59 651	37	10.40 349	9.96 853	5	27
34	9.56 536	32	9.59 688	37	10.40 312	9.96 848	5	26
35	9.56 568	31	9.59 725	37	10.40 275	9.96 843	5	25
36	9.56 599	32	9.59 762	37	10.40 238	9.96 838	5	24
37	9.56 631	32	9.59 799	36	10.40 201	9.96 833	5	23
38	9.56 663	32	9.59 835	37	10.40 165	9.96 828	5	22
39	9.56 695	32	9.59 872	37	10.40 128	9.96 823	5	21
40	9.56 727	32	9.59 909	37	10.40 091	9.96 818	5	20
41	9.56 759	31	9.59 946	37	10.40 054	9.96 813	5	19
42	9.56 790	32	9.59 983	36	10.40 017	9.96 808	5	18
43	9.56 822	32	9.60 019	37	10.39 981	9.96 803	5	17
44	9.56 854	32	9.60 056	37	10.39 944	9.96 798	5	16
45	9.56 886	31	9.60 093	37	10.39 907	9.96 793	5	15
46	9.56 917	32	9.60 130	36	10.39 870	9.96 788	5	14
47	9.56 949	31	9.60 166	37	10.39 834	9.96 783	5	13
48	9.56 980	32	9.60 203	37	10.39 797	9.96 778	6	12
49	9.57 012	32	9.60 240	36	10.39 760	9.96 772	5	11
50	9.57 044	31	9.60 276	37	10.39 724	9.96 767	5	10
51	9.57 075	32	9.60 313	36	10.39 687	9.96 762	5	9
52	9.57 107	31	9.60 349	37	10.39 651	9.96 757	5	8
53	9.57 138	31	9.60 386	36	10.39 614	9.96 752	5	7
54	9.57 169	32	9.60 422	37	10.39 578	9.96 747	5	6
55	9.57 201	31	9.60 459	36	10.39 541	9.96 742	5	5
56	9.57 232	32	9.60 495	37	10.39 505	9.96 737	5	4
57	9.57 264	31	9.60 532	36	10.39 468	9.96 732	5	3
58	9.57 295	31	9.60 568	37	10.39 432	9.96 727	5	2
59	9.57 326	32	9.60 605	36	10 39 395	9.96 722	5	1
60	9.57 358		9.60 641		10.39 359	9.96 717		0
	L. Cos.	d.	L. Cot.	c. d.	L. Tan.	L. Sin.	d.	'

P. P.

	38	37	36
1	3.8	3.7	3.6
2	7.6	7.4	7.2
3	11.4	11.1	10.8
4	15.2	14.8	14.4
5	19.0	18.5	18.0
6	22.8	22.2	21.6
7	26.6	25.9	25.2
8	30.4	29.6	28.8
9	34.2	33.3	32.4

	33	32	31
1	3.3	3.2	3.1
2	6.6	6.4	6.2
3	9.9	9.6	9.3
4	13.2	12.8	12.4
5	16.5	16.0	15.5
6	19.8	19.2	18.6
7	23.1	22.4	21.7
8	26.4	25.6	24.8
9	29.7	28.8	27.9

	6	5	4
1	0.6	0.5	0.4
2	1.2	1.0	0.8
3	1.8	1.5	1.2
4	2.4	2.0	1.6
5	3.0	2.5	2.0
6	3.6	3.0	2.4
7	4.2	3.5	2.8
8	4.8	4.0	3.2
9	5.4	4.5	3.6

22°

'	L. Sin.	d.	L. Tan.	c. d.	L. Cot.	L. Cos.	d.	'
0	9.57 358	31	9.60 641	36	10.39 359	9.96 717	6	60
1	9.57 389	31	9.60 677	37	10.39 323	9.96 711	5	59
2	9.57 420	31	9.60 714	36	10.39 286	9.96 706	5	58
3	9.57 451	31	9.60 750	36	10.39 250	9.96 701	5	57
4	9.57 482	32	9.60 786	37	10.39 214	9.96 696	5	56
5	9.57 514	31	9.60 823	36	10.39 177	9.96 691	5	55
6	9.57 545	31	9.60 859	36	10.39 141	9.96 686	5	54
7	9.57 576	31	9.60 895	36	10.39 105	9.96 681	5	53
8	9.57 607	31	9.60 931	36	10.39 069	9.96 676	6	52
9	9.57 638	31	9.60 967	37	10.39 033	9.96 670	5	51
10	9.57 669	31	9.61 004	36	10.38 996	9.96 665	5	50
11	9.57 700	31	9.61 040	36	10.38 960	9.96 660	5	49
12	9.57 731	31	9.61 076	36	10.38 924	9.96 655	5	48
13	9.57 762	31	9.61 112	36	10.38 888	9.96 650	5	47
14	9.57 793	31	9.61 148	36	10.38 852	9.96 645	5	46
15	9.57 824	31	9.61 184	36	10.38 816	9.96 640	6	45
16	9.57 855	30	9.61 220	36	10.38 780	9.96 634	5	44
17	9.57 885	31	9.61 256	36	10.38 744	9.96 629	5	43
18	9.57 916	31	9.61 292	36	10.38 708	9.96 624	5	42
19	9.57 947	31	9.61 328	36	10.38 672	9.96 619	5	41
20	9.57 978	30	9.61 364	36	10.38 636	9.96 614	6	40
21	9.58 008	31	9.61 400	36	10.38 600	9.96 608	5	39
22	9.58 039	31	9.61 436	36	10.38 564	9.96 603	5	38
23	9.58 070	31	9.61 472	36	10.38 528	9.96 598	5	37
24	9.58 101	30	9.61 508	36	10.38 492	9.96 593	5	36
25	9.58 131	31	9.61 544	35	10.38 456	9.96 588	6	35
26	9.58 162	30	9.61 579	36	10.38 421	9.96 582	5	34
27	9.58 192	31	9.61 615	36	10.38 385	9.96 577	5	33
28	9.58 223	30	9.61 651	36	10.38 349	9.96 572	5	32
29	9.58 253	31	9.61 687	35	10.38 313	9.96 567	6	31
30	9.58 284	30	9.61 722	36	10.38 278	9.96 562	6	30
31	9.58 314	31	9.61 758	36	10.38 242	9.96 556	5	29
32	9.58 345	30	9.61 794	36	10.38 206	9.96 551	5	28
33	9.58 375	31	9.61 830	35	10.38 170	9.96 546	5	27
34	9.58 406	30	9.61 865	36	10.38 135	9.96 541	6	26
35	9.58 436	31	9.61 901	35	10.38 099	9.96 535	5	25
36	9.58 467	30	9.61 936	36	10.38 064	9.96 530	5	24
37	9.58 497	30	9.61 972	36	10.38 028	9.96 525	5	23
38	9.58 527	30	9.62 008	35	10.37 992	9.96 520	6	22
39	9.58 557	31	9.62 043	36	10.37 957	9.96 514	5	21
40	9.58 588	30	9.62 079	35	10.37 921	9.96 509	5	20
41	9.58 618	30	9.62 114	36	10.37 886	9.96 504	6	19
42	9.58 648	30	9.62 150	35	10.37 850	9.96 498	5	18
43	9.58 678	31	9.62 185	36	10.37 815	9.96 493	5	17
44	9.58 709	30	9.62 221	35	10.37 779	9.96 488	5	16
45	9.58 739	30	9.62 256	36	10.37 744	9.96 483	6	15
46	9.58 769	30	9.62 292	35	10.37 708	9.96 477	5	14
47	9.58 799	30	9.62 327	35	10.37 673	9.96 472	5	13
48	9.58 829	30	9.62 362	36	10.37 638	9.96 467	6	12
49	9.58 859	30	9.62 398	35	10.37 602	9.96 461	5	11
50	9.58 889	30	9.62 433	35	10.37 567	9.96 456	5	10
51	9.58 919	30	9.62 468	36	10.37 532	9.96 451	6	9
52	9.58 949	30	9.62 504	35	10.37 496	9.96 445	5	8
53	9.58 979	30	9.62 539	35	10.37 461	9.96 440	5	7
54	9.59 009	30	9.62 574	35	10.37 426	9.96 435	6	6
55	9.59 039	30	9.62 609	36	10.37 391	9.96 429	5	5
56	9.59 069	29	9.62 645	35	10.37 355	9.96 424	5	4
57	9.59 098	30	9.62 680	35	10.37 320	9.96 419	6	3
58	9.59 128	30	9.62 715	35	10.37 285	9.96 413	5	2
59	9.59 158	30	9.62 750	35	10.37 250	9.96 408	5	1
60	9.59 188		9.62 785		10.37 215	9.96 403		0
	L. Cos.	d.	L. Cot.	c. d.	L. Tan.	L. Sin.	d.	'

P. P.

	37	36	35
1	3.7	3.6	3.5
2	7.4	7.2	7.0
3	11.1	10.8	10.5
4	14.8	14.4	14.0
5	18.5	18.0	17.5
6	22.2	21.6	21.0
7	25.9	25.2	24.5
8	29.6	28.8	28.0
9	33.3	32.4	31.5

	32	31	30
1	3.2	3.1	3.0
2	6.4	6.2	6.0
3	9.6	9.3	9.0
4	12.8	12.4	12.0
5	16.0	15.5	15.0
6	19.2	18.6	18.0
7	22.4	21.7	21.0
8	25.6	24.8	24.0
9	28.8	27.9	27.0

	29	6	5
1	2.9	0.6	0.5
2	5.8	1.2	1.0
3	8.7	1.8	1.5
4	11.6	2.4	2.0
5	14.5	3.0	2.5
6	17.4	3.6	3.0
7	20.3	4.2	3.5
8	23.2	4.8	4.0
9	26.1	5.4	4.5

TABLE III. LOGARITHMS OF FUNCTIONS | 235

23°

′	L. Sin.	d.	L. Tan.	c. d.	L. Cot.	L. Cos.	d.	″
0	9.59 188	30	9.62 785	35	10.37 215	9.96 403	6	60
1	9.59 218	29	9.62 820	35	10.37 180	9.96 397	5	59
2	9.59 247	30	9.62 855	35	10.37 145	9.96 392	5	58
3	9.59 277	30	9.62 890	36	10.37 110	9.96 387	6	57
4	9.59 307	29	9.62 926	35	10.37 074	9.96 381	5	56
5	9.59 336	30	9.62 961	35	10.37 039	9.96 376	6	55
6	9.59 366	30	9.62 996	35	10.37 004	9.96 370	5	54
7	9.59 396	29	9.63 031	35	10.36 969	9.96 365	5	53
8	9.59 425	30	9.63 066	35	10.36 934	9.96 360	6	52
9	9.59 455	29	9.63 101	34	10.36 899	9.96 354	5	51
10	9.59 484	30	9.63 135	35	10.36 865	9.96 349	6	50
11	9.59 514	29	9.63 170	35	10.36 830	9.96 343	5	49
12	9.59 543	30	9.63 205	35	10.36 795	9.96 338	5	48
13	9.59 573	29	9.63 240	35	10.36 760	9.96 333	6	47
14	9.59 602	30	9.63 275	35	10.36 725	9.96 327	5	46
15	9.59 632	29	9.63 310	35	10.36 690	9.96 322	6	45
16	9.59 661	29	9.63 345	34	10.36 655	9.96 316	5	44
17	9.59 690	30	9.63 379	35	10.36 621	9.96 311	6	43
18	9.59 720	29	9.63 414	35	10.36 586	9.96 305	5	42
19	9.59 749	29	9.63 449	35	10.36 551	9.96 300	6	41
20	9.59 778	30	9.63 484	35	10.36 516	9.96 294	5	40
21	9.59 808	29	9.63 519	34	10.36 481	9.96 289	5	39
22	9.59 837	29	9.63 553	35	10.36 447	9.96 284	6	38
23	9.59 866	29	9.63 588	35	10.36 412	9.96 278	5	37
24	9.59 895	29	9.63 623	34	10.36 377	9.96 273	6	36
25	9.59 924	30	9.63 657	35	10.36 343	9.96 267	5	35
26	9.59 954	29	9.63 692	34	10.36 308	9.96 262	6	34
27	9.59 983	29	9.63 726	35	10.36 274	9.96 256	5	33
28	9.60 012	29	9.63 761	35	10.36 239	9.96 251	6	32
29	9.60 041	29	9.63 796	34	10.36 204	9.96 245	5	31
30	9.60 070	29	9.63 830	35	10.36 170	9.96 240	6	30
31	9.60 099	29	9.63 865	34	10.36 135	9.96 234	5	29
32	9.60 128	29	9.63 899	35	10.36 101	9.96 229	6	28
33	9.60 157	29	9.63 934	34	10.36 066	9.96 223	5	27
34	9.60 186	29	9.63 968	35	10.36 032	9.96 218	6	26
35	9.60 215	29	9.64 003	34	10.35 997	9.96 212	5	25
36	9.60 244	29	9.64 037	35	10.35 963	9.96 207	6	24
37	9.60 273	29	9.64 072	34	10.35 928	9.96 201	5	23
38	9.60 302	29	9.64 106	34	10.35 894	9.96 196	6	22
39	9.60 331	28	9.64 140	35	10.35 860	9.96 190	5	21
40	9.60 359	29	9.64 175	34	10.35 825	9.96 185	6	20
41	9.60 388	29	9.64 209	34	10.35 791	9.96 179	5	19
42	9.60 417	29	9.64 243	35	10.35 757	9.96 174	6	18
43	9.60 446	28	9.64 278	34	10.35 722	9.96 168	6	17
44	9.60 474	29	9.64 312	34	10.35 688	9.96 162	5	16
45	9.60 503	29	9.64 346	35	10.35 654	9.96 157	6	15
46	9.60 532	29	9.64 381	34	10.35 619	9.96 151	5	14
47	9.60 561	28	9.64 415	34	10.35 585	9.96 146	6	13
48	9.60 589	29	9.64 449	34	10.35 551	9.96 140	5	12
49	9.60 618	28	9.64 483	34	10.35 517	9.96 135	6	11
50	9.60 646	29	9.64 517	35	10.35 483	9.96 129	6	10
51	9.60 675	29	9.64 552	34	10.35 448	9.96 123	5	9
52	9.60 704	28	9.64 586	34	10.35 414	9.96 118	6	8
53	9.60 732	29	9.64 620	34	10.35 380	9.96 112	5	7
54	9.60 761	28	9.64 654	34	10.35 346	9.96 107	6	6
55	9.60 789	29	9.64 688	34	10.35 312	9.96 101	6	5
56	9.60 818	28	9.64 722	34	10.35 278	9.96 095	5	4
57	9.60 846	29	9.64 756	34	10.35 244	9.96 090	6	3
58	9.60 875	28	9.64 790	34	10.35 210	9.96 084	5	2
59	9.60 903	28	9.64 824	34	10.35 176	9.96 079	6	1
60	9.60 931		9.64 858		10.35 142	9.96 073		0
	L. Cos.	d.	L. Cot.	c. d.	L. Tan.	L. Sin.	d.	′

P. P.

	36	35	34
1	3.6	3.5	3.4
2	7.2	7.0	6.8
3	10.8	10.5	10.2
4	14.4	14.0	13.6
5	18.0	17.5	17.0
6	21.6	21.0	20.4
7	25.2	24.5	23.8
8	28.8	28.0	27.2
9	32.4	31.5	30.6

	30	29	28
1	3.0	2.9	2.8
2	6.0	5.8	5.6
3	9.0	8.7	8.4
4	12.0	11.6	11.2
5	15.0	14.5	14.0
6	18.0	17.4	16.8
7	21.0	20.3	19.6
8	24.0	23.2	22.4
9	27.0	26.1	25.2

	6	5
1	0.6	0.5
2	1.2	1.0
3	1.8	1.5
4	2.4	2.0
5	3.0	2.5
6	3.6	3.0
7	4.2	3.5
8	4.8	4.0
9	5.4	4.5

24°

′	L. Sin.	d.	L. Tan.	c. d.	L. Cot.	L. Cos.	d.		
0	9.60 931	29	9.64 858	34	10.35 142	9.96 073	6	60	
1	9.60 960	28	9.64 892	34	10.35 108	9.96 067	5	59	
2	9.60 988	28	9.64 926	34	10.35 074	9.96 062	6	58	
3	9.61 016	29	9.64 960	34	10.35 040	9.96 056	6	57	
4	9.61 045	28	9.64 994	34	10.35 006	9.96 050	5	56	
5	9.61 073	28	9.65 028	34	10.34 972	9.96 045	6	55	
6	9.61 101	28	9.65 062	34	10.34 938	9.96 039	5	54	
7	9.61 129	29	9.65 096	34	10.34 904	9.96 034	6	53	
8	9.61 158	28	9.65 130	34	10.34 870	9.96 028	6	52	
9	9.61 186	28	9.65 164	33	10.34 836	9.96 022	5	51	
10	9.61 214	28	9.65 197	34	10.34 803	9.96 017	6	50	
11	9.61 242	28	9.65 231	34	10.34 769	9.96 011	6	49	
12	9.61 270	28	9.65 265	34	10.34 735	9.96 005	5	48	
13	9.61 298	28	9.65 299	34	10.34 701	9.96 000	6	47	
14	9.61 326	28	9.65 333	33	10.34 667	9.95 994	6	46	
15	9.61 354	28	9.65 366	34	10.34 634	9.95 988	6	45	
16	9.61 382	29	9.65 400	34	10.34 600	9.95 982	5	44	
17	9.61 411	27	9.65 434	33	10.34 566	9.95 977	6	43	
18	9.61 438	28	9.65 467	34	10.34 533	9.95 971	6	42	
19	9.61 466	28	9.65 501	34	10.34 499	9.95 965	5	41	
20	9.61 494	28	9.65 535	33	10.34 465	9.95 960	6	40	
21	9.61 522	28	9.65 568	34	10.34 432	9.95 954	6	39	
22	9.61 550	28	9.65 602	34	10.34 398	9.95 948	6	38	
23	9.61 578	28	9.65 636	33	10.34 364	9.95 942	6	37	
24	9.61 606	28	9.65 669	34	10.34 331	9.95 937	6	36	
25	9.61 634	28	9.65 703	33	10.34 297	9.95 931	6	35	
26	9.61 662	27	9.65 736	34	10.34 264	9.95 925	5	34	
27	9.61 689	28	9.65 770	33	10.34 230	9.95 920	6	33	
28	9.61 717	28	9.65 803	34	10.34 197	9.95 914	6	32	
29	9.61 745	28	9.65 837	33	10.34 163	9.95 908	6	31	
30	9.61 773	27	9.65 870	34	10.34 130	9.95 902	5	30	
31	9.61 800	28	9.65 904	33	10.34 096	9.95 897	6	29	
32	9.61 828	28	9.65 937	34	10.34 063	9.95 891	6	28	
33	9.61 856	27	9.65 971	33	10.34 029	9.95 885	6	27	
34	9.61 883	28	9.66 004	34	10.33 996	9.95 879	6	26	
35	9.61 911	28	9.66 038	33	10.33 962	9.95 873	5	25	
36	9.61 939	27	9.66 071	33	10.33 929	9.95 868	6	24	
37	9.61 966	28	9.66 104	34	10.33 896	9.95 862	6	23	
38	9.61 994	27	9.66 138	33	10.33 862	9.95 856	6	22	
39	9.62 021	28	9.66 171	33	10.33 829	9.95 850	6	21	
40	9.62 049	27	9.66 204	34	10.33 796	9.95 844	5	20	
41	9.62 076	28	9.66 238	33	10.33 762	9.95 839	6	19	
42	9.62 104	27	9.66 271	33	10.33 729	9.95 833	6	18	
43	9.62 131	28	9.66 304	33	10.33 696	9.95 827	6	17	
44	9.62 159	27	9.66 337	34	10.33 663	9.95 821	6	16	
45	9.62 186	28	9.66 371	33	10.33 629	9.95 815	5	15	
46	9.62 214	27	9.66 404	33	10.33 596	9.95 810	6	14	
47	9.62 241	27	9.66 437	33	10.33 563	9.95 804	6	13	
48	9.62 268	28	9.66 470	33	10.33 530	9.95 798	6	12	
49	9.62 296	27	9.66 503	34	10.33 497	9.95 792	6	11	
50	9.62 323	27	9.66 537	33	10.33 463	9.95 786	6	10	
51	9.62 350	27	9.66 570	33	10.33 430	9.95 780	5	9	
52	9.62 377	28	9.66 603	33	10.33 397	9.95 775	6	8	
53	9.62 405	27	9.66 636	33	10.33 364	9.95 769	6	7	
54	9.62 432	27	9.66 669	33	10.33 331	9.95 763	6	6	
55	9.62 459	27	9.66 702	33	10.33 298	9.95 757	6	5	
56	9.62 486	27	9.66 735	33	10.33 265	9.95 751	6	4	
57	9.62 513	28	9.66 768	33	10.33 232	9.95 745	6	3	
58	9.62 541	27	9.66 801	33	10.33 199	9.95 739	6	2	
59	9.62 568	27	9.66 834	33	10.33 166	9.95 733	5	1	
60	9.62 595		9.66 867		10.33 133	9.95 728		0	
	L. Cos.	d	L. Cot.	c.d.	L. Tan.	L. Sin.	d.	′	P. P.

P. P.

	34	33
1	3.4	3.3
2	6.8	6.6
3	10.2	9.9
4	13.6	13.2
5	17.0	16.5
6	20.4	19.8
7	23.8	23.1
8	27.2	26.4
9	30.6	29.7

	29	28	27
1	2.9	2.8	2.7
2	5.8	5.6	5.4
3	8.7	8.4	8.1
4	11.6	11.2	10.8
5	14.5	14.0	13.5
6	17.4	16.8	16.2
7	20.3	19.6	18.9
8	23.2	22.4	21.6
9	26.1	25.2	24.3

	6	5
1	0.6	0.5
2	1.2	1.0
3	1.8	1.5
4	2.4	2.0
5	3.0	2.5
6	3.6	3.0
7	4.2	3.5
8	4.8	4.0
9	5.4	4.5

65°

TABLE III. LOGARITHMS OF FUNCTIONS | 237

25°

′	L. Sin.	d.	L. Tan.	c. d.	L. Cot.	L. Cos.	d.		
0	9.62 595	27	9.66 867	33	10.33 133	9.95 728	6	60	
1	9.62 622	27	9.66 900	33	10.33 100	9.95 722	6	59	
2	9.62 649	27	9.66 933	33	10.33 067	9.95 716	6	58	
3	9.62 676	27	9.66 966	33	10.33 034	9.95 710	6	57	
4	9.62 703	27	9.66 999	33	10.33 001	9.95 704	6	56	
5	9.62 730	27	9.67 032	33	10.32 968	9.95 698	6	55	
6	9.62 757	27	9.67 065	33	10.32 935	9.95 692	6	54	
7	9.62 784	27	9.67 098	33	10.32 902	9.95 686	6	53	
8	9.62 811	27	9.67 131	32	10.32 869	9.95 680	6	52	
9	9.62 838	27	9.67 163	33	10.32 837	9.95 674	6	51	
10	9.62 865	27	9.67 196	33	10.32 804	9.95 668	5	50	
11	9.62 892	26	9.67 229	33	10.32 771	9.95 663	6	49	
12	9.62 918	27	9.67 262	33	10.32 738	9.95 657	6	48	
13	9.62 945	27	9.67 295	32	10.32 705	9.95 651	6	47	
14	9.62 972	27	9.67 327	33	10.32 673	9.95 645	6	46	
15	9.62 999	27	9.67 360	33	10.32 640	9.95 639	6	45	
16	9.63 026	26	9.67 393	33	10.32 607	9.95 633	6	44	
17	9.63 052	27	9.67 426	32	10.32 574	9.95 627	6	43	
18	9.63 079	27	9.67 458	33	10.32 542	9.95 621	6	42	
19	9.63 106	27	9.67 491	33	10.32 509	9.95 615	6	41	
20	9.63 133	26	9.67 524	32	10.32 476	9.95 609	6	40	
21	9.63 159	27	9.67 556	33	10.32 444	9.95 603	6	39	
22	9.63 186	27	9.67 589	33	10.32 411	9.95 597	6	38	
23	9.63 213	26	9.67 622	32	10.32 378	9.95 591	6	37	
24	9.63 239	27	9.67 654	33	10.32 346	9.95 585	6	36	
25	9.63 266	26	9.67 687	32	10.32 313	9.95 579	6	35	
26	9.63 292	27	9.67 719	33	10.32 281	9.95 573	6	34	
27	9.63 319	26	9.67 752	33	10.32 248	9.95 567	6	33	
28	9.63 345	27	9.67 785	32	10.32 215	9.95 561	6	32	
29	9.63 372	26	9.67 817	33	10.32 183	9.95 555	6	31	
30	9.63 398	27	9.67 850	32	10.32 150	9.95 549	6	30	
31	9.63 425	26	9.67 882	33	10.32 118	9.95 543	6	29	
32	9.63 451	27	9.67 915	32	10.32 085	9.95 537	6	28	
33	9.63 478	26	9.67 947	33	10.32 053	9.95 531	6	27	
34	9.63 504	27	9.67 980	32	10.32 020	9.95 525	6	26	
35	9.63 531	26	9.68 012	32	10.31 988	9.95 519	6	25	
36	9.63 557	26	9.68 044	33	10.31 956	9.95 513	6	24	
37	9.63 583	27	9.68 077	32	10.31 923	9.95 507	7	23	
38	9.63 610	26	9.68 109	33	10.31 891	9.95 500	6	22	
39	9.63 636	26	9.68 142	32	10.31 858	9.95 494	6	21	
40	9.63 662	27	9.68 174	32	10.31 826	9.95 488	6	20	
41	9.63 689	26	9.68 206	33	10.31 794	9.95 482	6	19	
42	9.63 715	26	9.68 239	32	10.31 761	9.95 476	6	18	
43	9.63 741	26	9.68 271	32	10.31 729	9.95 470	6	17	
44	9.63 767	27	9.68 303	33	10.31 697	9.95 464	6	16	
45	9.63 794	26	9.68 336	32	10.31 664	9.95 458	6	15	
46	9.63 820	26	9.68 368	32	10.31 632	9.95 452	6	14	
47	9.63 846	26	9.68 400	32	10.31 600	9.95 446	6	13	
48	9.63 872	26	9.68 432	33	10.31 568	9.95 440	6	12	
49	9.63 898	26	9.68 465	32	10.31 535	9.95 434	7	11	
50	9.63 924	26	9.68 497	32	10.31 503	9.95 427	6	10	
51	9.63 950	26	9.68 529	32	10.31 471	9.95 421	6	9	
52	9.63 976	26	9.68 561	32	10.31 439	9.95 415	6	8	
53	9.64 002	26	9.68 593	32	10.31 407	9.95 409	6	7	
54	9.64 028	26	9.68 626	32	10.31 374	9.95 403	6	6	
55	9.64 054	26	9.68 658	32	10.31 342	9.95 397	6	5	
56	9.64 080	26	9.68 690	32	10.31 310	9.95 391	7	4	
57	9.64 106	26	9.68 722	32	10.31 278	9.95 384	6	3	
58	9.64 132	26	9.68 754	32	10.31 246	9.95 378	6	2	
59	9.64 158	26	9.68 786	32	10.31 214	9.95 372	6	1	
60	9.64 184		9.68 818		10.31 182	9.95 366		0	
	L. Cos.	d.	L. Cot.	c. d.	L. Tan.	L. Sin.	d.	′	

P. P.

	33	32
1	3.3	3.2
2	6.6	6.4
3	9.9	9.6
4	13.2	12.8
5	16.5	16.0
6	19.8	19.2
7	23.1	22.4
8	26.4	25.6
9	29.7	28.8

	27	26
1	2.7	2.6
2	5.4	5.2
3	8.1	7.8
4	10.8	10.4
5	13.5	13.0
6	16.2	15.6
7	18.9	18.2
8	21.6	20.8
9	24.3	23.4

	7	6	5
1	0.7	0.6	0.5
2	1.4	1.2	1.0
3	2.1	1.8	1.5
4	2.8	2.4	2.0
5	3.5	3.0	2.5
6	4.2	3.6	3.0
7	4.9	4.2	3.5
8	5.6	4.8	4.0
9	6.3	5.4	4.5

64°

26°

'	L. Sin.	d.	L. Tan.	c. d.	L. Cot.	L. Cos.	d.	'
0	9.64 184	26	9.68 818	32	10.31 182	9.95 366	6	60
1	9.64 210	26	9.68 850	32	10.31 150	9.95 360	6	59
2	9.64 236	26	9.68 882	32	10.31 118	9.95 354	6	58
3	9.64 262	26	9.68 914	32	10.31 086	9.95 348	7	57
4	9.64 288	25	9.68 946	32	10.31 054	9.95 341	6	56
5	9.64 313	26	9.68 978	32	10.31 022	9.95 335	6	55
6	9.64 339	26	9.69 010	32	10.30 990	9.95 329	6	54
7	9.64 365	26	9.69 042	32	10.30 958	9.95 323	6	53
8	9.64 391	26	9.69 074	32	10.30 926	9.95 317	7	52
9	9.64 417	25	9.69 106	32	10.30 894	9.95 310	6	51
10	9.64 442	26	9.69 138	32	10.30 862	9.95 304	6	50
11	9.64 468	26	9.69 170	32	10.30 830	9.95 298	6	49
12	9.64 494	25	9.69 202	32	10.30 798	9.95 292	6	48
13	9.64 519	26	9.69 234	32	10.30 766	9.95 286	7	47
14	9.64 545	26	9.69 266	32	10.30 734	9.95 279	6	46
15	9.64 571	25	9.69 298	31	10.30 702	9.95 273	6	45
16	9.64 596	26	9.69 329	32	10.30 671	9.95 267	6	44
17	9.64 622	25	9.69 361	32	10.30 639	9.95 261	7	43
18	9.64 647	26	9.69 393	32	10.30 607	9.95 254	6	42
19	9.64 673	25	9.69 425	32	10.30 575	9.95 248	6	41
20	9.64 698	26	9.69 457	31	10.30 543	9.95 242	6	40
21	9.64 724	25	9.69 488	32	10.30 512	9.95 236	7	39
22	9.64 749	26	9.69 520	32	10.30 480	9.95 229	6	38
23	9.64 775	25	9.69 552	32	10.30 448	9.95 223	6	37
24	9.64 800	26	9.69 584	31	10.30 416	9.95 217	6	36
25	9.64 826	25	9.69 615	32	10.30 385	9.95 211	7	35
26	9.64 851	26	9.69 647	32	10.30 353	9.95 204	6	34
27	9.64 877	25	9.69 679	31	10.30 321	9.95 198	6	33
28	9.64 902	25	9.69 710	32	10.30 290	9.95 192	7	32
29	9.64 927	26	9.69 742	32	10.30 258	9.95 185	6	31
30	9.64 953	25	9.69 774	31	10.30 226	9.95 179	6	30
31	9.64 978	25	9.69 805	32	10.30 195	9.95 173	6	29
32	9.65 003	26	9.69 837	31	10.30 163	9.95 167	7	28
33	9.65 029	25	9.69 868	32	10.30 132	9.95 160	6	27
34	9.65 054	25	9.69 900	32	10.30 100	9.95 154	6	26
35	9.65 079	25	9.69 932	31	10.30 068	9.95 148	7	25
36	9.65 104	26	9.69 963	32	10.30 037	9.95 141	6	24
37	9.65 130	25	9.69 995	31	10.30 005	9.95 135	6	23
38	9.65 155	25	9.70 026	32	10.29 974	9.95 129	7	22
39	9.65 180	25	9.70 058	31	10.29 942	9.95 122	6	21
40	9.65 205	25	9.70 089	32	10.29 911	9.95 116	6	20
41	9.65 230	25	9.70 121	31	10.29 879	9.95 110	7	19
42	9.65 255	26	9.70 152	32	10.29 848	9.95 103	6	18
43	9.65 281	25	9.70 184	31	10.29 816	9.95 097	7	17
44	9.65 306	25	9.70 215	32	10.29 785	9.95 090	6	16
45	9.65 331	25	9.70 247	31	10.29 753	9.95 084	6	15
46	9.65 356	25	9.70 278	31	10.29 722	9.95 078	7	14
47	9.65 381	25	9.70 309	32	10.29 691	9.95 071	6	13
48	9.65 406	25	9.70 341	31	10.29 659	9.95 065	6	12
49	9.65 431	25	9.70 372	32	10.29 628	9.95 059	7	11
50	9.65 456	25	9.70 404	31	10.29 596	9.95 052	6	10
51	9.65 481	25	9.70 435	31	10.29 565	9.95 046	7	9
52	9.65 506	25	9.70 466	32	10.29 534	9.95 039	6	8
53	9.65 531	25	9.70 498	31	10.29 502	9.95 033	6	7
54	9.65 556	24	9.70 529	31	10.29 471	9.95 027	7	6
55	9.65 580	25	9.70 560	32	10.29 440	9.95 020	6	5
56	9.65 605	25	9.70 592	31	10.29 408	9.95 014	6	4
57	9.65 630	25	9.70 623	31	10.29 377	9.95 007	6	3
58	9.65 655	25	9.70 654	31	10.29 346	9.95 001	6	2
59	9.65 680	25	9.70 685	32	10.29 315	9.94 995	7	1
60	9.65 705		9.70 717		10.29 283	9.94 988		0
	L. Cos.	d.	L. Cot.	c. d.	L. Tan.	L. Sin.	d.	'

P. P.

	32	31
1	3.2	3.1
2	6.4	6.2
3	9.6	9.3
4	12.8	12.4
5	16.0	15.5
6	19.2	18.6
7	22.4	21.7
8	25.6	24.8
9	28.8	27.9

	26	25	24
1	2.6	2.5	2.4
2	5.2	5.0	4.8
3	7.8	7.5	7.2
4	10.4	10.0	9.6
5	13.0	12.5	12.0
6	15.6	15.0	14.4
7	18.2	17.5	16.8
8	20.8	20.0	19.2
9	23.4	22.5	21.6

	7	6
1	0.7	0.6
2	1.4	1.2
3	2.1	1.8
4	2.8	2.4
5	3.5	3.0
6	4.2	3.6
7	4.9	4.2
8	5.6	4.8
9	6.3	5.4

63°

TABLE III. LOGARITHMS OF FUNCTIONS | 239

27°

'	L. Sin.	d.	L. Tan.	c. d.	L. Cot.	L. Cos.	d.		P. P.
0	9.65 705	24	9.70 717	31	10.29 283	9.94 988	6	60	
1	9.65 729	25	9.70 748	31	10.29 252	9.94 982	7	59	
2	9.65 754	25	9.70 779	31	10.29 221	9.94 975	6	58	
3	9.65 779	25	9.70 810	31	10.29 190	9.94 969	7	57	
4	9.65 804	24	9.70 841	32	10.29 159	9.94 962	6	56	
5	9.65 828	25	9.70 873	31	10.29 127	9.94 956	7	55	
6	9.65 853	25	9.70 904	31	10.29 096	9.94 949	7	54	
7	9.65 878	24	9.70 935	31	10.29 065	9.94 943	6	53	
8	9.65 902	25	9.70 966	31	10.29 034	9.94 936	7	52	
9	9.65 927	25	9.70 997	31	10.29 003	9.94 930	6	51	
10	9.65 952	24	9.71 028	31	10.28 972	9.94 923	7	50	
11	9.65 976	25	9.71 059	31	10.28 941	9.94 917	6	49	
12	9.66 001	24	9.71 090	31	10.28 910	9.94 911	6	48	
13	9.66 025	25	9.71 121	32	10.28 879	9.94 904	7	47	
14	9.66 050	25	9.71 153	31	10.28 847	9.94 898	6	46	
15	9.66 075	24	9.71 184	31	10.28 816	9.94 891	7	45	
16	9.66 099	25	9.71 215	31	10.28 785	9.94 885	6	44	
17	9.66 124	24	9.71 246	31	10.28 754	9.94 878	7	43	
18	9.66 148	25	9.71 277	31	10.28 723	9.94 871	7	42	
19	9.66 173	24	9.71 308	31	10.28 692	9.94 865	6	41	
20	9.66 197	24	9.71 339	31	10.28 661	9.94 858	7	40	
21	9.66 221	25	9.71 370	31	10.28 630	9.94 852	6	39	
22	9.66 246	24	9.71 401	31	10.28 599	9.94 845	7	38	
23	9.66 270	25	9.71 431	31	10.28 569	9.94 839	6	37	
24	9.66 295	24	9.71 462	31	10.28 538	9.94 832	7	36	
25	9.66 319	24	9.71 493	31	10 8 507	9.94 826	6	35	
26	9.66 343	25	9.71 524	31	10.28 476	9.94 819	7	34	
27	9.66 368	24	9.71 555	31	10.28 445	9.94 813	6	33	
28	9.66 392	24	9.71 586	31	10.28 414	9.94 806	7	32	
29	9.66 416	25	9.71 617	31	10.28 383	9.94 799	7	31	
30	9.66 441	24	9.71 648	31	10.28 352	9.94 793	6	30	
31	9.66 465	24	9.71 679	30	10.28 321	9.94 786	7	29	
32	9.66 489	24	9.71 709	31	10.28 291	9.94 780	6	28	
33	9.66 513	24	9.71 740	31	10.28 260	9.94 773	7	27	
34	9.66 537	25	9.71 771	31	10.28 229	9.94 767	6	26	
35	9.66 562	24	9.71 802	31	10.28 198	9.94 760	7	25	
36	9.66 586	24	9.71 833	30	10.28 167	9.94 753	7	24	
37	9.66 610	24	9.71 863	31	10.28 137	9.94 747	6	23	
38	9.66 634	24	9.71 894	31	10.28 106	9.94 740	7	22	
39	9.66 658	24	9.71 925	30	10.28 075	9.94 734	6	21	
40	9.66 682	24	9.71 955	31	10.28 045	9.94 727	7	20	
41	9.66 706	25	9.71 986	31	10.28 014	9.94 720	6	19	
42	9.66 731	24	9.72 017	31	10.27 983	9.94 714	7	18	
43	9.66 755	24	9.72 048	30	10.27 952	9.94 707	7	17	
44	9.66 779	24	9.72 078	31	10.27 922	9.94 700	6	16	
45	9.66 803	24	9.72 109	31	10.27 891	9.94 694	7	15	
46	9.66 827	24	9.72 140	30	10.27 860	9.94 687	7	14	
47	9.66 851	24	9.72 170	31	10.27 830	9.94 680	6	13	
48	9.66 875	24	9.72 201	30	10.27 799	9.94 674	7	12	
49	9.66 899	23	9.72 231	31	10.27 769	9.94 667	7	11	
50	9.66 922	24	9.72 262	31	10.27 738	9.94 660	6	10	
51	9.66 946	24	9.72 293	30	10.27 707	9.94 654	7	9	
52	9.66 970	24	9.72 323	31	10.27 677	9.94 647	7	8	
53	9.66 994	24	9.72 354	30	10.27 646	9.94 640	6	7	
54	9.67 018	24	9.72 384	31	10.27 616	9.94 634	7	6	
55	9.67 042	24	9.72 415	30	10.27 585	9.94 627	7	5	
56	9.67 066	24	9.72 445	31	10.27 555	9.94 620	6	4	
57	9.67 090	23	9.72 476	30	10.27 524	9.94 614	7	3	
58	9.67 113	24	9.72 506	31	10.27 494	9.94 607	7	2	
59	9.67 137	24	9.72 537	30	10.27 463	9.94 600	7	1	
60	9.67 161		9.72 567		10.27 433	9.94 593		0	
	L. Cos.	d.	L. Cot.	c. d.	L. Tan.	L. Sin.	d.	'	P. P.

P. P.

	32	31	30
1	3.2	3.1	3.0
2	6.4	6.2	6.0
3	9.6	9.3	9.0
4	12.8	12.4	12.0
5	16.0	15.5	15.0
6	19.2	18.6	18.0
7	22.4	21.7	21.0
8	25.6	24.8	24.0
9	28.8	27.9	27.0

	25	24	23
1	2.5	2.4	2.3
2	5.0	4.8	4.6
3	7.5	7.2	6.9
4	10.0	9.6	9.2
5	12.5	12.0	11.5
6	15.0	14.4	13.8
7	17.5	16.8	16.1
8	20.0	19.2	18.4
9	22.5	21.6	20.7

	7	6
1	0.7	0.6
2	1.4	1.2
3	2.1	1.8
4	2.8	2.4
5	3.5	3.0
6	4.2	3.6
7	4.9	4.2
8	5.6	4.8
9	6.3	5.4

62°

28°

'	L. Sin.	d.	L. Tan.	c. d.	L. Cot.	L. Cos.	d.	'
0	9.67 161	24	9.72 567	31	10.27 433	9.94 593	6	60
1	9.67 185	23	9.72 598	30	10.27 402	9.94 587	7	59
2	9.67 208	24	9.72 628	31	10.27 372	9.94 580	7	58
3	9.67 232	24	9.72 659	30	10.27 341	9.94 573	6	57
4	9.67 256	24	9.72 689	31	10.27 311	9.94 567	7	56
5	9.67 280	23	9.72 720	30	10.27 280	9.94 560	7	55
6	9.67 303	24	9.72 750	30	10.27 250	9.94 553	7	54
7	9.67 327	23	9.72 780	31	10.27 220	9.94 546	6	53
8	9.67 350	24	9.72 811	30	10.27 189	9.94 540	7	52
9	9.67 374	24	9.72 841	31	10.27 159	9.94 533	7	51
10	9.67 398	23	9.72 872	30	10.27 128	9.94 526	7	50
11	9.67 421	24	9.72 902	30	10.27 098	9.94 519	6	49
12	9.67 445	23	9.72 932	31	10.27 068	9.94 513	7	48
13	9.67 468	24	9.72 963	30	10.27 037	9.94 506	7	47
14	9.67 492	23	9.72 993	30	10.27 007	9.94 499	7	46
15	9.67 515	24	9.73 023	31	10.26 977	9.94 492	7	45
16	9.67 539	23	9.73 054	30	10.26 946	9.94 485	6	44
17	9.67 562	24	9.73 084	30	10.26 916	9.94 479	7	43
18	9.67 586	23	9.73 114	30	10.26 886	9.94 472	7	42
19	9.67 609	24	9.73 144	31	10.26 856	9.94 465	7	41
20	9.67 633	23	9.73 175	30	10.26 825	9.94 458	7	40
21	9.67 656	24	9.73 205	30	10.26 795	9.94 451	6	39
22	9.67 680	23	9.73 235	30	10.26 765	9.94 445	7	38
23	9.67 703	23	9.73 265	30	10.26 735	9.94 438	7	37
24	9.67 726	24	9.73 295	31	10.26 705	9.94 431	7	36
25	9.67 750	23	9.73 326	30	10.26 674	9.94 424	7	35
26	9.67 773	23	9.73 356	30	10.26 644	9.94 417	7	34
27	9.67 796	24	9.73 386	30	10.26 614	9.94 410	6	33
28	9.67 820	23	9.73 416	30	10.26 584	9.94 404	7	32
29	9.67 843	23	9.73 446	30	10.26 554	9.94 397	7	31
30	9.67 866	24	9.73 476	31	10.26 524	9.94 390	7	30
31	9.67 890	23	9.73 507	30	10.26 493	9.94 383	7	29
32	9.67 913	23	9.73 537	30	10.26 463	9.94 376	7	28
33	9.67 936	23	9.73 567	30	10.26 433	9.94 369	7	27
34	9.67 959	23	9.73 597	30	10.26 403	9.94 362	7	26
35	9.67 982	24	9.73 627	30	10.26 373	9.94 355	6	25
36	9.68 006	23	9.73 657	30	10.26 343	9.94 349	7	24
37	9.68 029	23	9.73 687	30	10.26 313	9.94 342	7	23
38	9.68 052	23	9.73 717	30	10.26 283	9.94 335	7	22
39	9.68 075	23	9.73 747	30	10.26 253	9.94 328	7	21
40	9.68 098	23	9.73 777	30	10.26 223	9.94 321	7	20
41	9.68 121	23	9.73 807	30	10.26 193	9.94 314	7	19
42	9.68 144	23	9.73 837	30	10.26 163	9.94 307	7	18
43	9.68 167	23	9.73 867	30	10.26 133	9.94 300	7	17
44	9.68 190	23	9.73 897	30	10.26 103	9.94 293	7	16
45	9.68 213	24	9.73 927	30	10.26 073	9.94 286	7	15
46	9.68 237	23	9.73 957	30	10.26 043	9.94 279	6	14
47	9.68 260	23	9.73 987	30	10.26 013	9.94 273	7	13
48	9.68 283	22	9.74 017	30	10.25 983	9.94 266	7	12
49	9.68 305	23	9.74 047	30	10.25 953	9.94 259	7	11
50	9.68 328	23	9.74 077	30	10.25 923	9.94 252	7	10
51	9.68 351	23	9.74 107	30	10.25 893	9.94 245	7	9
52	9.68 374	23	9.74 137	29	10.25 863	9.94 238	7	8
53	9.68 397	23	9.74 166	30	10.25 834	9.94 231	7	7
54	9.68 420	23	9.74 196	30	10.25 804	9.94 224	7	6
55	9.68 443	23	9.74 226	30	10.25 774	9.94 217	7	5
56	9.68 466	23	9.74 256	30	10.25 744	9.94 210	7	4
57	9.68 489	23	9.74 286	30	10.25 714	9.94 203	7	3
58	9.68 512	22	9.74 316	29	10.25 684	9.94 196	7	2
59	9.68 534	23	9.74 345	30	10.25 655	9.94 189	7	1
60	9.68 557		9.74 375		10.25 625	9.94 182		0
	L. Cos.	d.	L. Cot.	c. d.	L. Tan.	L. Sin.	d.	'

P. P.

	31	30	29
1	3.1	3.0	2.9
2	6.2	6.0	5.8
3	9.3	9.0	8.7
4	12.4	12.0	11.6
5	15.5	15.0	14.5
6	18.6	18.0	17.4
7	21.7	21.0	20.3
8	24.8	24.0	23.2
9	27.9	27.0	26.1

	24	23	22
1	2.4	2.3	2.2
2	4.8	4.6	4.4
3	7.2	6.9	6.6
4	9.6	9.2	8.8
5	12.0	11.5	11.0
6	14.4	13.8	13.2
7	16.8	16.1	15.4
8	19.2	18.4	17.6
9	21.6	20.7	19.8

	7	6
1	0.7	0.6
2	1.4	1.2
3	2.1	1.8
4	2.8	2.4
5	3.5	3.0
6	4.2	3.6
7	4.9	4.2
8	5.6	4.8
9	6.3	5.4

TABLE III. LOGARITHMS OF FUNCTIONS | 241

29°

'	L. Sin.	d.	L. Tan.	c. d.	L. Cot.	L. Cos.	d.	'	P. P.
0	9.68 557	23	9.74 375	30	10.25 625	9.94 182	7	60	
1	9.68 580	23	9.74 405	30	10.25 595	9.94 175	7	59	
2	9.68 603	22	9.74 435	30	10.25 565	9.94 168	7	58	
3	9.68 625	23	9.74 465	29	10.25 535	9.94 161	7	57	
4	9.68 648	23	9.74 494	30	10.25 506	9.94 154	7	56	
5	9.68 671	23	9.74 524	30	10.25 476	9.94 147	7	55	
6	9.68 694	22	9.74 554	29	10.25 446	9.94 140	7	54	
7	9.68 716	23	9.74 583	30	10.25 417	9.94 133	7	53	
8	9.68 739	23	9.74 613	30	10.25 387	9.94 126	7	52	
9	9.68 762	22	9.74 643	30	10.25 357	9.94 119	7	51	
10	9.68 784	23	9.74 673	29	10.25 327	9.94 112	7	50	
11	9.68 807	22	9.74 702	30	10.25 298	9.94 105	7	49	
12	9.68 829	23	9.74 732	30	10.25 268	9.94 098	8	48	
13	9.68 852	23	9.74 762	29	10.25 238	9.94 090	7	47	
14	9.68 875	22	9.74 791	30	10.25 209	9.94 083	7	46	
15	9.68 897	23	9.74 821	30	10.25 179	9.94 076	7	45	
16	9.68 920	22	9.74 851	29	10.25 149	9.94 069	7	44	
17	9.68 942	23	9.74 880	30	10.25 120	9.94 062	7	43	
18	9.68 965	22	9.74 910	29	10.25 090	9.94 055	7	42	
19	9.68 987	23	9.74 939	30	10.25 061	9.94 048	7	41	
20	9.69 010	22	9.74 969	29	10.25 031	9.94 041	7	40	
21	9.69 032	23	9.74 998	30	10.25 002	9.94 034	7	39	
22	9.69 055	22	9.75 028	30	10.24 972	9.94 027	7	38	
23	9.69 077	23	9.75 058	29	10.24 942	9.94 020	8	37	
24	9.69 100	22	9.75 087	30	10.24 913	9.94 012	7	36	
25	9.69 122	22	9.75 117	29	10.24 883	9.94 005	7	35	
26	9.69 144	23	9.75 146	30	10.24 854	9.93 998	7	34	
27	9.69 167	22	9.75 176	29	10.24 824	9.93 991	7	33	
28	9.69 189	23	9.75 205	30	10.24 795	9.93 984	7	32	
29	9.69 212	22	9.75 235	29	10.24 765	9.93 977	7	31	
30	9.69 234	22	9.75 264	30	10.24 736	9.93 970	7	30	
31	9.69 256	23	9.75 294	29	10.24 706	9.93 963	8	29	
32	9.69 279	22	9.75 323	30	10.24 677	9.93 955	7	28	
33	9.69 301	22	9.75 353	29	10.24 647	9.93 948	7	27	
34	9.69 323	22	9.75 382	29	10.24 618	9.93 941	7	26	
35	9.69 345	23	9.75 411	30	10.24 589	9.93 934	7	25	
36	9.69 368	22	9.75 441	29	10.24 559	9.93 927	7	24	
37	9.69 390	22	9.75 470	30	10.24 530	9.93 920	8	23	
38	9.69 412	22	9.75 500	29	10.24 500	9.93 912	7	22	
39	9.69 434	22	9.75 529	29	10.24 471	9.93 905	7	21	
40	9.69 456	23	9.75 558	30	10.24 442	9.93 898	7	20	
41	9.69 479	22	9.75 588	29	10.24 412	9.93 891	7	19	
42	9.69 501	22	9.75 617	30	10.24 383	9.93 884	8	18	
43	9.69 523	22	9.75 647	29	10.24 353	9.93 876	7	17	
44	9.69 545	22	9.75 676	29	10.24 324	9.93 869	7	16	
45	9.69 567	22	9.75 705	30	10.24 295	9.93 862	7	15	
46	9.69 589	22	9.75 735	29	10.24 265	9.93 855	8	14	
47	9.69 611	22	9.75 764	29	10.24 236	9.93 847	7	13	
48	9.69 633	22	9.75 793	29	10.24 207	9.93 840	7	12	
49	9.69 655	22	9.75 822	30	10.24 178	9.93 833	7	11	
50	9.69 677	22	9.75 852	29	10.24 148	9.93 826	7	10	
51	9.69 699	22	9.75 881	29	10.24 119	9.93 819	8	9	
52	9.69 721	22	9.75 910	29	10.24 090	9.93 811	7	8	
53	9.69 743	22	9.75 939	30	10.24 061	9.93 804	7	7	
54	9.69 765	22	9.75 969	29	10.24 031	9.93 797	8	6	
55	9.69 787	22	9.75 998	29	10.24 002	9.93 789	7	5	
56	9.69 809	22	9.76 027	29	10.23 973	9.93 782	7	4	
57	9.69 831	22	9.76 056	30	10.23 944	9.93 775	7	3	
58	9.69 853	22	9.76 086	29	10.23 914	9.93 768	8	2	
59	9.69 875	22	9.76 115	29	10.23 885	9.93 760	7	1	
60	9.69 897		9.76 144		10.23 856	9.93 753		0	
	L. Cos.	d.	L. Cot.	c. d.	L. Tan.	L. Sin.	d.	'	P. P.

P. P.

	30	29	23
1	3.0	2.9	2.3
2	6.0	5.8	4.6
3	9.0	8.7	6.9
4	12.0	11.6	9.2
5	15.0	14.5	11.5
6	18.0	17.4	13.8
7	21.0	20.3	16.1
8	24.0	23.2	18.4
9	27.0	26.1	20.7

	22	8	7
1	2.2	0.8	0.7
2	4.4	1.6	1.4
3	6.6	2.4	2.1
4	8.8	3.2	2.8
5	11.0	4.0	3.5
6	13.2	4.8	4.2
7	15.4	5.6	4.9
8	17.6	6.4	5.6
9	19.8	7.2	6.3

30°

'	L. Sin.	d.	L. Tan.	c. d.	L. Cot.	L. Cos.	d.	
0	9.69 897	22	9.76 144	29	10.23 856	9.93 753	7	60
1	9.69 919	22	9.76 173	29	10.23 827	9.93 746	8	59
2	9.69 941	22	9.76 202	29	10.23 798	9.93 738	7	58
3	9.69 963	21	9.76 231	30	10.23 769	9.93 731	7	57
4	9.69 984	22	9.76 261	29	10.23 739	9.93 724	7	56
5	9.70 006	22	9.76 290	29	10.23 710	9.93 717	8	55
6	9.70 028	22	9.76 319	29	10.23 681	9.93 709	7	54
7	9.70 050	22	9.76 348	29	10.23 652	9.93 702	7	53
8	9.70 072	21	9.76 377	29	10.23 623	9.93 695	8	52
9	9.70 093	22	9.76 406	29	10.23 594	9.93 687	7	51
10	9.70 115	22	9.76 435	29	10.23 565	9.93 680	7	50
11	9.70 137	22	9.76 464	29	10.23 536	9.93 673	8	49
12	9.70 159	21	9.76 493	29	10.23 507	9.93 665	7	48
13	9.70 180	22	9.76 522	29	10.23 478	9.93 658	8	47
14	9.70 202	22	9.76 551	29	10.23 449	9.93 650	7	46
15	9.70 224	21	9.76 580	29	10.23 420	9.93 643	7	45
16	9.70 245	22	9.76 609	30	10.23 391	9.93 636	8	44
17	9.70 267	21	9.76 639	29	10.23 361	9.93 628	7	43
18	9.70 288	22	9.76 668	29	10.23 332	9.93 621	7	42
19	9.70 310	22	9.76 697	28	10.23 303	9.93 614	8	41
20	9.70 332	21	9.76 725	29	10.23 275	9.93 606	7	40
21	9.70 353	22	9.76 754	29	10.23 246	9.93 599	8	39
22	9.70 375	21	9.76 783	29	10.23 217	9.93 591	7	38
23	9.70 396	22	9.76 812	29	10.23 188	9.93 584	7	37
24	9.70 418	21	9.76 841	29	10.23 159	9.93 577	8	36
25	9.70 439	22	9.76 870	29	10.23 130	9.93 569	7	35
26	9.70 461	21	9.76 899	29	10.23 101	9.93 562	8	34
27	9.70 482	22	9.76 928	29	10.23 072	9.93 554	7	33
28	9.70 504	21	9.76 957	29	10.23 043	9.93 547	8	32
29	9.70 525	22	9.76 986	29	10.23 014	9.93 539	7	31
30	9.70 547	21	9.77 015	29	10.22 985	9.93 532	7	30
31	9.70 568	22	9.77 044	29	10.22 956	9.93 525	8	29
32	9.70 590	21	9.77 073	28	10.22 927	9.93 517	7	28
33	9.70 611	22	9.77 101	29	10.22 899	9.93 510	8	27
34	9.70 633	21	9.77 130	29	10.22 870	9.93 502	7	26
35	9.70 654	21	9.77 159	29	10.22 841	9.93 495	8	25
36	9.70 675	22	9.77 188	29	10.22 812	9.93 487	7	24
37	9.70 697	21	9.77 217	29	10.22 783	9.93 480	8	23
38	9.70 718	21	9.77 246	28	10.22 754	9.93 472	7	22
39	9.70 739	22	9.77 274	29	10.22 726	9.93 465	8	21
40	9.70 761	21	9.77 303	29	10.22 697	9.93 457	7	20
41	9.70 782	21	9.77 332	29	10.22 668	9.93 450	8	19
42	9.70 803	21	9.77 361	29	10.22 639	9.93 442	7	18
43	9.70 824	22	9.77 390	28	10.22 610	9.93 435	8	17
44	9.70 846	21	9.77 418	29	10.22 582	9.93 427	7	16
45	9.70 867	21	9.77 447	29	10.22 553	9.93 420	8	15
46	9.70 888	21	9.77 476	29	10.22 524	9.93 412	7	14
47	9.70 909	22	9.77 505	28	10.22 495	9.93 405	8	13
48	9.70 931	21	9.77 533	29	10.22 467	9.93 397	7	12
49	9.70 952	21	9.77 562	29	10.22 438	9.93 390	8	11
50	9.70 973	21	9.77 591	28	10.22 409	9.93 382	7	10
51	9.70 994	21	9.77 619	29	10.22 381	9.93 375	8	9
52	9.71 015	21	9.77 648	29	10.22 352	9.93 367	7	8
53	9.71 036	22	9.77 677	29	10.22 323	9.93 360	8	7
54	9.71 058	21	9.77 706	28	10.22 294	9.93 352	7	6
55	9.71 079	21	9.77 734	29	10.22 266	9.93 344	8	5
56	9.71 100	21	9.77 763	28	10.22 237	9.93 337	7	4
57	9.71 121	21	9.77 791	29	10.22 209	9.93 329	8	3
58	9.71 142	21	9.77 820	29	10.22 180	9.93 322	8	2
59	9.71 163	21	9.77 849	28	10.22 151	9.93 314	8	1
60	9.71 184		9.77 877		10.22 123	9.93 307	7	0
	L. Cos.	d.	L. Cot.	c. d.	L. Tan.	L. Sin.	d.	'

P. P.

	30	29	28
1	3.0	2.9	2.8
2	6.0	5.8	5.6
3	9.0	8.7	8.4
4	12.0	11.6	11.2
5	15.0	14.5	14.0
6	18.0	17.4	16.8
7	21.0	20.3	19.6
8	24.0	23.2	22.4
9	27.0	26.1	25.2

	22	21
1	2.2	2.1
2	4.4	4.2
3	6.6	6.3
4	8.8	8.4
5	11.0	10.5
6	13.2	12.6
7	15.4	14.7
8	17.6	16.8
9	19.8	18.9

	8	7
1	0.8	0.7
2	1.6	1.4
3	2.4	2.1
4	3.2	2.8
5	4.0	3.5
6	4.8	4.2
7	5.6	4.9
8	6.4	5.6
9	7.2	6.3

59°

TABLE III. LOGARITHMS OF FUNCTIONS | 243

31°

'	L. Sin.	d.	L. Tan.	c. d.	L. Cot.	L. Cos.	d.	
0	9.71 184	21	9.77 877	29	10.22 123	9.93 307	8	60
1	9.71 205	21	9.77 906	29	10.22 094	9.03 299	8	59
2	9.71 226	21	9.77 935	28	10.22 065	9.93 291	8	58
3	9.71 247	21	9.77 963	29	10.22 037	9.93 284	7	57
4	9.71 268	21	9.77 992	28	10.22 008	9.93 276	8	56
5	9.71 289	21	9.78 020	29	10.21 980	9.93 269	7	55
6	9.71 310	21	9.78 049	28	10.21 951	9.93 261	8	54
7	9.71 331	21	9.78 077	29	10.21 923	9.93 253	8	53
8	9.71 352	21	9.78 106	29	10.21 894	9.93 246	7	52
9	9.71 373	20	9.78 135	28	10.21 865	9.93 238	8	51
10	9.71 393	21	9.78 163	29	10.21 837	9.93 230	8	50
11	9.71 414	21	9.78 192	28	10.21 808	9.93 223	7	49
12	9.71 435	21	9.78 220	29	10.21 780	9.93 215	8	48
13	9.71 456	21	9.78 249	28	10.21 751	9.93 207	8	47
14	9.71 477	21	9.78 277	29	10.21 723	9.93 200	7	46
15	9.71 498	21	9.78 306	28	10.21 694	9.93 192	8	45
16	9.71 519	20	9.78 334	29	10.21 666	9.03 184	8	44
17	9.71 539	21	9.78 363	28	10.21 637	9.93 177	7	43
18	9.71 560	21	9.78 391	28	10.21 609	9.93 169	8	42
19	9.71 581	21	9.78 419	29	10.21 581	9.93 161	7	41
20	9.71 602	20	9.78 448	28	10.21 552	9.93 154	8	40
21	9.71 622	21	9.78 476	29	10.21 524	9.93 146	8	39
22	9.71 643	21	9.78 505	28	10.21 495	9.03 138	7	38
23	9.71 664	21	9.78 533	29	10.21 467	9.03 131	8	37
24	9.71 685	20	9.78 562	28	10.21 438	9.93 123	8	36
25	9.71 705	21	9.78 590	28	10.21 410	9.93 115	7	35
26	9.71 726	21	9.78 618	29	10.21 382	9.93 108	8	34
27	9.71 747	20	9.78 647	28	10.21 353	9.93 100	8	33
28	9.71 767	21	9.78 675	29	10.21 325	9.93 092	8	32
29	9.71 788	21	9.78 704	28	10.21 296	9.93 084	7	31
30	9.71 809	20	9.78 732	28	10.21 268	9.93 077	8	30
31	9.71 829	21	9.78 760	29	10.21 240	9.93 069	8	29
32	9.71 850	20	9.78 789	28	10.21 211	9.93 061	8	28
33	9.71 870	21	9.78 817	28	10.21 183	9.93 053	7	27
34	9.71 891	20	9.78 845	29	10.21 155	9.93 046	8	26
35	9.71 911	21	9.78 874	28	10.21 126	9.93 038	8	25
36	9.71 932	20	9.78 902	28	10.21 098	9.93 030	8	24
37	9.71 952	21	9.78 930	29	10.21 070	9.93 022	8	23
38	9.71 973	21	9.78 959	28	10.21 041	9.93 014	7	22
39	9.71 994	20	9.78 987	28	10.21 013	9.93 007	8	21
40	9.72 014	20	9.79 015	28	10.20 985	9.92 999	8	20
41	9.72 034	21	9.79 043	29	10.20 957	9.92 991	8	19
42	9.72 055	20	9.79 072	28	10.20 928	9.92 983	7	18
43	9.72 075	21	9.79 100	28	10.20 900	9.92 976	8	17
44	9.72 096	20	9.79 128	28	10.20 872	9.92 968	8	16
45	9.72 116	21	9.79 156	29	10.20 844	9.92 960	8	15
46	9.72 137	20	9.79 185	28	10.20 815	9.92 952	8	14
47	9.72 157	20	9.79 213	28	10.20 787	9.92 944	8	13
48	9.72 177	21	9.79 241	28	10.20 759	9.92 936	7	12
49	9.72 198	20	9.79 269	28	10.20 731	9.92 929	8	11
50	9.72 218	20	9.79 297	29	10.20 703	9.92 921	8	10
51	9.72 238	21	9.79 326	28	10.20 674	9.92 913	8	9
52	9.72 259	20	9.79 354	28	10.20 646	9.92 905	8	8
53	9.72 279	20	9.79 382	28	10.20 618	9.92 897	8	7
54	9.72 299	21	9.79 410	28	10.20 590	9.92 889	8	6
55	9.72 320	20	9.79 438	28	10.20 562	9.92 881	7	5
56	9.72 340	20	9.79 466	29	10.20 534	9.92 874	8	4
57	9.72 360	21	9.79 495	28	10.20 505	9.92 866	8	3
58	9.72 381	20	9.79 523	28	10.20 477	9.92 858	8	2
59	9.72 401	20	9.79 551	28	10.20 449	9.92 850	8	1
60	9.72 421		9.79 579		10.20 421	9.92 842		0
	L. Cos.	d.	L. Cot.	c. d.	L. Tan.	L. Sin.	d.	'

P. P.

	29	28
1	2.9	2.8
2	5.8	5.6
3	8.7	8.4
4	11.6	11.2
5	14.5	14.0
6	17.4	16.8
7	20.3	19.6
8	23.2	22.4
9	26.1	25.2

	21	20
1	2.1	2.0
2	4.2	4.0
3	6.3	6.0
4	8.4	8.0
5	10.5	10.0
6	12.6	12.0
7	14.7	14.0
8	16.8	16.0
9	18.9	18.0

	8	7
1	0.8	0.7
2	1.6	1.4
3	2.4	2.1
4	3.2	2.8
5	4.0	3.5
6	4.8	4.2
7	5.3	4.9
8	6.4	5.6
9	7.2	6.3

58°

32°

'	L. Sin.	d.	L. Tan.	c. d.	L. Cot.	L. Cos.	d.	
0	9.72 421	20	9.79 579	28	10.20 421	9.92 842	8	60
1	9.72 441	20	9.79 607	28	10.20 393	9.92 834	8	59
2	9.72 461	21	9.79 635	28	10.20 365	9.92 826	8	58
3	9.72 482	20	9.79 663	28	10.20 337	9.92 818	8	57
4	9.72 502	20	9.79 691	28	10.20 309	9.92 810	7	56
5	9.72 522	20	9.79 719	28	10.20 281	9.92 803	8	55
6	9.72 542	20	9.79 747	29	10.20 253	9.92 795	8	54
7	9.72 562	20	9.79 776	28	10.20 224	9.92 787	8	53
8	9.72 582	20	9.79 804	28	10.20 196	9.92 779	8	52
9	9.72 602	20	9.79 832	28	10.20 168	9.92 771	8	51
10	9.72 622	21	9.79 860	28	10.20 140	9.92 763	8	50
11	9.72 643	20	9.79 888	28	10.20 112	9.92 755	8	49
12	9.72 663	20	9.79 916	28	10.20 084	9.92 747	8	48
13	9.72 683	20	9.79 944	28	10.20 056	9.92 739	8	47
14	9.72 703	20	9.79 972	28	10.20 028	9.92 731	8	46
15	9.72 723	20	9.80 000	28	10.20 000	9.92 723	8	45
16	9.72 743	20	9.80 028	28	10.19 972	9.92 715	8	44
17	9.72 763	20	9.80 056	28	10.19 944	9.92 707	8	43
18	9.72 783	20	9.80 084	28	10.19 916	9.92 699	8	42
19	9.72 803	20	9.80 112	28	10.19 888	9.92 691	8	41
20	9.72 823	20	9.80 140	28	10.19 860	9.92 683	8	40
21	9.72 843	20	9.80 168	27	10.19 832	9.92 675	8	39
22	9.72 863	20	9.80 195	28	10.19 805	9.92 667	8	38
23	9.72 883	19	9.80 223	28	10.19 777	9.92 659	8	37
24	9.72 902	20	9.80 251	28	10.19 749	9.92 651	8	36
25	9.72 922	20	9.80 279	28	10.19 721	9.92 643	8	35
26	9.72 942	20	9.80 307	28	10.19 693	9.92 635	8	34
27	9.72 962	20	9.80 335	28	10.19 665	9.92 627	8	33
28	9.72 982	20	9.80 363	28	10.19 637	9.92 619	8	32
29	9.73 002	20	9.80 391	28	10.19 609	9.92 611	8	31
30	9.73 022	19	9.80 419	28	10.19 581	9.92 603	8	30
31	9.73 041	20	9.80 447	27	10.19 553	9.92 595	8	29
32	9.73 061	20	9.80 474	28	10.19 526	9.92 587	8	28
33	9.73 081	20	9.80 502	28	10.19 498	9.92 579	8	27
34	9.73 101	20	9.80 530	28	10.19 470	9.92 571	8	26
35	9.73 121	19	9.80 558	28	10.19 442	9.92 563	8	25
36	9.73 140	20	9.80 586	28	10.19 414	9.92 555	9	24
37	9.73 160	20	9.80 614	28	10.19 386	9.92 546	8	23
38	9.73 180	20	9.80 642	27	10.19 358	9.92 538	8	22
39	9.73 200	19	9.80 669	28	10.19 331	9.92 530	8	21
40	9.73 219	20	9.80 697	28	10.19 303	9.92 522	8	20
41	9.73 239	20	9.80 725	28	10.19 275	9.92 514	8	19
42	9.73 259	19	9.80 753	28	10.19 247	9.92 506	8	18
43	9.73 278	20	9.80 781	27	10.19 219	9.92 498	8	17
44	9.73 298	20	9.80 808	28	10.19 192	9.92 490	8	16
45	9.73 318	19	9.80 836	28	10.19 164	9.92 482	9	15
46	9.73 337	20	9.80 864	28	10.19 136	9.92 473	8	14
47	9.73 357	20	9.80 892	27	10.19 108	9.92 465	8	13
48	9.73 377	19	9.80 919	28	10.19 081	9.92 457	8	12
49	9.73 396	20	9.80 947	28	10.19 053	9.92 449	8	11
50	9.73 416	19	9.80 975	28	10.19 025	9.92 441	8	10
51	9.73 435	20	9.81 003	27	10.18 997	9.92 433	8	9
52	9.73 455	19	9.81 030	28	10.18 970	9.92 425	9	8
53	9.73 474	20	9.81 058	28	10.18 942	9.92 416	8	7
54	9.73 494	19	9.81 086	27	10.18 914	9.92 408	8	6
55	9.73 513	20	9.81 113	28	10.18 887	9.92 400	8	5
56	9.73 533	19	9.81 141	28	10.18 859	9.92 392	8	4
57	9.73 552	20	9.81 169	27	10.18 831	9.92 384	8	3
58	9.73 572	19	9.81 196	28	10.18 804	9.92 376	9	2
59	9.73 591	20	9.81 224	28	10.18 776	9.92 367	8	1
60	9.73 611		9.81 252		10.18 748	9.92 359		0
	L. Cos.	d.	L. Cot.	c. d.	L. Tan.	L. Sin.	d.	'

P. P.

	29	·28	27
1	2.9	2.8	2.7
2	5.8	5.6	5.4
3	8.7	8.4	8.1
4	11.6	11.2	10.8
5	14.5	14.0	13.5
6	17.4	16.8	16.2
7	20.3	19.6	18.9
8	23.2	22.4	21.6
9	26.1	25.2	24.3

	21	20	19
1	2.1	2.0	1.9
2	4.2	4.0	3.8
3	6.3	6.0	5.7
4	8.4	8.0	7.6
5	10.5	10.0	9.5
6	12.6	12.0	11.4
7	14.7	14.0	13.3
8	16.8	16.0	15.2
9	18.9	18.0	17.1

	9	8	7
1	0.9	0.8	0.7
2	1.8	1.6	1.4
3	2.7	2.4	2.1
4	3.6	3.2	2.8
5	4.5	4.0	3.5
6	5.4	4.8	4.2
7	6.3	5.6	4.9
8	7.2	6.4	5.6
9	8.1	7.2	6.3

TABLE III. LOGARITHMS OF FUNCTIONS | 245

33°

′	L. Sin.	d.	L. Tan.	c. d.	L. Cot.	L. Cos.	d.	′
0	9.73 611	19	9.81 252	27	10.18 748	9.92 359	8	60
1	9.73 630	20	9.81 279	28	10.18 721	9.92 351	8	59
2	9.73 650	19	9.81 307	28	10 18 693	9.92 343	8	58
3	9.73 669	20	9.81 335	27	10.18 665	9.92 335	9	57
4	9.73 689	19	9.81 362	28	10.18 638	9.92 326	8	56
5	9.73 708	19	9.81 390	28	10.18 610	9.92 318	8	55
6	9.73 727	20	9.81 418	27	10.18 582	9.92 310	8	54
7	9.73 747	19	9.81 445	28	10.18 555	9.92 302	9	53
8	9.73 766	19	9.81 473	27	10.18 527	9.92 293	8	52
9	9.73 785	20	9.81 500	28	10.18 500	9.92 285	8	51
10	9.73 805	19	9.81 528	28	10.18 472	9.92 277	8	50
11	9.73 824	19	9.81 556	27	10.18 444	9.92 269	9	49
12	9.73 843	20	9.81 583	28	10.18 417	9.92 260	8	48
13	9.73 863	19	9.81 611	27	10.18 389	9.92 252	8	47
14	9.73 882	19	9.81 638	28	10.18 362	9.92 244	9	46
15	9.73 901	20	9.81 666	27	10.18 334	9.92 235	8	45
16	9.73 921	19	9.81 693	28	10.18 307	9.92 227	8	44
17	9.73 940	19	9.81 721	27	10.18 279	9.92 219	8	43
18	9.73 959	19	9.81 748	28	10.18 252	9.92 211	9	42
19	9.73 978	19	9.81 776	27	10.18 224	9.92 202	8	41
20	9.73 997	20	9.81 803	28	10.18 197	9.92 194	8	40
21	9.74 017	19	9.81 831	27	10.18 169	9.92 186	9	39
22	9.74 036	19	9.81 858	28	10.18 142	9.92 177	8	38
23	9.74 055	19	9.81 886	27	10.18 114	9.92 169	8	37
24	9.74 074	19	9.81 913	28	10.18 087	9.92 161	9	36
25	9.74 093	20	9.81 941	27	10.18 059	9.92 152	8	35
26	9.74 113	19	9.81 968	28	10.18 032	9.92 144	8	34
27	9.74 132	19	9.81 996	27	10.18 004	9.92 136	9	33
28	9.74 151	19	9.82 023	28	10.17 977	9.92 127	8	32
29	9.74 170	19	9.82 051	27	10.17 949	9.92 119	8	31
30	9.74 189	19	9.82 078	28	10.17 922	9.92 111	9	30
31	9.74 208	19	9.82 106	27	10.17 894	9.92 102	8	29
32	9.74 227	19	9.82 133	28	10.17 867	9.92 094	8	28
33	9.74 246	19	9.82 161	27	10.17 839	9.92 086	9	27
34	9.74 265	19	9.82 188	27	10.17 812	9.92 077	8	26
35	9.74 284	19	9.82 215	28	10.17 785	9.92 069	9	25
36	9.74 303	19	9.82 243	27	10.17 757	9.92 060	8	24
37	9.74 322	19	9.82 270	28	10.17 730	9.92 052	8	23
38	9.74 341	19	9.82 298	27	10.17 702	9.92 044	9	22
39	9.74 360	19	9.82 325	27	10.17 675	9.92 035	8	21
40	9.74 379	19	9.82 352	28	10.17 648	9.92 027	9	20
41	9.74 398	19	9.82 380	27	10.17 620	9.92 018	8	19
42	9.74 417	19	9.82 407	28	10.17 593	9.02 010	8	18
43	9.74 436	19	9.82 435	27	10.17 565	9.92 002	9	17
44	9.74 455	19	9.82 462	27	10.17 538	9.91 993	8	16
45	9.74 474	19	9.82 489	28	10.17 511	9.91 985	9	15
46	9.74 493	19	9.82 517	27	10.17 483	9.91 976	8	14
47	9.74 512	19	9.82 544	27	10.17 456	9.91 968	9	13
48	9.74 531	18	9.82 571	28	10.17 429	9.91 959	8	12
49	9.74 549	19	9.82 599	27	10.17 401	9.91 951	9	11
50	9.74 568	19	9.82 626	27	10.17 374	9.91 942	8	10
51	9.74 587	19	9.82 653	28	10.17 347	9.91 934	9	9
52	9.74 606	19	9.82 681	27	10.17 319	9.91 925	8	8
53	9.74 625	19	9.82 708	27	10.17 292	9.91 917	9	7
54	9.74 644	18	9.82 735	27	10.17 265	9.91 908	8	6
55	9.74 662	19	9.82 762	28	10.17 238	9.91 900	9	5
56	9.74 681	19	9.82 790	27	10.17 210	9.91 891	8	4
57	9.74 700	19	9.82 817	27	10 17 183	9.91 883	9	3
58	9.74 719	18	9.82 844	27	10.17 156	9.91 874	8	2
59	9.74 737	19	9.82 871	28	10.17 129	9.91 866	9	1
60	9.74 756		9.82 899		10.17 101	9.91 857		0
	L. Cos.	d.	L. Cot.	c. d.	L. Tan.	L. Sin.	d.	′

P. P.

	28	27
1	2.8	2.7
2	5.6	5.4
3	8.4	8.1
4	11.2	10.8
5	14.0	13.5
6	16.8	16.2
7	19.6	18.9
8	22.4	21.6
9	25.2	24.3

	20	19	18
1	2.0	1.9	1.8
2	4.0	3.8	3.6
3	6.0	5.7	5.4
4	8.0	7.6	7.2
5	10.0	9.5	9.0
6	12.0	11.4	10.8
7	14.0	13.3	12.6
8	16.0	15.2	14.4
9	18.0	17.1	16.2

	9	8
1	0.9	0.8
2	1.8	1.6
3	2.7	2.4
4	3.6	3.2
5	4.5	4.0
6	5.4	4.8
7	6.3	5.6
8	7.2	6.4
9	8.1	7.2

56°

34°

′	L. Sin.	d.	L. Tan.	c. d.	L. Cot.	L. Cos.	d.		P. P.
0	9.74 756	19	9.82 899	27	10.17 101	9.91 857	8	60	
1	9.74 775	19	9.82 926	27	10.17 074	9.91 849	9	59	
2	9.74 794	18	9.82 953	27	10.17 047	9.91 840	8	58	
3	9.74 812	19	9.82 980	28	10.17 020	9.91 832	9	57	
4	9.74 831	19	9.83 008	27	10.16 992	9.91 823	8	56	
5	9.74 850	18	9.83 035	27	10.16 965	9.91 815	9	55	
6	9.74 868	19	9.83 062	27	10.16 938	9.91 806	8	54	
7	9.74 887	19	9.83 089	28	10.16 911	9.91 798	9	53	
8	9.74 906	18	9.83 117	27	10.16 883	9.91 789	8	52	
9	9.74 924	19	9.83 144	27	10.16 856	9.91 781	9	51	
10	9.74 943	18	9.83 171	27	10.16 829	9.91 772	9	50	
11	9.74 961	19	9.83 198	27	10.16 802	9.91 763	8	49	
12	9.74 980	19	9.83 225	27	10.16 775	9.91 755	9	48	
13	9.74 999	18	9.83 252	28	10.16 748	9.91 746	8	47	
14	9.75 017	19	9.83 280	27	10.16 720	9.91 738	9	46	
15	9.75 036	18	9.83 307	27	10.16 693	9.91 729	9	45	
16	9.75 054	19	9.83 334	27	10.16 666	9.91 720	8	44	
17	9.75 073	18	9.83 361	27	10.16 639	9.91 712	9	43	
18	9.75 091	19	9.83 388	27	10.16 612	9.91 703	8	42	
19	9.75 110	18	9.83 415	27	10.16 585	9.91 695	9	41	
20	9.75 128	19	9.83 442	28	10.16 558	9.91 686	9	40	
21	9.75 147	18	9.83 470	27	10.16 530	9.91 677	8	39	
22	9.75 165	19	9.83 497	27	10.16 503	9.91 669	9	38	
23	9.75 184	18	9.83 524	27	10.16 476	9.91 660	9	37	
24	9.75 202	19	9.83 551	27	10.16 449	9.91 651	8	36	
25	9.75 221	18	9.83 578	27	10.16 422	9.91 643	9	35	
26	9.75 239	19	9.83 605	27	10.16 395	9.91 634	9	34	
27	9.75 258	18	9.83 632	27	10.16 368	9.91 625	8	33	
28	9.75 276	18	9.83 659	27	10.16 341	9.91 617	9	32	
29	9.75 294	19	9.83 686	27	10.16 314	9.91 608	9	31	
30	9.75 313	18	9.83 713	27	10.16 287	9.91 599	8	30	
31	9.75 331	19	9.83 740	28	10.16 260	9.91 591	9	29	
32	9.75 350	18	9.83 768	27	10.16 232	9.91 582	9	28	
33	9.75 368	18	9.83 795	27	10.16 205	9.91 573	8	27	
34	9.75 386	19	9.83 822	27	10.16 178	9.91 565	9	26	
35	9.75 405	18	9.83 849	27	10.16 151	9.91 556	9	25	
36	9.75 423	18	9.83 876	27	10 16 124	9.91 547	9	24	
37	9.75 441	18	9.83 903	27	10.16 097	9.91 538	8	23	
38	9.75 459	19	9.83 930	27	10.16 070	9.91 530	9	22	
39	9.75 478	18	9.83 957	27	10.16 043	9.91 521	9	21	
40	9.75 496	18	9.83 984	27	10.16 016	9.91 512	8	20	
41	9.75 514	19	9.84 011	27	10.15 989	9.91 504	9	19	
42	9.75 533	18	9.84 038	27	10.15 962	9.91 495	9	18	
43	9.75 551	18	9.84 065	27	10.15 935	9.91 486	3	17	
44	9.75 569	18	9.84 092	27	10.15 908	9.91 477	8	16	
45	9.75 587	18	9.84 119	27	10.15 881	9.91 469	9	15	
46	9.75 605	19	9.84 146	27	10.15 854	9.91 460	9	14	
47	9.75 624	18	9.84 173	27	10.15 827	9.91 451	9	13	
48	9.75 642	18	9.84 200	27	10.15 800	9.91 442	9	12	
49	9.75 660	18	9.84 227	27	10.15 773	9.91 433	8	11	
50	9.75 678	18	9.84 254	26	10.15 746	9.91 425	9	10	
51	9.75 696	18	9.84 280	27	10.15 720	9.91 416	9	9	
52	9.75 714	19	9.84 307	27	10.15 693	9.91 40˙	9	8	
53	9.75 733	18	9.84 334	27	10.15 666	9.91 398	9	7	
54	9.75 751	18	9.84 361	27	10.15 639	9.91 389	9	6	
55	9.75 769	18	9.84 388	27	10.15 612	9.91 381	9	5	
56	9.75 787	18	9.84 415	27	10.15 585	9.91 372	9	4	
57	9.75 805	18	9.84 442	27	10.15 558	9.91 363	9	3	
58	9.75 823	18	9.84 469	27	10.15 531	9.91 354	9	2	
59	9.75 841	18	9.84 496	27	10.15 504	9.91 345	9	1	
60	9.75 859		9.84 523		10.15 477	9.91 336		0	
	L. Cos.	d.	L. Cot.	c. d.	L. Tan.	L. Sin.	d.	′	P. P.

P. P.

	28	27	26
1	2.8	2.7	2.6
2	5.6	5.4	5.2
3	8.4	8.1	7.8
4	11.2	10.8	10.4
5	14.0	13.5	13.0
6	16.8	16.2	15.6
7	19.6	18.9	18.2
8	22.4	21.6	20.8
9	25.2	24.3	23.4

	19	18
1	1.9	1.8
2	3.8	3.6
3	5.7	5.4
4	7.6	7.2
5	9.5	9.0
6	11.4	10.8
7	13.3	12.6
8	15.2	14.4
9	17.1	16.2

	9	8
1	0.9	0.8
2	1.8	1.6
3	2.7	2.4
4	3.6	3.2
5	4.5	4.0
6	5.4	4.8
7	6.3	5.6
8	7.2	6.4
9	8.1	7.2

55°

TABLE III. LOGARITHMS OF FUNCTIONS | 247

35°

′	L. Sin.	d.	L. Tan.	c. d.	L. Cot.	L. Cos.	d.		P. P.
0	9.75 859		9.84 523		10.15 477	9.91 336		60	
1	9.75 877	18	9.84 550	27	10.15 450	9.91 328	8	59	
2	9.75 895	18	9.84 576	26	10.15 424	9.91 319	9	58	
3	9.75 913	18	9.84 603	27	10.15 397	9.91 310	9	57	
4	9.75 931	18	9.84 630	27	10.15 370	9.91 301	9	56	
5	9.75 949	18	9.84 657	27	10.15 343	9.91 292	9	55	
6	9.75 967	18	9.84 684	27	10.15 316	9.91 283	9	54	
7	9.75 985	18	9.84 711	27	10.15 289	9.91 274	9	53	
8	9.76 003	18	9.84 738	27	10.15 262	9.91 266	8	52	
9	9.76 021	18	9.84 764	26	10.15 236	9.91 257	9	51	27 26
10	9.76 039	18	9.84 791	27	10.15 209	9.91 248	9	50	
11	9.76 057	18	9.84 818	27	10.15 182	9.91 239	9	49	1 2.7 2.6
12	9.76 075	18	9.84 845	27	10.15 155	9.91 230	9	48	2 5.4 5.2
13	9.76 093	18	9.84 872	27	10.15 128	9.91 221	9	47	3 8.1 7.8
14	9.76 111	18	9.84 899	26	10.15 101	9.91 212	9	46	4 10.8 10.4
15	9.76 129	17	9.84 925	27	10.15 075	9.91 203	9	45	5 13.5 13.0
16	9.76 146	18	9.84 952	27	10.15 048	9.91 194	9	44	6 16.2 15.6
17	9.76 164	18	9.84 979	27	10.15 021	9.91 185	9	43	7 18.9 18.2
18	9.76 182	18	9.85 006	27	10.14 994	9.91 176	9	42	8 21.6 20.8
19	9.76 200	18	9.85 033	26	10.14 967	9.91 167	9	41	9 24.3 23.4
20	9.76 218	18	9.85 059	27	10.14 941	9.91 158	9	40	
21	9.76 236	17	9.85 086	27	10.14 914	9.91 149	8	39	
22	9.76 253	18	9.85 113	27	10.14 887	9.91 141	9	38	
23	9.76 271	18	9.85 140	26	10.14 860	9.91 132	9	37	
24	9.76 289	18	9.85 166	27	10.14 834	9.91 123	9	36	
25	9.76 307	17	9.85 193	27	10.14 807	9.91 114	9	35	
26	9.76 324	18	9.85 220	27	10.14 780	9.91 105	9	34	
27	9.76 342	18	9.85 247	26	10.14 753	9.91 096	9	33	18 17
28	9.76 360	18	9.85 273	27	10.14 727	9.91 087	9	32	
29	9.76 378	17	9.85 300	27	10.14 700	9.91 078	9	31	1 1.8 1.7
30	9.76 395	18	9.85 327	27	10.14 673	9.91 069	9	30	2 3.6 3.4
31	9.76 413	18	9.85 354	26	10.14 646	9.91 060	9	29	3 5.4 5.1
32	9.76 431	17	9.85 380	27	10.14 620	9.91 051	9	28	4 7.2 6.8
33	9.76 448	18	9.85 407	27	10.14 593	9.91 042	9	27	5 9.0 8.5
34	9.76 466	18	9.85 434	26	10.14 566	9.91 033	10	26	6 10.8 10.2
35	9.76 484	17	9.85 460	27	10.14 540	9.91 023	9	25	7 12.6 11.9
36	9.76 501	18	9.85 487	27	10.14 513	9.91 014	9	24	8 14.4 13.6
37	9.76 519	18	9.85 514	26	10.14 486	9.91 005	9	23	9 16.2 15.3
38	9.76 537	17	9.85 540	27	10.14 460	9.90 996	9	22	
39	9.76 554	18	9.85 567	27	10.14 433	9.90 987	9	21	
40	9.76 572	18	9.85 594	26	10.14 406	9.90 978	9	20	
41	9.76 590	17	9.85 620	27	10.14 380	9.90 969	9	19	
42	9.76 607	18	9.85 647	27	10.14 353	9.90 960	9	18	
43	9.76 625	17	9.85 674	26	10.14 326	9.90 951	9	17	10 9 8
44	9.76 642	18	9.85 700	27	10.14 300	9.90 942	9	16	
45	9.76 660	17	9.85 727	27	10.14 273	9.90 933	9	15	1 1.0 0.9 0.8
46	9.76 677	18	9.85 754	26	10.14 246	9.90 924	9	14	2 2.0 1.8 1.6
47	9.76 695	17	9.85 780	27	10.14 220	9.90 915	9	13	3 3.0 2.7 2.4
48	9.76 712	18	9.85 807	27	10.14 193	9.90 906	10	12	4 4.0 3.6 3.2
49	9.76 730	17	9.85 834	26	10.14 166	9.90 896	9	11	5 5.0 4.5 4.0
50	9.76 747	18	9.85 860	27	10.14 140	9.90 887	9	10	6 6.0 5.4 4.8
51	9.76 765	17	9.85 887	26	10.14 113	9.90 878	9	9	7 7.0 6.3 5.6
52	9.76 782	18	9.85 913	27	10.14 087	9.90 869	9	8	8 8.0 7.2 6.4
53	9.76 800	17	9.85 940	27	10.14 060	9.90 860	9	7	9 9.0 8.1 7.2
54	9.76 817	18	9.85 967	26	10.14 033	9.90 851	9	6	
55	9.76 835	17	9.85 993	27	10.14 007	9.90 842	10	5	
56	9.76 852	18	9.86 020	26	10.13 980	9.90 832	9	4	
57	9.76 870	17	9.86 046	27	10.13 954	9.90 823	9	3	
58	9.76 887	17	9.86 073	27	10.13 927	9.90 814	9	2	
59	9.76 904	18	9.86 100	26	10.13 900	9.90 805	9	1	
60	9.76 922		9.86 126		10.13 874	9.90 796		0	
	L. Cos.	d.	L. Cot.	c. d.	L. Tan.	L. Sin.	d.	′	P. P.

36°

′	L. Sin.	d.	L. Tan.	c. d.	L. Cot.	L. Cos.	d.		P. P.
0	9.76 922		9.86 126		10.13 874	9.90 796		60	
1	9.76 939	17	9.86 153	27	10.13 847	9.90 787	9	59	
2	9.76 957	18	9.86 179	26	10.13 821	9.90 777	10	58	
3	9.76 974	17	9.86 206	27	10.13 794	9.90 768	9	57	
4	9.76 991	17	9.86 232	26	10.13 768	9.90 759	9	56	
5	9.77 009	18	9.86 259	27	10.13 741	9.90 750	9	55	
6	9.77 026	17	9.86 285	26	10.13 715	9.90 741	9	54	
7	9.77 043	17	9.86 312	27	10.13 688	9.90 731	10	53	
8	9.77 061	18	9.86 338	26	10.13 662	9.90 722	9	52	
9	9.77 078	17	9.86 365	27	10.13 635	9.90 713	9	51	
10	9.77 095	17	9.86 392	27	10.13 608	9.90 704	9	50	**27** **26**
11	9.77 112	17	9.86 418	26	10.13 582	9.90 694	10	49	1 2.7 2.6
12	9.77 130	18	9.86 445	27	10.13 555	9.90 685	9	48	2 5.4 5.2
13	9.77 147	17	9.86 471	26	10.13 529	9.90 676	9	47	3 8.1 7.8
14	9.77 164	17	9.86 498	27	10.13 502	9.90 667	9	46	4 10.8 10.4
15	9.77 181	17	9.86 524	26	10.13 476	9.90 657	10	45	5 13.5 13.0
16	9.77 199	18	9.86 551	27	10.13 449	9.90 648	9	44	6 16.2 15.6
17	9.77 216	17	9.86 577	26	10.13 423	9.90 639	9	43	7 18.9 18.2
18	9.77 233	17	9.86 603	26	10.13 397	9.90 630	9	42	8 21.6 20.8
19	9.77 250	17	9.86 630	27	10.13 370	9.90 620	10	41	9 24.3 23.4
20	9.77 268	18	9.86 656	26	10.13 344	9.90 611	9	40	
21	9.77 285	17	9.86 683	27	10.13 317	9.90 602	9	39	
22	9.77 302	17	9.86 709	26	10.13 291	9.90 592	10	38	
23	9.77 319	17	9.86 736	27	10.13 264	9.90 583	9	37	
24	9.77 336	17	9.86 762	26	10.13 238	9.90 574	9	36	
25	9.77 353	17	9.86 789	27	10.13 211	9.90 565	9	35	
26	9.77 370	17	9.86 815	26	10.13 185	9.90 555	10	34	**18** **17** **16**
27	9.77 387	17	9.86 842	27	10.13 158	9.90 546	9	33	1 1.8 1.7 1.6
28	9.77 405	18	9.86 868	26	10.13 132	9.90 537	9	32	2 3.6 3.4 3.2
29	9.77 422	17	9.86 894	26	10.13 106	9.90 527	10	31	3 5.4 5.1 4.8
30	9.77 439	17	9.86 921	27	10.13 079	9.90 518	9	30	4 7.2 6.8 6.4
31	9.77 456	17	9.86 947	26	10.13 053	9.90 509	9	29	5 9.0 8.5 8.0
32	9.77 473	17	9.86 974	27	10.13 026	9.90 500	10	28	6 10.8 10.2 9.6
33	9.77 490	17	9.87 000	26	10.13 000	9.90 490	9	27	7 12.6 11.9 11.2
34	9.77 507	17	9.87 027	26	10.12 973	9.90 480	10	26	8 14.4 13.6 12.8
35	9.77 524	17	9.87 053	26	10.12 947	9.90 471	9	25	9 16.2 15.3 14.4
36	9.77 541	17	9.87 079	26	10.12 921	9.90 462	10	24	
37	9.77 558	17	9.87 106	27	10.12 894	9.90 452	10	23	
38	9.77 575	17	9.87 132	26	10.12 868	9.90 443	9	22	
39	9.77 592	17	9.87 158	26	10.12 842	9.90 434	10	21	
40	9.77 609	17	9.87 185	27	10.12 815	9.90 424	9	20	
41	9.77 626	17	9.87 211	26	10.12 789	9.90 415	10	19	
42	9.77 643	17	9.87 238	27	10.12 762	9.90 405	9	18	
43	9.77 660	17	9.87 264	26	10.12 736	9.90 396	10	17	
44	9.77 677	17	9.87 290	26	10.12 710	9.90 386	9	16	**10** **9**
45	9.77 694	17	9.87 317	27	10.12 683	9.90 377	9	15	1 1.0 0.9
46	9.77 711	17	9.87 343	26	10.12 657	9.90 368	10	14	2 2.0 1.8
47	9.77 728	16	9.87 369	27	10.12 631	9.90 358	9	13	3 3.0 2.7
48	9.77 744	17	9.87 396	26	10.12 604	9.90 349	10	12	4 4.0 3.6
49	9.77 761	17	9.87 422	26	10.12 578	9.90 339	9	11	5 5.0 4.5
50	9.77 778	17	9.87 448	27	10.12 552	9.90 330	10	10	6 6.0 5.4
51	9.77 795	17	9.87 475	26	10.12 525	9.90 320	9	9	7 7.0 6.3
52	9.77 812	17	9.87 501	26	10.12 499	9.90 311	10	8	8 8.0 7.2
53	9.77 829	17	9.87 527	27	10.12 473	9.90 301	9	7	9 9.0 8.1
54	9.77 846	16	9.87 554	26	10.12 446	9.90 292	10	6	
55	9.77 862	17	9.87 580	26	10.12 420	9.90 282	9	5	
56	9.77 879	17	9.87 606	27	10.12 394	9.90 273	10	4	
57	9.77 896	17	9.87 633	26	10.12 367	9.90 263	9	3	
58	9.77 913	17	9.87 659	26	10.12 341	9.90 254	10	2	
59	9.77 930	16	9.87 685	26	10.12 315	9.90 244	9	1	
60	9.77 946		9.87 711		10.12 289	9.90 235		0	
	L. Cos.	d.	L. Cot.	c. d.	L. Tan.	L. Sin.	d.	′	P. P.

TABLE III. LOGARITHMS OF FUNCTIONS | 249

37°

′	L. Sin.	d.	L. Tan.	c. d.	L. Cot.	L. Cos.	d.	′	P. P.
0	9.77 946	17	9.87 711	27	10.12 289	9.90 235	10	60	
1	9.77 963	17	9.87 738	26	10.12 262	9.90 225	9	59	
2	9.77 980	17	9.87 764	26	10.12 236	9.90 216	10	58	
3	9.77 997	16	9.87 790	27	10.12 210	9.90 206	9	57	
4	9.78 013	17	9.87 817	26	10.12 183	9.90 197	10	56	
5	9.78 030	17	9.87 843	26	10.12 157	9.90 187	9	55	
6	9.78 047	16	9.87 869	26	10.12 131	9.90 178	10	54	
7	9.78 063	17	9.87 895	27	10.12 105	9.90 168	9	53	
8	9.78 080	17	9.87 922	26	10.12 078	9.90 159	10	52	
9	9.78 097	16	9.87 948	26	10.12 052	9.90 149	10	51	
10	9.78 113	17	9.87 974	26	10.12 026	9.90 139	9	50	**27** **26**
11	9.78 130	17	9.88 000	27	10.12 000	9.90 130	10	49	1 | 2.7 | 2.6
12	9.78 147	16	9.88 027	26	10.11 973	9.90 120	9	48	2 | 5.4 | 5.2
13	9.78 163	17	9.88 053	26	10.11 947	9.90 111	10	47	3 | 8.1 | 7.8
14	9.78 180	17	9.88 079	26	10.11 921	9.90 101	10	46	4 | 10.8 | 10.4
15	9.78 197	16	9.88 105	26	10.11 895	9.90 091	9	45	5 | 13.5 | 13.0
16	9.78 213	17	9.88 131	27	10.11 869	9.90 082	10	44	6 | 16.2 | 15.6
17	9.78 230	16	9.88 158	26	10.11 842	9.90 072	9	43	7 | 18.9 | 18.2
18	9.78 246	17	9.88 184	26	10.11 816	9.90 063	10	42	8 | 21.6 | 20.8
19	9.78 263	17	9.88 210	26	10.11 790	9.90 053	10	41	9 | 24.3 | 23.4
20	9.78 280	16	9.88 236	26	10.11 764	9.90 043	9	40	
21	9.78 296	17	9.88 262	27	10.11 738	9.90 034	10	39	
22	9.78 313	16	9.88 289	26	10.11 711	9.90 024	10	38	
23	9.78 329	17	9.88 315	26	10.11 685	9.90 014	9	37	
24	9.78 346	16	9.88 341	26	10.11 659	9.90 005	10	36	
25	9.78 362	17	9.88 367	26	10.11 633	9.89 995	10	35	
26	9.78 379	16	9.88 393	27	10.11 607	9.89 985	9	34	**17** **16**
27	9.78 395	17	9.88 420	26	10.11 580	9.89 976	10	33	1 | 1.7 | 1.6
28	9.78 412	16	9.88 446	26	10.11 554	9.89 966	10	32	2 | 3.4 | 3.2
29	9.78 428	17	9.88 472	26	10.11 528	9.89 956	9	31	3 | 5.1 | 4.8
30	9.78 445	16	9.88 498	26	10.11 502	9.89 947	10	30	4 | 6.8 | 6.4
31	9.78 461	17	9.88 524	26	10.11 476	9.89 937	10	29	5 | 8.5 | 8.0
32	9.78 478	16	9.88 550	27	10.11 450	9.89 927	9	28	6 | 10.2 | 9.6
33	9.78 494	16	9.88 577	26	10.11 423	9.89 918	10	27	7 | 11.9 | 11.2
34	9.78 510	17	9.88 603	26	10.11 397	9.89 908	10	26	8 | 13.6 | 12.8
35	9.78 527	16	9.88 629	26	10.11 371	9.89 898	10	25	9 | 15.3 | 14.4
36	9.78 543	17	9.88 655	26	10.11 345	9.89 888	9	24	
37	9.78 560	16	9.88 681	26	10.11 319	9.89 879	10	23	
38	9.78 576	16	9.88 707	26	10.11 293	9.89 869	10	22	
39	9.78 592	17	9.88 733	26	10.11 267	9.89 859	10	21	
40	9.78 609	16	9.88 759	27	10.11 241	9.89 849	9	20	
41	9.78 625	17	9.88 786	26	10.11 214	9.89 840	10	19	
42	9.78 642	16	9.88 812	26	10.11 188	9.89 830	10	18	
43	9.78 658	16	9.88 838	26	10.11 162	9.89 820	10	17	
44	9.78 674	17	9.88 864	26	10.11 136	9.89 810	9	16	
45	9.78 691	16	9.88 890	26	10.11 110	9.89 801	10	15	**10** **9**
46	9.78 707	16	9.88 916	26	10.11 084	9.89 791	10	14	1 | 1.0 | 0.9
47	9.78 723	16	9.88 942	26	10.11 058	9.89 781	10	13	2 | 2.0 | 1.8
48	9.78 739	17	9.88 968	26	10.11 032	9.89 771	10	12	3 | 3.0 | 2.7
49	9.78 756	16	9.88 994	26	10.11 006	9.89 761	9	11	4 | 4.0 | 3.6
50	9.78 772	16	9.89 020	26	10.10 980	9.89 752	10	10	5 | 5.0 | 4.5
51	9.78 788	17	9.89 046	27	10.10 954	9.89 742	10	9	6 | 6.0 | 5.4
52	9.78 805	16	9.89 073	26	10.10 927	9.89 732	10	8	7 | 7.0 | 6.3
53	9.78 821	16	9.89 099	26	10.10 901	9.89 722	10	7	8 | 8.0 | 7.2
54	9.78 837	16	9.89 125	26	10.10 875	9.89 712	10	6	9 | 9.0 | 8.1
55	9.78 853	16	9.89 151	26	10.10 849	9.89 702	9	5	
56	9.78 869	17	9.89 177	26	10.10 823	9.89 693	10	4	
57	9.78 886	16	9.89 203	26	10.10 797	9.89 683	10	3	
58	9.78 902	16	9.89 229	26	10.10 771	9.89 673	10	2	
59	9.78 918	16	9.89 255	26	10.10 745	9.89 663	10	1	
60	9.78 934		9.89 281		10.10 719	9.89 653		0	
	L. Cos.	d.	L. Cot.	c. d.	L. Tan.	L. Sin.	d.	′	P. P.

52°

38°

'	L. Sin.	d.	L. Tan.	c. d.	L. Cot.	L. Cos.	d.		
0	9.78 934	16	9.89 281	26	10.10 719	9.89 653	10	60	
1	9.78 950	17	9.89 307	26	10.10 693	9.89 643	10	59	
2	9.78 967	16	9.89 333	26	10.10 667	9.89 633	9	58	
3	9.78 983	16	9.89 359	26	10.10 641	9.89 624	10	57	
4	9.78 999	16	9.89 385	26	10.10 615	9.89 614	10	56	
5	9.79 015	16	9.89 411	26	10.10 589	9.89 604	10	55	
6	9.79 031	16	9.89 437	26	10.10 563	9.89 594	10	54	
7	9.79 047	16	9.89 463	26	10.10 537	9.89 584	10	53	
8	9.79 063	16	9.89 489	26	10.10 511	9.89 574	10	52	
9	9.79 079	16	9.89 515	26	10.10 485	9.89 564	10	51	
10	9.79 095	16	9.89 541	26	10.10 459	9.89 554	10	50	
11	9.79 111	17	9.89 567	26	10.10 433	9.89 544	10	49	
12	9.79 128	16	9.89 593	26	10.10 407	9.89 534	10	48	
13	9.79 144	16	9.89 619	26	10.10 381	9.89 524	10	47	
14	9.79 160	16	9.89 645	26	10.10 355	9.89 514	10	46	
15	9.79 176	16	9.89 671	26	10.10 329	9.89 504	9	45	
16	9.79 192	16	9.89 697	26	10.10 303	9.89 495	10	44	
17	9.79 208	16	9.89 723	26	10.10 277	9.89 485	10	43	
18	9.79 224	16	9.89 749	26	10.10 251	9.89 475	10	42	
19	9.79 240	16	9.89 775	26	10.10 225	9.89 465	10	41	
20	9.79 256	16	9.89 801	26	10.10 199	9.89 455	10	40	
21	9.79 272	16	9.89 827	26	10.10 173	9.89 445	10	39	
22	9.79 288	16	9.89 853	26	10.10 147	9.89 435	10	38	
23	9.79 304	15	9.89 879	26	10.10 121	9.89 425	10	37	
24	9.79 319	16	9.89 905	26	10.10 095	9.89 415	10	36	
25	9.79 335	16	9.89 931	26	10.10 069	9.89 405	10	35	
26	9.79 351	16	9.89 957	26	10.10 043	9.89 395	10	34	
27	9.79 367	16	9.89 983	26	10.10 017	9.89 385	10	33	
28	9.79 383	16	9.90 009	26	10.09 991	9.89 375	11	32	
29	9.79 399	16	9.90 035	26	10.09 965	9.89 364	10	31	
30	9.79 415	16	9.90 061	25	10.09 939	9.89 354	10	30	
31	9.79 431	16	9.90 086	26	10.09 914	9.89 344	10	29	
32	9.79 447	16	9.90 112	26	10.09 888	9.89 334	10	28	
33	9.79 463	15	9.90 138	26	10.09 862	9.89 324	10	27	
34	9.79 478	16	9.90 164	26	10.09 836	9.89 314	10	26	
35	9.79 494	16	9.90 190	26	10.09 810	9.89 304	10	25	
36	9.79 510	16	9.90 216	26	10.09 784	9.89 294	10	24	
37	9.79 526	16	9.90 242	26	10.09 758	9.89 284	10	23	
38	9.79 542	16	9.90 268	26	10.09 732	9.89 274	10	22	
39	9.79 558	15	9.90 294	26	10.09 706	9.89 264	10	21	
40	9.79 573	16	9.90 320	26	10.09 680	9.89 254	10	20	
41	9.79 589	16	9.90 346	25	10.09 654	9.89 244	11	19	
42	9.79 605	16	9.90 371	26	10.09 629	9.89 233	10	18	
43	9.79 621	15	9.90 397	26	10.09 603	9.89 223	10	17	
44	9.79 636	16	9.90 423	26	10.09 577	9.89 213	10	16	
45	9.79 652	16	9.90 449	26	10.09 551	9.89 203	10	15	
46	9.79 668	16	9.90 475	26	10.09 525	9.89 193	10	14	
47	9.79 684	15	9.90 501	26	10.09 499	9.89 183	10	13	
48	9.79 699	16	9.90 527	26	10.09 473	9.89 173	11	12	
49	9.79 715	16	9.90 553	25	10.09 447	9.89 162	10	11	
50	9.79 731	15	9.90 578	26	10.09 422	9.89 152	10	10	
51	9.79 746	16	9.90 604	26	10.09 396	9.89 142	10	9	
52	9.79 762	16	9.90 630	26	10.09 370	9.89 132	10	8	
53	9.79 778	15	9.90 656	26	10.09 344	9.89 122	10	7	
54	9.79 793	16	9.90 682	26	10.09 318	9.89 112	11	6	
55	9.79 809	16	9.90 708	26	10.09 292	9.89 101	10	5	
56	9.79 825	15	9.90 734	25	10.09 266	9.89 091	10	4	
57	9.79 840	16	9.90 759	26	10.09 241	9.89 081	10	3	
58	9.79 856	16	9.90 785	26	10.09 215	9.89 071	11	2	
59	9.79 872	15	9.90 811	26	10.09 189	9.89 060	10	1	
60	9.79 887		9.90 837		10.09 163	9.89 050		0	
	L. Cos.	d.	L. Cot.	c.d.	L. Tan.	L. Sin.	d.	'	P. P.

P. P.

	26	25
1	2.6	2.5
2	5.2	5.0
3	7.8	7.5
4	10.4	10.0
5	13.0	12.5
6	15.6	15.0
7	18.2	17.5
8	20.8	20.0
9	23.4	22.5

	17	16	15
1	1.7	1.6	1.5
2	3.4	3.2	3.0
3	5.1	4.8	4.5
4	6.8	6.4	6.0
5	8.5	8.0	7.5
6	10.2	9.6	9.0
7	11.9	11.2	10.5
8	13.6	12.8	12.0
9	15.3	14.4	13.5

	11	10	9
1	1.1	1.0	0.9
2	2.2	2.0	1.8
3	3.3	3.0	2.7
4	4.4	4.0	3.6
5	5.5	5.0	4.5
6	6.6	6.0	5.4
7	7.7	7.0	6.3
8	8.8	8.0	7.2
9	9.9	9.0	8.1

TABLE III. LOGARITHMS OF FUNCTIONS | 251

39°

'	L. Sin.	d.	L. Tan.	c. d.	L. Cot.	L. Cos.	d.	'
0	9.79 887	16	9.90 837	26	10.09 163	9.89 050	10	60
1	9.79 903	15	9.90 863	26	10.09 137	9.89 040	10	59
2	9.79 918	16	9.90 889	25	10.09 111	9.89 030	10	58
3	9.79 934	16	9.90 914	26	10.09 086	9.89 020	10	57
4	9.79 950	15	9.90 940	26	10.09 060	9.89 009	11	56
							10	
5	9.79 965	16	9.90 966	26	10.09 034	9.88 999	10	55
6	9.79 981	15	9.90 992	26	10.09 008	9.88 989	11	54
7	9.79 996	16	9.91 018	25	10.08 982	9.88 978	10	53
8	9.80 012	15	9.91 043	26	10.08·957	9.88 968	10	52
9	9.80 027	16	9.91 069	26	10.08 931	9.88 958	10	51
10	9.80 043	15	9.91 095	26	10.08 905	9.88 948	10	50
11	9.80 058	16	9.91 121	26	10.08 879	9.88 937	11	49
12	9.80 074	15	9.91 147	25	10.08 853	9.88 927	10	48
13	9.80 089	16	9.91 172	26	10.08 828	9.88 917	10	47
14	9.80 105	15	9.91 198	26	10.08 802	9.88 906	11	46
							10	
15	9.80 120	16	9.91 224	26	10.08 776	9.88 896	10	45
16	9.80 136	15	9.91 250	26	10.08 750	9.88 886	10	44
17	9.80 151	15	9.91 276	25	10.08 724	9.88 875	11	43
18	9.80 166	16	9.91 301	26	10.08 699	9.88 865	10	42
19	9.80 182	15	9.91 327	26	10.08 673	9.88 855	10	41
20	9.80 197	16	9.91 353	26	10.08 647	9.88 844	11	40
21	9.80 213	15	9.91 379	25	10.08 621	9.88 834	10	39
22	9.80 228	16	9.91 404	26	10.08 596	9.88 824	10	38
23	9.80 244	15	9.91 430	26	10.08 570	9.88 813	11	37
24	9.80 259	15	9.91 456	26	10.08 544	9.88 803	10	36
25	9.80 274	16	9.91 482	25	10.08 518	9.88 793	10	35
26	9.80 290	15	9.91 507	26	10.08 493	9.88 782	11	34
27	9.80 305	15	9.91 533	26	10.08 467	9.88 772	10	33
28	9.80 320	16	9.91 559	26	10.08 441	9.88 761	11	32
29	9.80 336	15	9.91 585	25	10.08 415	9.88 751	10	31
30	9.80 351	15	9.91 610	26	10.08 390	9.88 741	11	30
31	9.80 366	16	9.91 636	26	10.08 364	9.88 730	10	29
32	9.80 382	15	9.91 662	26	10.08 338	9.88 720	11	28
33	9.80 397	15	9.91 688	25	10.08 312	9.88 709	10	27
34	9.80 412	16	9.91 713	26	10.08 287	9.88 699	11	26
35	9.80 428	15	9.91 739	26	10.08 261	9.88 688	10	25
36	9.80 443	15	9.91 765	26	10.08 235	9.88 678	10	24
37	9.80 458	15	9.91 791	25	10.08 209	9.88 668	10	23
38	9.80 473	16	9.91 816	26	10.08 184	9.88 657	10	22
39	9.80 489	15	9.91 842	26	10.08 158	9.88 647	11	21
40	9.80 504	15	9.91 868	25	10.08 132	9.88 636	10	20
41	9.80 519	15	9.91 893	26	10.08 107	9.88 626	10	19
42	9.80 534	16	9.91 919	26	10.08 081	9.88 615	10	18
43	9.80 550	15	9.91 945	26	10.08 055	9.88 605	11	17
44	9.80 565	15	9.91 971	25	10.08 029	9.88 594	10	16
45	9.80 580	15	9.91 996	26	10.08 004	9.88 584	11	15
46	9.80 595	15	9.92 022	26	10.07 978	9.88 573	10	14
47	9.80 610	15	9.92 048	25	10.07 952	9.88 563	11	13
48	9.80 625	16	9.92 073	26	10.07 927	9.88 552	10	12
49	9.80 641	15	9.92 099	26	10.07 901	9.88 542	11	11
50	9.80 656	15	9.92 125	25	10.07 875	9.88 531	10	10
51	9.80 671	15	9.92 150	26	10.07 850	9.88 521	11	9
52	9.80 686	15	9.92 176	26	10.07 824	9.88 510	11	8
53	9.80 701	15	9.92 202	25	10.07 798	9.88 499	10	7
54	9.80 716	15	9.92 227	26	10.07 773	9.88 489	11	6
55	9.80 731	15	9.92 253	26	10.07 747	9.88 478	10	5
56	9.80 746	16	9.92 279	25	10.07 721	9.88 468	11	4
57	9.80 762	15	9.92 304	26	10.07 696	9.88 457	10	3
58	9.80 777	15	9.92 330	26	10.07 670	9.88 447	11	2
59	9.80 792	15	9.92 356	25	10.07 644	9.88 436	11	1
60	9.80 807		9.92 381		10.07 619	9.88 425		0
	L. Cos.	d.	L. Cot.	c. d.	L. Tan.	L. Sin.	d.	'

P. P.

	26	25
1	2.6	2.5
2	5.2	5.0
3	7.8	7.5
4	10.4	10.0
5	13.0	12.5
6	15.6	15.0
7	18.2	17.5
8	20.8	20.0
9	23.4	22.5

	16	15
1	1.6	1.5
2	3.2	3.0
3	4.8	4.5
4	6.4	6.0
5	8.0	7.5
6	9.6	9.0
7	11.2	10.5
8	12.8	12.0
9	14.4	13.5

	11	10
1	1.1	1.0
2	2.2	2.0
3	3.3	3.0
4	4.4	4.0
5	5.5	5.0
6	6.6	6.0
7	7.7	7.0
8	8.8	8.0
9	9.9	9.0

P. P.

40°

′	L. Sin.	d.	L. Tan.	c. d.	L. Cot.	L. Cos.	d.	
0	9.80 807	15	9.92 381	26	10.07 619	9.88 425	10	60
1	9.80 822	15	9.92 407	26	10.07 593	9.88 415	11	59
2	9.80 837	15	9.92 433	25	10.07 567	9.88 404	10	58
3	9.80 852	15	9.92 458	26	10.07 542	9.88 394	11	57
4	9.80 867	15	9.92 484	26	10.07 516	9.88 383	11	56
5	9.80 882	15	9.92 510	25	10.07 490	9.88 372	10	55
6	9.80 897	15	9.92 535	26	10.07 465	9.88 362	11	54
7	9.80 912	15	9.92 561	26	10.07 439	9.88 351	11	53
8	9.80 927	15	9.92 587	25	10.07 413	9.88 340	11	52
9	9.80 942	15	9.92 612	26	10.07 388	9.88 330	11	51
10	9.80 957	15	9.92 638	25	10.07 362	9.88 319	11	50
11	9.80 972	15	9.92 663	26	10.07 337	9.88 308	10	49
12	9.80 987	15	9.92 689	26	10.07 311	9.88 298	11	48
13	9.81 002	15	9.92 715	25	10.07 285	9.88 287	11	47
14	9.81 017	15	9.92 740	26	10.07 260	9.88 276	10	46
15	9.81 032	15	9.92 766	26	10.07 234	9.88 266	11	45
16	9.81 047	14	9.92 792	25	10.07 208	9.88 255	11	44
17	9.81 061	15	9.92 817	26	10.07 183	9.88 244	10	43
18	9.81 076	15	9.92 843	25	10.07 157	9.88 234	11	42
19	9.81 091	15	9.92 868	26	10.07 132	9.88 223	11	41
20	9.81 106	15	9.92 894	26	10.07 106	9.88 212	11	40
21	9.81 121	15	9.92 920	25	10.07 080	9.88 201	10	39
22	9.81 136	15	9.92 945	26	10.07 055	9.88 191	11	38
23	9.81 151	15	9.92 971	25	10.07 029	9.88 180	11	37
24	9.81 166	14	9.92 996	26	10.07 004	9.88 169	11	36
25	9.81 180	15	9.93 022	26	10.06 978	9.88 158	10	35
26	9.81 195	15	9.93 048	25	10.06 952	9.88 148	11	34
27	9.81 210	15	9.93 073	26	10.06 927	9.88 137	11	33
28	9.81 225	15	9.93 099	25	10.06 901	9.88 126	11	32
29	9.81 240	14	9.93 124	26	10.06 876	9.88 115	10	31
30	9.81 254	15	9.93 150	25	10.06 850	9.88 105	11	30
31	9.81 269	15	9.93 175	26	10.06 825	9.88 094	11	29
32	9.81 284	15	9.93 201	26	10.06 799	9.88 083	11	28
33	9.81 299	15	9.93 227	25	10.06 773	9.88 072	11	27
34	9.81 314	14	9.93 252	26	10.06 748	9.88 061	10	26
35	9.81 328	15	9.93 278	25	10.06 722	9.88 051	11	25
36	9.81 343	15	9.93 303	26	10.06 697	9.88 040	11	24
37	9.81 358	14	9.93 329	25	10.06 671	9.88 029	11	23
38	9.81 372	15	9.93 354	26	10.06 646	9.88 018	11	22
39	9.81 387	15	9.93 380	26	10.06 620	9.88 007	11	21
40	9.81 402	15	9.93 406	25	10.06 594	9.87 996	11	20
41	9.81 417	14	9.93 431	26	10.06 569	9.87 985	10	19
42	9.81 431	15	9.93 457	25	10.06 543	9.87 975	11	18
43	9.81 446	15	9.93 482	26	10.06 518	9.87 964	11	17
44	9.81 461	14	9.93 508	25	10.06 492	9.87 953	11	16
45	9.81 475	15	9.93 533	26	10.06 467	9.87 942	11	15
46	9.81 490	15	9.93 559	25	10.06 441	9.87 931	11	14
47	9.81 505	14	9.93 584	26	10.06 416	9.87 920	11	13
48	9.81 519	15	9.93 610	26	10.06 390	9.87 909	11	12
49	9.81 534	15	9.93 636	25	10.06 364	9.87 898	11	11
50	9.81 549	14	9.93 661	26	10.06 339	9.87 887	10	10
51	9.81 563	15	9.93 687	25	10.06 313	9.87 877	11	9
52	9.81 578	14	9.93 712	26	10.06 288	9.87 866	11	8
53	9.81 592	15	9.93 738	25	10.06 262	9.87 855	11	7
54	9.81 607	15	9.93 763	26	10.06 237	9.87 844	11	6
55	9.81 622	14	9.93 789	25	10.06 211	9.87 833	11	5
56	9.81 636	15	9.93 814	26	10.06 186	9.87 822	11	4
57	9.81 651	14	9.93 840	25	10.06 160	9.87 811	11	3
58	9.81 665	15	9.93 865	26	10.06 135	9.87 800	11	2
59	9.81 680	14	9.93 891	25	10.06 109	9.87 789	11	1
60	9.81 694		9.93 916		10.06 084	9.87 778		0
	L. Cos.	d.	L. Cot.	c. d.	L. Tan.	L. Sin.	d.	′

P. P.

	26	25
1	2.6	2.5
2	5.2	5.0
3	7.8	7.5
4	10.4	10.0
5	13.0	12.5
6	15.6	15.0
7	18.2	17.5
8	20.8	20.0
9	23.4	22.5

	15	14
1	1.5	1.4
2	3.0	2.8
3	4.5	4.2
4	6.0	5.6
5	7.5	7.0
6	9.0	8.4
7	10.5	9.8
8	12.0	11.2
9	13.5	12.6

	11	10
1	1.1	1.0
2	2.2	2.0
3	3.3	3.0
4	4.4	4.0
5	5.5	5.0
6	6.6	6.0
7	7.7	7.0
8	8.8	8.0
9	9.9	9.0

TABLE III. LOGARITHMS OF FUNCTIONS | 253

41°

′	L. Sin.	d.	L. Tan.	c. d.	L. Cot.	L. Cos.	d.	′
0	9.81 694	15	9.93 916	26	10.06 084	9.87 778	11	60
1	9.81 709	14	9.93 942	25	10.06 058	9.87 767	11	59
2	9.81 723	15	9.93 967	26	10.06 033	9.87 756	11	58
3	9.81 738	14	9.93 993	25	10.06 007	9.87 745	11	57
4	9.81 752	15	9.94 018	26	10.05 982	9.87 734	11	56
5	9.81 767	14	9.94 044	25	10.05 956	9.87 723	11	55
6	9.81 781	15	9.94 069	26	10.05 931	9.87 712	11	54
7	9.81 796	14	9.94 095	25	10.05 905	9.87 701	11	53
8	9.81 810	15	9.94 120	26	10.05 880	9.87 690	11	52
9	9.81 825	14	9.94 146	25	10.05 854	9.87 679	11	51
10	9.81 839	15	9.94 171	26	10.05 829	9.87 668	11	50
11	9.81 854	14	9.94 197	25	10.05 803	9.87 657	11	49
12	9.81 868	14	9.94 222	26	10.05 778	9.87 646	11	48
13	9.81 882	15	9.94 248	25	10.05 752	9.87 635	11	47
14	9.81 897	14	9.94 273	26	10.05 727	9.87 624	11	46
15	9.81 911	15	9.94 299	25	10.05 701	9.87 613	12	45
16	9.81 926	14	9.94 324	26	10.05 676	9.87 601	11	44
17	9.81 940	15	9.94 350	25	10.05 650	9.87 590	11	43
18	9.81 955	14	9.94 375	26	10.05 625	9.87 579	11	42
19	9.81 969	14	9.94 401	25	10.05 599	9.87 568	11	41
20	9.81 983	15	9.94 426	26	10.05 574	9.87 557	11	40
21	9.81 998	14	9.94 452	25	10.05 548	9.87 546	11	39
22	9.82 012	14	9.94 477	26	10.05 523	9.87 535	11	38
23	9.82 026	15	9.94 503	25	10.05 497	9.87 524	11	37
24	9.82 041	14	9.94 528	26	10.05 472	9.87 513	12	36
25	9.82 055	14	9.94 554	25	10.05 446	9.87 501	11	35
26	9.82 069	15	9.94 579	25	10.05 421	9.87 490	11	34
27	9.82 084	14	9.94 604	26	10.05 396	9.87 479	11	33
28	9.82 098	14	9.94 630	25	10.05 370	9.87 468	11	32
29	9.82 112	14	9.94 655	26	10.05 345	9.87 457	11	31
30	9.82 126	15	9.94 681	25	10.05 319	9.87 446	12	30
31	9.82 141	14	9.94 706	26	10.05 294	9.87 434	11	29
32	9.82 155	14	9.94 732	25	10.05 268	9.87 423	11	28
33	9.82 169	15	9.94 757	26	10.05 243	9.87 412	11	27
34	9.82 184	14	9.94 783	25	10.05 217	9.87 401	11	26
35	9.82 198	14	9.94 808	26	10.05 192	9.87 390	12	25
36	9.82 212	14	9.94 834	25	10.05 166	9.87 378	11	24
37	9.82 226	14	9.94 859	25	10.05 141	9.87 367	11	23
38	9.82 240	15	9.94 884	26	10.05 116	9.87 356	11	22
39	9.82 255	14	9.94 910	25	10.05 090	9.87 345	11	21
40	9.82 269	14	9.94 935	26	10.05 065	9.87 334	12	20
41	9.82 283	14	9.94 961	25	10.05 039	9.87 322	11	19
42	9.82 297	14	9.94 986	26	10.05 014	9.87 311	11	18
43	9.82 311	15	9.95 012	25	10.04 988	9.87 300	12	17
44	9.82 326	14	9.95 037	25	10.04 963	9.87 288	11	16
45	9.82 340	14	9.95 062	26	10.04 938	9.87 277	11	15
46	9.82 354	14	9.95 088	25	10.04 912	9.87 266	11	14
47	9.82 368	14	9.95 113	26	10.04 887	9.87 255	12	13
48	9.82 382	14	9.95 139	25	10.04 861	9.87 243	11	12
49	9.82 396	14	9.95 164	26	10.04 836	9.87 232	11	11
50	9.82 410	14	9.95 190	25	10.04 810	9.87 221	12	10
51	9.82 424	15	9.95 215	25	10.04 785	9.87 209	11	9
52	9.82 439	14	9.95 240	26	10.04 760	9.87 198	11	8
53	9.82 453	14	9.95 266	25	10.04 734	9.87 187	12	7
54	9.82 467	14	9.95 291	26	10.04 709	9.87 175	11	6
55	9.82 481	14	9.95 317	25	10.04 683	9.87 164	11	5
56	9.82 495	14	9.95 342	26	10.04 658	9.87 153	12	4
57	9.82 509	14	9.95 368	25	10.04 632	9.87 141	11	3
58	9.82 523	14	9.95 393	25	10.04 607	9.87 130	11	2
59	9.82 537	14	9.95 418	26	10.04 581	9.87 119	12	1
60	9.82 551		9.95 444		10.04 556	9.87 107		0
	L. Cos.	d.	L. Cot.	c. d.	L. Tan.	L. Sin.	d.	′

P. P.

	26	25
1	2.6	2.5
2	5.2	5.0
3	7.8	7.5
4	10.4	10.0
5	13.0	12.5
6	15.6	15.0
7	18.2	17.5
8	20.8	20.0
9	23.4	22.5

	15	14
1	1.5	1.4
2	3.0	2.8
3	4.5	4.2
4	6.0	5.6
5	7.5	7.0
6	9.0	8.4
7	10.5	9.8
8	12.0	11.2
9	13.5	12.6

	12	11
1	1.2	1.1
2	2.4	2.2
3	3.6	3.3
4	4.8	4.4
5	6.0	5.5
6	7.2	6.6
7	8.4	7.7
8	9.6	8.8
9	10.8	9.9

48°

42°

′	L. Sin.	d.	L. Tan.	c. d.	L. Cot.	L. Cos.	d.			P. P.
0	9.82 551	14	9.95 444	25	10.04 556	9.87 107	11	60		
1	9.82 565	14	9.95 469	26	10.04 531	9.87 096	11	59		
2	9.82 579	14	9.95 495	25	10.04 505	9.87 085	12	58		
3	9.82 593	14	9.95 520	25	10.04 480	9.87 073	11	57		
4	9.82 607	14	9.95 545	26	10.04 455	9.87 062	12	56		
5	9.82 621	14	9.95 571	25	10.04 429	9.87 050	11	55		
6	9.82 635	14	9.95 596	26	10.04 404	9.87 039	11	54		
7	9.82 649	14	9.95 622	25	10.04 378	9.87 028	12	53		
8	9.82 663	14	9.95 647	25	10.04 353	9.87 016	11	52		
9	9.82 677	14	9.95 672	26	10.04 328	9.87 005	12	51		**26** **25**
10	9.82 691	14	9.95 698	25	10.04 302	9.86 993	11	50		
11	9.82 705	14	9.95 723	25	10.04 277	9.86 982	12	49		1 2.6 2.5
12	9.82 719	14	9.95 748	26	10.04 252	9.86 970	11	48		2 5.2 5.0
13	9.82 733	14	9.95 774	25	10.04 226	9.86 959	12	47		3 7.8 7.5
14	9.82 747	14	9.95 799	26	10.04 201	9.86 947	11	46		4 10.4 10.0
15	9.82 761	14	9.95 825	25	10.04 175	9.86 936	12	45		5 13.0 12.5
16	9.82 775	13	9.95 850	25	10.04 150	9.86 924	11	44		6 15.6 15.0
17	9.82 788	14	9.95 875	26	10.04 125	9.86 913	11	43		7 18.2 17.5
18	9.82 802	14	9.95 901	25	10.04 099	9.86 902	12	42		8 20.8 20.0
19	9.82 816	14	9.95 926	26	10.04 074	9.86 890	11	41		9 23.4 22.5
20	9.82 830	14	9.95 952	25	10.04 048	9.86 879	12	40		
21	9.82 844	14	9.95 977	25	10.04 023	9.86 867	12	39		
22	9.82 858	14	9.96 002	26	10.03 998	9.86 855	11	38		
23	9.82 872	13	9.96 028	25	10.03 972	9.86 844	12	37		
24	9.82 885	14	9.96 053	25	10.03 947	9.86 832	11	36		
25	9.82 899	14	9.96 078	26	10.03 922	9.86 821	12	35		
26	9.82 913	14	9.96 104	25	10.03 896	9.86 809	11	34		**14** **13**
27	9.82 927	14	9.96 129	26	10.03 871	9.86 798	12	33		
28	9.82 941	14	9.96 155	25	10.03 845	9.86 786	11	32		1 1.4 1.3
29	9.82 955	13	9.96 180	25	10.03 820	9.86 775	12	31		2 2.8 2.6
30	9.82 968	14	9.96 205	26	10.03 795	9.86 763	11	30		3 4.2 3.9
31	9.82 982	14	9.96 231	25	10.03 769	9.86 752	12	29		4 5.6 5.2
32	9.82 996	14	9.96 256	25	10.03 744	9.86 740	12	28		5 7.0 6.5
33	9.83 010	13	9.96 281	26	10.03 719	9.86 728	11	27		6 8.4 7.8
34	9.83 023	14	9.96 307	25	10.03 693	9.86 717	12	26		7 9.8 9.1
35	9.83 037	14	9.96 332	25	10.03 668	9.86 705	11	25		8 11.2 10.4
36	9.83 051	14	9.96 357	26	10.03 643	9.86 694	12	24		9 12.6 11.7
37	9.83 065	13	9.96 383	25	10.03 617	9.86 682	12	23		
38	9.83 078	14	9.96 408	25	10.03 592	9.86 670	11	22		
39	9.83 092	14	9.96 433	26	10.03 567	9.86 659	12	21		
40	9.83 106	14	9.96 459	25	10.03 541	9.86 647	12	20		
41	9.83 120	13	9.96 484	26	10.03 516	9.86 635	11	19		
42	9.83 133	14	9.96 510	25	10.03 490	9.86 624	12	18		
43	9.83 147	14	9.96 535	25	10.03 465	9.86 612	12	17		
44	9.83 161	13	9.96 560	26	10.03 440	9.86 600	11	16		**12** **11**
45	9.83 174	14	9.96 586	25	10.03 414	9.86 589	12	15		
46	9.83 188	14	9.96 611	25	10.03 389	9.86 577	12	14		1 1.2 1.1
47	9.83 202	13	9.96 636	26	10.03 364	9.86 565	11	13		2 2.4 2.2
48	9.83 215	14	9.96 662	25	10.03 338	9.86 554	12	12		3 3.6 3.3
49	9.83 229	13	9.96 687	25	10.03 313	9.86 542	12	11		4 4.8 4.4
50	9.83 242	14	9.96 712	26	10.03 288	9.86 530	12	10		5 6.0 5.5
51	9.83 256	14	9.96 738	25	10.03 262	9.86 518	11	9		6 7.2 6.6
52	9.83 270	13	9.96 763	25	10.03 237	9.86 507	12	8		7 8.4 7.7
53	9.83 283	14	9.96 788	26	10.03 212	9.86 495	12	7		8 9.6 8.8
54	9.83 297	13	9.96 814	25	10.03 186	9.86 483	11	6		9 10.8 9.9
55	9.83 310	14	9.96 839	25	10.03 161	9.86 472	12	5		
56	9.83 324	14	9.96 864	26	10.03 136	9.86 460	12	4		
57	9.83 338	13	9.96 890	25	10.03 110	9.86 448	12	3		
58	9.83 351	14	9.96 915	25	10.03 085	9.86 436	11	2		
59	9.83 365	13	9.96 940	26	10.03 060	9.86 425	12	1		
60	9.83 378		9.96 966		10.03 034	9.86 413		0		
	L. Cos.	d.	L. Cot.	c. d.	L. Tan.	L. Sin.	d.	′		P. P.

TABLE III. LOGARITHMS OF FUNCTIONS | 255

43°

′	L. Sin.	d.	L. Tan.	c. d.	L. Cot.	L. Cos.	d.		P. P.
0	9.83 378	14	9.96 966	25	10.03 034	9.86 413	12	60	
1	9.83 392	13	9.96 991	25	10.03 009	9.86 401	12	59	
2	9.83 405	14	9.97 016	26	10.02 984	9.86 389	12	58	
3	9.83 419	13	9.97 042	25	10.02 958	9.86 377	11	57	
4	9.83 432	14	9.97 067	25	10.02 933	9.86 366	12	56	
5	9.83 446	13	9.97 092	26	10.02 908	9.86 354	12	55	
6	9.83 459	14	9.97 118	25	10.02 882	9.86 342	12	54	
7	9.83 473	13	9.97 143	25	10.02 857	9.86 330	12	53	
8	9.83 486	14	9.97 168	25	10.02 832	9.86 318	12	52	
9	9.83 500	13	9.97 193	26	10.02 807	9.86 306	11	51	26 25
10	9.83 513	14	9.97 219	25	10.02 781	9.86 295	12	50	1	2.6 2.5
11	9.83 527	13	9.97 244	25	10.02 756	9.86 283	12	49	2	5.2 5.0
12	9.83 540	14	9.97 269	26	10.02 731	9.86 271	12	48	3	7.8 7.5
13	9.83 554	13	9.97 295	25	10.02 705	9.86 259	12	47	4	10.4 10.0
14	9.83 567	14	9.97 320	25	10.02 680	9.86 247	12	46	5	13.0 12.5
15	9.83 581	13	9.97 345	26	10.02 655	9.86 235	12	45	6	15.6 15.0
16	9.83 594	14	9.97 371	25	10.02 629	9.86 223	12	44	7	18.2 17.5
17	9.83 608	13	9.97 396	25	10.02 604	9.86 211	11	43	8	20.8 20.0
18	9.83 621	13	9.97 421	26	10.02 579	9.86 200	12	42	9	23.4 22.5
19	9.83 634	14	9.97 447	25	10.02 553	9.86 188	12	41	
20	9.83 648	13	9.97 472	25	10.02 528	9.86 176	12	40	
21	9.83 661	13	9.97 497	26	10.02 503	9.86 164	12	39	
22	9.83 674	14	9.97 523	25	10.02 477	9.86 152	12	38	
23	9.83 688	13	9.97 548	25	10.02 452	9.86 140	12	37	
24	9.83 701	14	9.97 573	25	10.02 427	9.86 128	12	36	
25	9.83 715	13	9.97 598	26	10.02 402	9.86 116	12	35	
26	9.83 728	13	9.97 624	25	10.02 376	9.86 104	12	34	14 13
27	9.83 741	14	9.97 649	25	10.02 351	9.86 092	12	33	1	1.4 1.3
28	9.83 755	13	9.97 674	26	10.02 326	9.86 080	12	32	2	2.8 2.6
29	9.83 768	13	9.97 700	25	10.02 300	9.86 068	12	31	3	4.2 3.9
30	9.83 781	14	9.97 725	25	10.02 275	9.86 056	12	30	4	5.6 5.2
31	9.83 795	13	9.97 750	26	10.02 250	9.86 044	12	29	5	7.0 6.5
32	9.83 808	13	9.97 776	25	10.02 224	9.86 032	12	28	6	8.4 7.8
33	9.83 821	13	9.97 801	25	10.02 199	9.86 020	12	27	7	9.8 9.1
34	9.83 834	14	9.97 826	25	10.02 174	9.86 008	12	26	8	11.2 10.4
35	9.83 848	13	9.97 851	26	10.02 149	9.85 996	12	25	9	12.6 11.7
36	9.83 861	13	9.97 877	25	10.02 123	9.85 984	12	24	
37	9.83 874	13	9.97 902	25	10.02 098	9.85 972	12	23	
38	9.83 887	14	9.97 927	26	10.02 073	9.85 960	12	22	
39	9.83 901	13	9.97 953	25	10.02 047	9.85 948	12	21	
40	9.83 914	13	9.97 978	25	10.02 022	9.85 936	12	20	
41	9.83 927	13	9.98 003	26	10.01 997	9.85 924	12	19	
42	9.83 940	14	9.98 029	25	10.01 971	9.85 912	12	18	
43	9.83 954	13	9.98 054	25	10.01 946	9 85 900	12	17	12 11
44	9.83 967	13	9.98 079	25	10.01 921	9.85 888	12	16	1	1.2 1.1
45	9.83 980	13	9.98 104	26	10.01 896	9.85 876	12	15	2	2.4 2.2
46	9.83 993	13	9.98 130	25	10.01 870	9.85 864	13	14	3	3.6 3.3
47	9.84 006	14	9.98 155	25	10.01 845	9.85 851	12	13	4	4.8 4.4
48	9.84 020	13	9.98 180	26	10.01 820	9.85 839	12	12	5	6.0 5.5
49	9.84 033	13	9.98 206	25	10.01 794	9.85 827	12	11	6	7.2 6.6
50	9.84 046	13	9.98 231	25	10.01 769	9.85 815	12	10	7	8.4 7.7
51	9.84 059	13	9.98 256	25	10.01 744	9.85 803	12	9	8	9.6 8.8
52	9.84 072	13	9.98 281	26	10.01 719	9.85 791	12	8	9	10.8 9.9
53	9.84 085	13	9.98 307	25	10.01 693	9.85 779	13	7	
54	9.84 098	14	9.98 332	25	10.01 668	9.85 766	12	6	
55	9.84 112	13	9.98 357	26	10.01 643	9.85 754	12	5	
56	9.84 125	13	9.98 383	25	10.01 617	9.85 742	12	4	
57	9.84 138	13	9.98 408	25	10.01 592	9.85 730	12	3	
58	9.84 151	13	9.98 433	25	10.01 567	9.85 718	12	2	
59	9.84 164	13	9.98 458	26	10.01 542	9.85 706	13	1	
60	9.84 177		9.98 484		10.01 516	9.85 693		0	
	L. Cos.	d.	L. Cot.	c. d.	L. Tan.	L. Sin.	d.	′	P. P.

46°

44°

′	L. Sin.	d.	L. Tan.	c. d.	L. Cot.	L. Cos.	d.	
0	9.84 177	13	9.98 484	25	10.01 516	9.85 693	12	60
1	9.84 190	13	9.98 509	25	10.01 491	9.85 681	12	59
2	9.84 203	13	9.98 534	26	10.01 466	9.85 669	12	58
3	9.84 216	13	9.98 560	25	10.01 440	9.85 657	12	57
4	9.84 229	13	9.98 585	25	10.01 415	9.85 645	13	56
5	9.84 242	13	9.98 610	25	10.01 390	9.85 632	12	55
6	9.84 255	14	9.98 635	26	10.01 365	9.85 620	12	54
7	9.84 269	13	9.98 661	25	10.01 339	9.85 608	12	53
8	9.84 282	13	9.98 686	25	10.01 314	9.85 596	13	52
9	9.84 295	13	9.98 711	26	10.01 289	9.85 583	12	51
10	9.84 308	13	9.98 737	25	10.01 263	9.85 571	12	50
11	9.84 321	13	9.98 762	25	10.01 238	9.85 559	12	49
12	9.84 334	13	9.98 787	25	10.01 213	9.85 547	13	48
13	9.84 347	13	9.98 812	26	10.01 188	9.85 534	12	47
14	9.84 360	13	9.98 838	25	10.01 162	9.85 522	12	46
15	9.84 373	12	9.98 863	25	10.01 137	9.85 510	13	45
16	9.84 385	13	9.98 888	25	10.01 112	9.85 497	12	44
17	9.84 398	13	9.98 913	26	10.01 087	9.85 485	12	43
18	9.84 411	13	9.98 939	25	10.01 061	9.85 473	13	42
19	9.84 424	13	9.98 964	25	10.01 036	9.85 460	12	41
20	9.84 437	13	9.98 989	26	10.01 011	9.85 448	12	40
21	9.84 450	13	9.99 015	25	10.00 985	9.85 436	13	39
22	9.84 463	13	9.99 040	25	10.00 960	9.85 423	12	38
23	9.84 476	13	9.99 065	25	10.00 935	9.85 411	12	37
24	9.84 489	13	9.99 090	26	10.00 910	9.85 399	13	36
25	9.84 502	13	9.99 116	25	10.00 884	9.85 386	12	35
26	9.84 515	13	9.99 141	25	10.00 859	9.85 374	13	34
27	9.84 528	12	9.99 166	25	10.00 834	9.85 361	12	33
28	9.84 540	13	9.99 191	26	10.00 809	9.85 349	12	32
29	9.84 553	13	9.99 217	25	10.00 783	9.85 337	13	31
30	9.84 566	13	9.99 242	25	10.00 758	9.85 324	12	30
31	9.84 579	13	9.99 267	26	10.00 733	9.85 312	13	29
32	9.84 592	13	9.99 293	25	10.00 707	9.85 299	12	28
33	9.84 605	13	9.99 318	25	10.00 682	9.85 287	13	27
34	9.84 618	12	9.99 343	25	10.00 657	9.85 274	12	26
35	9.84 630	13	9.99 368	26	10.00 632	9.85 262	12	25
36	9.84 643	13	9.99 394	25	10.00 606	9.85 250	12	24
37	9.84 656	13	9.99 419	25	10.00 581	9.85 237	12	23
38	9.84 669	13	9.99 444	25	10.00 556	9.85 225	13	22
39	9.84 682	13	9.99 469	26	10.00 531	9.85 212	12	21
40	9.84 694	13	9.99 495	25	10.00 505	9.85 200	13	20
41	9.84 707	13	9.99 520	25	10.00 480	9.85 187	12	19
42	9.84 720	13	9.99 545	25	10.00 455	9.85 175	13	18
43	9.84 733	12	9.99 570	26	10.00 430	9.85 162	12	17
44	9.84 745	13	9.99 596	25	10.00 404	9.85 150	13	16
45	9.84 758	13	9.99 621	25	10.00 379	9.85 137	12	15
46	9.84 771	13	9.99 646	26	10.00 354	9.85 125	13	14
47	9.84 784	12	9.99 672	25	10.00 328	9.85 112	12	13
48	9.84 796	13	9.99 697	25	10.00 303	9.85 100	13	12
49	9.84 809	13	9.99 722	25	10.00 278	9.85 087	13	11
50	9.84 822	13	9.99 747	26	10.00 253	9.85 074	12	10
51	9.84 835	12	9.99 773	25	10.00 227	9.85 062	13	9
52	9.84 847	13	9.99 798	25	10.00 202	9.85 049	12	8
53	9.84 860	13	9.99 823	25	10.00 177	9.85 037	13	7
54	9.84 873	12	9.99 848	26	10.00 152	9.85 024	12	6
55	9.84 885	13	9.99 874	25	10.00 126	9.85 012	13	5
56	9.84 898	13	9.99 899	25	10.00 101	9.84 999	13	4
57	9.84 911	12	9.99 924	25	10.00 076	9.84 986	12	3
58	9.84 923	13	9.99 949	26	10.00 051	9.84 974	13	2
59	9.84 936	13	9.99 975	25	10.00 025	9.84 961	12	1
60	9.84 949		10.00 000		10.00 000	9.84 949		0

P. P.

	26	25	14
1	2.6	2.5	1.4
2	5.2	5.0	2.8
3	7.8	7.5	4.2
4	10.4	10.0	5.6
5	13.0	12.5	7.0
6	15.6	15.0	8.4
7	18.2	17.5	9.8
8	20.8	20.0	11.2
9	23.4	22.5	12.6

	13	12
1	1.3	1.2
2	2.6	2.4
3	3.9	3.6
4	5.2	4.8
5	6.5	6.0
6	7.8	7.2
7	9.1	8.4
8	10.4	9.6
9	11.7	10.8

	L. Cos.	d.	L. Cot.	c. d.	L. Tan.	L. Sin.	d.	′	P. P.

45°

Table IV

DEGREES, MINUTES, AND SECONDS
TO RADIANS

DEGREES, MINUTES, AND SECONDS, TO RADIANS							
Deg.	Radians	Deg.	Radians	Min.	Radians	Sec.	Radians
0	0.00000	60	1.04720	0	0.00000	0	0.00000
1	0.01745	61	1.06465	1	0.00029	1	0.00000
2	0.03491	62	1.08210	2	0.00058	2	0.00001
3	0.05236	63	1.09956	3	0.00087	3	0.00001
4	0.06981	64	1.11701	4	0.00116	4	0.00002
5	0.08727	65	1.13446	5	0.00145	5	0.00002
6	0.10472	66	1.15192	6	0.00175	6	0.00003
7	0.12217	67	1.16937	7	0.00204	7	0.00003
8	0.13963	68	1.18682	8	0.00233	8	0.00004
9	0.15708	69	1.20428	9	0.00262	9	0.00004
10	0.17453	70	1.22173	10	0.00291	10	0.00005
11	0.19199	71	1.23918	11	0.00320	11	0.00005
12	0.20944	72	1.25664	12	0.00349	12	0.00006
13	0.22689	73	1.27409	13	0.00378	13	0.00006
14	0.24435	74	1.29154	14	0.00407	14	0.00007
15	0.26180	75	1.30900	15	0.00436	15	0.00007
16	0.27925	76	1.32645	16	0.00465	16	0.00008
17	0.29671	77	1.34390	17	0.00495	17	0.00008
18	0.31416	78	1.36136	18	0.00524	18	0.00009
19	0.33161	79	1.37881	19	0.00553	19	0.00009
20	0.34907	80	1.39626	20	0.00582	20	0.00010
21	0.36652	81	1.41372	21	0.00611	21	0.00010
22	0.38397	82	1.43117	22	0.00640	22	0.00011
23	0.40143	83	1.44862	23	0.00669	23	0.00011
24	0.41888	84	1.46608	24	0.00698	24	0.00012
25	0.43633	85	1.48353	25	0.00727	25	0.00012
26	0.45379	86	1.50098	26	0.00756	26	0.00013
27	0.47124	87	1.51844	27	0.00785	27	0.00013
28	0.48869	88	1.53589	28	0.00814	28	0.00014
29	0.50615	89	1.55334	29	0.00844	29	0.00014
30	0.52360	90	1.57080	30	0.00873	30	0.00015
31	0.54105	91	1.58825	31	0.00902	31	0.00015
32	0.55851	92	1.60570	32	0.00931	32	0.00016
33	0.57596	93	1.62316	33	0.00960	33	0.00016
34	0.59341	94	1.64061	34	0.00989	34	0.00016
35	0.61087	95	1.65806	35	0.01018	35	0.00017
36	0.62832	96	1.67552	36	0.01047	36	0.00017
37	0.64577	97	1.69297	37	0.01076	37	0.00018
38	0.66323	98	1.71042	38	0.01105	38	0.00018
39	0.68068	99	1.72788	39	0.01134	39	0.00019
40	0.69813	100	1.74533	40	0.01164	40	0.00019
41	0.71558	101	1.76278	41	0.01193	41	0.00020
42	0.73304	102	1.78024	42	0.01222	42	0.00020
43	0.75049	103	1.79769	43	0.01251	43	0.00021
44	0.76794	104	1.81514	44	0.01280	44	0.00021
45	0.78540	105	1.83260	45	0.01309	45	0.00022
46	0.80285	106	1.85004	46	0.01338	46	0.00022
47	0.82030	107	1.86750	47	0.01367	47	0.00023
48	0.83776	108	1.88496	48	0.01396	48	0.00023
49	0.85521	109	1.90241	49	0.01425	49	0.00024
50	0.87266	110	1.91986	50	0.01454	50	0.00024
51	0.89012	111	1.93732	51	0.01484	61	0.00025
52	0.90757	112	1.95477	52	0.01513	52	0.00025
53	0.92502	113	1.97222	53	0.01542	53	0.00026
54	0.94248	114	1.98968	54	0.01571	54	0.00026
55	0.95993	115	2.00713	55	0.01600	55	0.00027
56	0.97738	116	2.02458	56	0.01629	56	0.00027
57	0.99484	117	2.04204	57	0.01658	57	0.00028
58	1.01229	118	2.05949	58	0.01687	58	0.00028
59	1.02974	119	2.07694	59	0.01716	59	0.00029
60	1.04720	120	2.09440	60	0.01745	60	0.00029

ANSWERS
TO
PROBLEMS

Answers are provided for most odd-numbered problems.

Set 2.1 page 6

1. Void set.
3. Yes.
5. $\{1/2, 1/4, 3/2, 3/4, 5/2, 5/4\}$.

Set 2.2 page 8

3. (a) 14,   (b) 31,   (c) 17.
5. $b - (a + 1)$.
7. (a) $1.222 \cdots$,   (b) 0.8,   (c) $0.0909 \cdots$,   (d) $0.8181 \cdots$.

Set 2.3 page 12

1. (b), (c), (e).
7. (a) $-4 \leqq f(x) \leqq 2$,   (c) $-5 \leqq f(x) \leqq 7$,
   (b) $0 \leqq f(x) \leqq 3$,   (d) 1 and $-3 \leqq f(x) \leqq 0$.
9. (a) 1 and -1,   (b) 1/3 and 1,   (c) None,   (d) $-\pi$, 0, and $\sqrt{2}$.

Set 2.4 page 16

1. I, I, II, II, None, III, IV, IV, None, III.
3. Each has 2 as its second co-ordinate.
5. (a) I and II,   (b) II and III,   (c) I and III.
7. (a) 3,   (b) 7,   (c) 5,   (d) 8.
9. Dist $(O, P) = \sqrt{x^2 + y^2}$.

Miscellaneous Problems page 17

1. "an" and "the".
3. $\{1, 2\}$, $\{1, 3\}$, $\{2, 3\}$.
5. $\{3, 5, 7, 11, 13\}$.
7. $b - (a + 1)$.
9. (a) Irrational,   (b) Rational.
13. (a) $0.1999 \cdots$,   (b) $0.24999 \cdots$,   (c) $0.008999 \cdots$.
19. (a) $x < 0$,   (b) $x \leqq 0$,   (c) $x > 1$,   (d) $x \geqq 1$.
23. (a) 10 square units,   (b) No,   (c) Yes,   (d) 10.

Set 3.1 page 23

1. $7\pi/30$, $-4\pi/45$, $52\pi/9$, $-143\pi/36$, $\pi/8$.
3. (a) $s = \theta$, (b) $s = (\pi/180)\theta$.
5. (a) $3/2, 270°/\pi$, (b) $12/\pi, 2160°/\pi^2$, (c) $1, 180°/\pi$, (d) $6\pi, 1080°$, (e) $4\pi, 720°$.
7. (a) 2, (b) $1/\pi$, (c) π, (d) $\frac{1}{4}$.

Set 3.2 page 25

1. (a) $1/2$, (b) $\pi/360$, (c) $\pi/12$, (d) $5/8$, (e) $5\pi/6$.
3. That from the first pie.
5. (a) $2\pi/5$, (b) $20\sqrt{5}/\pi$ inches, (c) 6 seconds.
7. (a) $5\pi/12$ inches, (b) 24π inches.

Set 3.3 page 26

1. I, II, III, I, I, IV, IV, I, IV, II, III, I.
7. None.
9. $\{\pi \pm 2n\pi\}$.

Set 3.4 page 30

1. (a), (d)., (g) tangent and secant; (b), (c), (h), (i) cotangent and cosecant.
3. $\sin \theta = -1/2$, $\cos \theta = \sqrt{3}/2$, $\tan \theta = -\sqrt{3}/3$.
5. $\sin \theta = 3/5$, $\cos \theta = -4/5$, $\tan \theta = -3/4$.
7. $\sin \theta = -\sqrt{2}/2$, $\cos \theta = \sqrt{2}/2$, $\tan \theta = -1$.

Set 3.5 page 32

1. (a) III, IV; (b) I, II; (c) I, IV; (d) I, IV; (e) III, IV; (f) II, IV; (g) II, III;
   (h) I, III; (i) II, IV.
3. $\cos \theta = -\sqrt{7}/4$, $\tan \theta = -3\sqrt{7}/7$.
5. $\sin \theta = 5\sqrt{29}/29$, $\cos \theta = 2\sqrt{29}/29$.
7. $\tan \theta = -\sqrt{3}/3$.
9. $\tan \theta = -\sqrt{5}/2$.

Miscellaneous Problems page 32

5. (a) right triangle, (c) isosceles right triangle.
7. (a) $\pi/1,800$ rad/sec
   (b) $\pi/21,600$ rad/sec

9. (a) $50\pi/9$, (b) 1000.

11. $11\pi/30$.

13. $11\pi/30r$.

15. (a) 2, (b) $-5/3$, (c) $1/3$, (d) $-14/5$, (e) $5/\pi$, (f) $5/6$.

17. $\{(1 \pm n)\pi/2\} = \{0 \pm n\pi/2\}$.

19. $\{\pi(1 \pm 8n)/4\}$.

21. (a) $x/y = (x/r)/(y/r)$,
  (b) $(r/y)(x/r) = x/y$,
  (c) $(r/x)(y/r) = y/x$.

23. (a) for all θ, $-r \leqq y \leqq r$, hence $-1 \leqq y/r \leqq 1$;
  (b) for all θ, $-r \leqq x \leqq r$, hence $-1 \leqq x/r \leqq 1$.

25. (a) II, (b) No, (c) No.

27. $\sin \theta = 24/25$, $\cos \theta = 7/25$, $\tan \theta = 24/7$.

29. $\cos \theta = 3/5$, $\tan \theta = -4/3$.

Set 4.1 page 36

1. (a) $0 \leqq \sin \theta \leqq 1$,   (b) $0 \leqq \sin \theta \leqq 1$,
  $\quad -1 \leqq \cos \theta \leqq 1$, $0 \leqq \cos \theta \leqq 1$,
  $\quad \tan \theta = R$, $\tan \theta \geqq 0$,
  $\quad \cot \theta = R$, $\cot \theta \geqq 0$,
  $\quad \begin{cases} \sec \theta \geqq 1 \text{ or} \\ \sec \theta \leqq -1, \end{cases}$ $\sec \theta \geqq 1$,
  $\quad \csc \theta \geqq 1$; $\csc \theta \geqq 1$.

3. (a) R except $\{\pi/2 \pm n\pi\}$,
  (b) R except $\{\pm n\pi/2\}$,
  (c) R except $\{3\pi/4 \pm n\pi\}$.

5. (a) 0, $\pi/2$, π, $3\pi/2$;
  (b) $\pi/2$, $3\pi/2$;
  (c) $\pi/2$, $3\pi/2$;
  (d) 0, $\pi/2$, π, $3\pi/2$.

7. $-2 \leqq f(\theta) \leqq 2$.

9. $0 \leqq f(\theta) \leqq 2$.

Set 4.2 page 37

1. (a) $-5\pi/2$, -2π, $-3\pi/2$, $-\pi$, $-\pi/2$, 0, $\pi/2$, π;
  (b) π, $3\pi/2$, 2π, $5\pi/2$, 3π.

3. (a) 1,   (b) 3,   (c) 8.

5. $\sin \pi/2 = 1$, $\cos \pi/2 = 0$, $\tan \pi/2$ undefined, $\cot \pi/2 = 0$, $\sec \pi/2$ undefined, $\csc \pi/2 = 1$.

7. $\sin 7\pi/2 = -1$, $\cos 7\pi/2 = 0$, $\tan 7\pi/2$ undefined, $\cot 7\pi/2 = 0$, $\sec 7\pi/2$ undefined, $\csc 7\pi/2 = -1$.

9. $\sin 2\pi = 0$, $\cos 2\pi = 1$, $\tan 2\pi = 0$, $\cot 2\pi$ undefined, $\sec 2\pi = 1$, $\csc 2\pi$ undefined.

Set 4.3 page 40

1. (a) $P(2,2)$,   (b) $P(\sqrt{2}, \sqrt{2})$,   (c) $P(\pi\sqrt{2}/2, \pi\sqrt{2}/2)$.

3. (a) $3/4$,   (b) $(\sqrt{6} - 1)/2$,   (c) $\sqrt{3}/2$.

5. (a) $1 \neq \sqrt{2}$,   (b) $\frac{1}{2} \neq \sqrt{3}$.

9. (a) is $\sin \pi/3$,   (b) is $\sin \pi/2$,   (c) is $\cos \pi/3$.

Set 4.4 page 46

1. (a) $\pi + \pi/3$,
   (b) $\pi/2$,
   (c) $2\pi/5$,
   (d) $\pi/3$,
   (e) $-\pi/3$.

3. (a) $\sin 15°$
   (b) $\cos 50°$,
   (c) $-\sec 5\pi/12$,
   (d) $\tan 80°$
   (e) $-\csc \pi/3$,
   (f) $-\sin \pi/3$,
   (g) $-\cos 2\pi/11$.

5. (a) $\pi/3, 2\pi/3$; (b) $5\pi/6, 11\pi/6$; (c) $3\pi/4, 5\pi/4$; (d) $\pi/4, 5\pi/4$.

7. (a) -1, (b) undefined, (c) 1, (d) $-4\sqrt{3}/3$,
   (e) $-\sqrt{3}/6$.

Miscellaneous Problems page 51

1. $\sin 3\pi/4 = \sqrt{2}/2$.
3. (a) -1, (b) 1.
5. (a) $3\pi/2$, (b) $\pi/2, \pi, 3\pi/2$.
7. $-1/2 \leqq \sin \theta \leqq 1/2$.
9. $f(0) = 1$, $f(\pi/2) = 1$, $f(\pi) = -1$, $f(3\pi/2) = -1$.
11. $-2, 0, 2$.
13. (a) $x = 2, r = 4$; (b) $x = 10, r = 20$.
15. $3\sqrt{2}/2$.
17. $-\sqrt{6}/24$.
19. -1.
23. (a) $\sqrt{2}/2$,
    (b) $-\sqrt{3}/2$,
    (c) $-\sqrt{3}/3$,
    (d) $-\sqrt{3}$.

Set 5.1 page 54

1. (a) $(\sqrt{3}/2, \frac{1}{2})$,
   (b) $(\sqrt{2}/2, \sqrt{2}/2)$,
   (c) $(-\frac{1}{2}, -\sqrt{3}/2)$,
   (d) $(-\frac{1}{2}, \sqrt{3}/2)$,
   (e) $(\sqrt{3}/2, -\frac{1}{2})$,
   (f) $(0, -1)$,
   (g) $(-\sqrt{2}/2, \sqrt{2}/2)$,
   (h) $(\frac{1}{2}, -\sqrt{3}/2)$.

3. (a) $(\frac{1}{2})^2 + (\sqrt{3}/2)^2 = 1$,
   (b) $(-\frac{4}{5})^2 + (-\frac{3}{5})^2 = 1$,
   (c) $(-\sqrt{3}/4)^2 + (\sqrt{13}/4)^2 = 1$,
   (d) $(\frac{2}{3})^2 + (\sqrt{5}/3)^2 = 1$.

Set 5.2 page 55

7. $\sin 7\pi/10 = 0.81$, $\cos 7\pi/10 = -0.59$, $\tan 7\pi/10 = -1.38$.

Set 5.3 page 61

7. (a) 6, (b) 6

Set 5.4 page 63

1. (a) $\pi/4$,
   (b) $4\pi/3$,
   (c) $11\pi/6$,
   (d) $13\pi/18$,
   (e) $4\pi/3$,
   (f) $11\pi/6$.

3. (a) $2\pi/3, 4\pi/3$; (b) $2\pi/3, 4\pi/3$.

5. (a) $\{3\pi/2 \pm 2n\pi\}$, (b) $\{(2n \pm 1)\pi\}$, (c) $\{\pi/4 \pm n\pi\}$.

7. Let $0 \leqq \theta < 2\pi$. Each positive value occurs twice on the interval $0 < \theta < \pi$ except the value 1 at $\pi/2$. Each negative value occurs twice on the interval $\pi < \theta < 2\pi$ except the value -1 at $3\pi/2$. The value 0 occurs at 0 and π.

Set 5.5 page 69

7. $x = \pi/2$.

Miscellaneous Problems page 70

1. (a) $\pm 7/25$,   (b) $\pm 12/13$,   (c) ± 1.
13. *Hint.* The periods form an irrational ratio.
17. (a) any number > 1,   (b) any number > 2,   (c) any number > 2,
     (d) any number > 0.
19. 2π.
21. 4.
23. (a) 4,   (b) 2.
25. Only the first.

Set 6.1 page 73

1. (a) $\{\pi/2 \pm n\pi\}$,   (b) $\{\pm n\pi/2\}$,   (c) $\{\pm n\pi\}$.
3. No.
5. (a) Null,   (b) Identity.
7. The equality does not hold at (for example):
    (a) $\pi/4$,   (b) $3\pi/4$,   (c) $3\pi/4$.

Set 6.2 page 76

3. (a) Null,   (b) Conditional.
5. (a) Identity,   (b) Conditional.
7. (a) $0 \leqq x \leqq \pi/4$, $\pi/2 < x \leqq 5\pi/4$, $3\pi/2 < x \leqq 2\pi$;
    (b) $\pi/4 \leqq x < \pi$, $5\pi/4 \leqq x < 2\pi$.

Set 6.3 page 78

7. The equality does not hold at (for example):
    (a) 0,   (b) 0,   (c) $\pi/4$,   (d) $\pi/4$,   (e) 0.
9. (a) $x \geqq 5$;   (b) $x \leqq 0, x \geqq 1$;   (c) $-1 \leqq x \leqq 1$;   (d) $-1/2 \leqq x \leqq 2$.

Set 6.5 page 87

1. $\{\pi/4 \pm n\pi/2\}$.
3. $\{\pi/4 \pm n\pi/2\}$.
5. $\{3\pi/4 \pm n\pi\}$.
7. $\{5\pi/4 \pm n\pi\}$.
9. $\{\pi/6 \pm 2n\pi\}$, $\{5\pi/6 \pm 2n\pi\}$.
11. $y = x \pm 2n\pi$ or $y = x + (1 \pm 2n)\pi$.

Miscellaneous Problems page 87

1. (a) Conditional,   (b) Null.
7. (a) No.   (b) No.
9. $1/(\sin^2\theta + \sin\theta \cdot \cos\theta)$.

11. (a) $\pi/4 \leqq x < \pi/2,\, 3\pi/4 \leqq x < \pi,\, 5\pi/4 \leqq x < 3\pi/2,\, 7\pi/4 \leqq x < 2\pi;$
(b) $0 \leqq x < \pi/2,\, 3\pi/2 < x \leqq 2\pi.$

13. (a) and (b) $\pi/4 \leqq x < \pi/2,\, \pi/2 < x \leqq 3\pi/4.$

21. $0 \leqq x < \pi/2,\, 3\pi/2 < x \leqq 2\pi.$

23. (a) $\sin x \cos x \tan x \cot x \sec x,$
(b) $\sin x \cos x \cot x \sec x \csc x.$

25. (a) $\{\pm n\pi\},\, \{\pi/4 \pm n\pi\};$ (c) $\{53°8' \pm n\,360°\}$ (approximately),
(b) null; (d) $\{\pm 2n\pi\}.$

27. $y = x \pm 2n\pi$ or $y = x + (1 \pm 2n)\pi.$

29. 0.

Set 7.1 page 94

1. (a) $(\sqrt{6} - \sqrt{2})/4,$ (b) $\sqrt{3} - 2,$ (c) and (d) $(\sqrt{2} - \sqrt{6})/4.$

3. (a) $\sin \pi/12 = (\sqrt{6} - \sqrt{2})/4,$
  $\cos \pi/12 = (\sqrt{6} + \sqrt{2})/4,$
  $\tan \pi/12 = 2 - \sqrt{3};$
(b) $\sin (-\pi/12) = (\sqrt{2} - \sqrt{6})/4,$
  $\cos (-\pi/12) = (\sqrt{6} + \sqrt{2})/4,$
  $\tan (-\pi/12) = \sqrt{3} - 2.$

5. $\theta = \phi = \pm n\pi,\quad \theta + \phi = \pm n\pi.$

Set 7.2 page 95

1. $\{\pm n\pi/2\}.$

7. (a) $24/25,$ (b) $-7/25,$ (c) $-24/7.$

9. $-\sqrt{2},\, \sqrt{2}/2.$

Set 7.3 page 97

5. (a) $\sqrt{2 - \sqrt{2}}/2,$ (c) $2 - \sqrt{3},$ (e) $-\sqrt{2 - \sqrt{3}}/2,$
(b) $-\sqrt{2 + \sqrt{3}}/2,$ (d) $\sqrt{3} - 2,$ (f) $1 - \sqrt{2}.$

7. $(2 - \sqrt{2 + \sqrt{2 + \sqrt{3}}})/4.$

Set 7.4 page 99

1. (a) $\cos 5\theta,$ (b) $\sin (-\theta/2),$ (c) $\cos (\theta - \pi/5),$ (d) $\sin 9\pi/40.$

9. $\{2\pi/3 \pm 2n\pi\}.$

11. $\{\pi/4 \pm n\pi/2\}.$

13. $\{\pi/6 \pm 2n\pi\}.$

Miscellaneous Problems page 102

1. $\sin 5\pi/12 = (\sqrt{6} + \sqrt{2})/4,$ $\cos 5\pi/12 = (\sqrt{6} - \sqrt{2})/4,$
$\tan 5\pi/12 = \sqrt{3} + 2.$

11. (a) $4\sqrt{2}/9,$ (b) $\pm\sqrt{(3 + \sqrt{8})}/6,$ (c) $-4\sqrt{2}/7.$

13. (a) III, IV; (b) any.

15. (a) yes, (b) no.

25. $\{56°19' \pm n180°\}$ (approximately).

27. $\{323° \pm n360°\}$ (approximately).

29. (a) $2 \cos \left(\dfrac{\theta - \phi}{2} \right) = 2 \sin \theta.$

    (b) 0,

    (c) 0,

    (d) $-2 \sin \left(\dfrac{\theta - \phi}{2} \right) = 2 \cos \theta.$

Set 8.1 page 106

3. 1 (a),   1 (b) and inverse of 1 (b),   inverse of 2 (b).
5. (b) No.
7. (a) younger,   (b) younger.

Set 8.2 page 109

1. $y = x$, $-1 \leqq x \leqq 1$,   yes.
3. Every horizontal line through an element in the range intersects the graph in exactly one point.
7. $y = \sqrt[3]{x^2}$, $-1 \leqq x \leqq 1$,   yes.

Set 8.3 page 111

1. Yes.
3. The inverse relation is a function.

Set 8.5 page 118

3. (a) $\pi/2$,   (c) $\pi/4$,   (e) $\pi/3$,
    (b) $-\pi/2$,   (d) $3\pi/4$,   (f) $-\pi/3$.
5. (a) 0.   (b) 0,   (c) undefined,   (d) 1.
7. (a) $u/\sqrt{1 + u^2}$,   (b) $u/\sqrt{1 - u^2}$,   (c) $1/\sqrt{2 + 2u + u^2}$.
13. ± 1.

Miscellaneous Problems page 119

3. Inverse of (a),   (b) and its inverse,   (c),   (e).
7. $f^{-1}(x) = \begin{cases} z \cdot \pi \leqq y < (z + 1)\pi & \text{if } x = 1, \\ (z - 1)\pi \leqq y < z \cdot \pi & \text{if } x = -1. \end{cases}$
    Domain: ± 1, Range: all real numbers.
    $g^{-1}(x) = \begin{cases} z \leqq y < z + 1 & \text{if } x = 1/2, \\ z - 1 \leqq y < z & \text{if } x = -1/2. \end{cases}$
    Domain: $\pm 1/2$, Range: all real numbers.
9. (b) No.
11. (a) $Y = 2 \text{ arc sin } \theta.$
        Domain: $-1 \leqq \theta \leqq 1$,   Range: $0 \leqq y \leqq 4\pi.$
    (b) $Y = \frac{1}{2} \text{ arc sin } (x/2).$
        Domain: $-2 \leqq x \leqq 2$,   Range: $0 \leqq y \leqq \pi.$

13. (a) $\{\pi/3 \pm 2n\pi\}$, $\{2\pi/3 \pm 2n\pi\}$, (b) $\{\pi/2 \pm n\pi\}$; (c) $\{3\pi/2 \pm 2n\pi\}$,
(d) $\{\pi/4 \pm n\pi\}$, (e) $\{\pm n\pi\}$, (f) void.
15. (a) $\sqrt{2}/2$, (b) $\sqrt{2}/2$, (c) Undefined, (d) $-\sqrt{3}$.
17. (a) $u^2/\sqrt{1-u^4}$, (b) $2u\sqrt{1-u^2}$, (c) $2u^2-1$, (d) 1, (e) $2u\sqrt{1-u^2}$.
23. $\{\pi/2 \pm n\pi\}$.
25. $\sqrt{3}/6$.

Set 9.1 page 126

1. $a = 6$, $c = 9$, $\gamma = 57°$.
3. $b = 6.44$, $c = 6.30$, $\alpha = 11°50'$.
5. $b = 294$, $\alpha = 26°10'$, $\gamma = 63°50'$.
7. $17°$.
9. 11.8 feet.
11. 190 feet.
13. 349 feet, $57°10'$.

Set 9.2 page 131

1. (a) No solution; (b) $\alpha = 106°$, $\beta = 22°$, $\gamma = 52°$.
3. (a) $a = 3.31$, $c = 1.65$, $\beta = 26°45'$;
(b) $b = 170.90$, $c = 139.20$, $\alpha = 56°54'54''$.
7. $29°40'$, $81°50'$, $68°30'$.
9. 3.7 miles.
11. 619 feet, 418 feet.
13. Street 52.4 feet, observer 136 feet.

Set 9.3 page 135

1. (a) Unique solution (3a), (c) No solution (1),
(b) No solution (1), (d) No solution (3 c ii).
3. 1.
5. $b = 16.913$ or 3.053; $\beta = 144°58'36''$ or $5°56'48''$;
$\gamma = 20°29'6''$ or $159°30'54''$.
7. No solution.
9. 3,361 feet.

Miscellaneous Problems page 136

1. (a) $a = 2,590$, $b = 2,620$, $\gamma = 9°10'$,
(b) $a = 5.4260$, $c = 6.3850$, $\alpha = 30°21'30''$.
3. (a) 1.3406,
(b) 14.693.

5. (a) No solution,
(b) $a = 7.9$, $\beta = 102°$, $\gamma = 38°$.
7. (a) $a = 5.44$, $b = 12.2$, $c = 8.74$,
$\beta = 116°40'$, $\gamma = 39°50'$,
(b) $a = 8.91$, $b = 10.4$, $\alpha = 28°0'$,
$\beta = 141°50'$, $\gamma = 10°10'$;
(c) $b = 21.9$, $c = 18.0$, $\beta = 124°50'$, $\gamma = 42°20'$.

9. $a = 23.865$, $\alpha = 138°50'25''$, $\beta = 16°9'5''$.
11. 4,760 feet.
15. (a) $75\sqrt{3}$, (b) 200, (c) 237.8 (approximately), (d) $150\sqrt{3}$.
17. 15.55, 17.47, 22.92.
23. (b) 2.1.
25. 1.2951, Not possible.

Set 10.1 page 145

7. Amplitude $3/2$, period π, phase shift $\pi/2$.
9. Amplitude π, period 2, phase shift 0.

Set 10.2 page 148

1. Amplitude 2, period 2π, phase shift $\pi/3$.
3. Amplitude 4, period 2π, phase shift $\pi/6$.
5. Amplitude $3\sqrt{2}$, period π, phase shift $\pi/8$.
7. $a = b = m\sqrt{2}/2$.

Miscellaneous Problems page 152

5. Amplitude $7/2$, period 6π, phase shift π.
7. Period 2, phase shift $1/\pi$.
11. $\{\phi/2 + (1 \pm 2n)\pi/4\}$, $\phi = 53°8'$ (approximately).
13. $\{6\pi/10 \pm 2n\pi\}$.
17. 2π radians, 1 radian, $2\pi m$, m.

Set 11.1 page 158

1. (a) $\sqrt{2}$, (b) $\sqrt{2}$, (c) 2, (d) -2, (e) 1, (f) -1.
3. (a) $-3\sqrt{2}/2 - i3\sqrt{2}/2$, (b) $-i2$, (c) -1.
5. (a) $\sqrt{2}/2 + i\sqrt{2}/2$, (b) $-4 + i0$.

Set 11.2 page 161

3. (a) $(x + iy) + (x - iy) = 2x + i0$,
   (b) $(x + iy) - (x - iy) = 0 + i2y$.
9. $\sqrt{5} - i\sqrt{5}$.
11. (a) $(1 - \sqrt{2}) + i(\sqrt{2} - 1)$, (b) $-1 + i5$, (c) $6 - i$, (d) $-2 - i$.
13. (a) $i3$, (b) $10 + i10$, (c) $-5 + i5$, (d) $-2 + i2$.
15. (a) $3\sqrt{2}(\cos 3\pi/4 + i \sin 3\pi/4)$, (b) $25(\cos \pi + i \sin \pi)$.
17. (a) -1, (b) $-i$, (c) $-i$, (d) i, (e) 1, (f) i.
19. (a) $5(\cos 5\pi/12 + i \sin 5\pi/12)$, (b) $2\sqrt{2}[\cos(-\pi/2) + i \sin(-\pi/2)]$.

Set 11.3 page 165

5. $r = \sqrt[8]{2}$, $\theta = -9\pi/16, -\pi/16, 7\pi/16, 15\pi/16$.
7. $r = 1$, $\theta = -9\pi/12, -5\pi/12, -\pi/12, 3\pi/12, 7\pi/12, 11\pi/12$.

Miscellaneous Problems page 166

7. (a) $\sqrt{3} - i3$, (b) $2\sqrt{2} + i3\sqrt{2}/2$, (c) $\sqrt{10}/2 + i5\sqrt{10}/4$.

9. (a) 4, (b) 0, (c) $(\sqrt{3}/2 - 1) - i/2$.

17. (a) $\dfrac{x^2 - y^2 + i2xy}{x^2 + y^2}$, (b) $\cos 2\theta + i \sin 2\theta$.

19. $r = 1,\ \theta = -7\pi/8,\ -5\pi/8,\ -3\pi/8,\ -\pi/8,\ \pi/8,\ 3\pi/8,\ 5\pi/8,\ 7\pi/8.$

Set A.1 page 170

1. (a) 1.4821×10^3, (c) 4.23×10^{-8},
(b) 1.000000001×10^9, (d) 1.872×10^{-1}.

3. (a) 9.9×10, (b) 1×10^{12}, (c) 5×10^{-3}.

Set A.2 page 173

1. (a) 0.143, (b) 8.22, (c) 38,200, (d) 1,820,000.

3. (a) $1.3985 < x + y < 1.4095$, (b) $39{,}751.5 < x + y < 39{,}852.5$.

Set A.3 page 180

1. (a) 3, (b) 1/125, (c) 4, (d) ± 2, (e) 1, (f) 1.

3. (a) $x > 0$, (b) All real numbers, (c) $y > 0$.

5. No.

7. (a) 1.07954, (c) 205,580, (e) $9.84516 - 10$,
(b) 6.12368, (d) 0.00000052482, (f) 147,570,000,000.

Set A.4 page 184

1. (a) 0.2292, (b) 0.9888, (c) 0.9942, (d) 0.0218.

3. (a) $9.42699 - 10$, (b) $9.65700 - 10$, (c) 1.15791, (d) 0.18210

INDEX

INDEX

271

C